Indie Press Guide
3rd edition

The Mslexia guide to small and independent
book publishers and literary magazines in the
UK and the Republic of Ireland

First published 2019 by Mslexia Publications Ltd

PO Box 656, Newcastle upon Tyne NE99 1PZ
www.mslexia.co.uk

ISBN 978-0-9955250-3-0

Editorial Director: Debbie Taylor
Editor and Production Manager: Françoise Harvey
Reviewers: Maxine Davies, Charlea Harrison, Françoise Harvey, Laura Steven
Production Assistants: Maxine Davies, Kay Hadden, Chloe Shakesby, Casey Spence, Laura Steven
Advertising: Laura Steven

Printed and bound in the UK by TJ International
Designed by Juliette Boisseau, www.outlinedesign.co.uk

Supported using public funding by
**ARTS COUNCIL
ENGLAND**

Contents

INTRODUCTION   5

HOW TO USE THIS GUIDE   7

PART 1: Book publishers   **9**
Indie publishers: an introduction   11
Poetry publishers (including pamphlets/chapbooks)   13
Prose publishers (fiction, non-fiction, other)   89

PART 2: Literary magazines and e-zines   **207**
Literary magazines: ebbs and flows   209
Mixed-form magazines   211
Poetry magazines   267
Prose magazines   287

PART 3: Competitions   **301**
Competitions: taking your shot   303
Competition listings   305

Afterword and thanks   315

INDEX   **317**

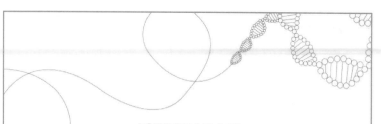

LONDON LIT LAB

Critique and Mentoring

London Lit Lab's Zoe Gilbert and Lily Dunn are both published authors with years of teaching and mentoring experience, and a friendly and open attitude. We offer tailored mentoring packages and critical feedback services for writers at all stages, whether you are developing an idea, honing a story, or need a trusted eye to check your beloved manuscript.

Get in touch at **info@londonlitlab.co.uk** for a chat.

Courses

Our popular courses include:

- ➤ Writing Compelling Memoir (London)
- ➤ Folk Tales in Fiction (London)
- ➤ LGBTQ Writing (London)
- ➤ Commercial Fiction (Bristol)
- ➤ Post-MA Sessions (London & Bristol)

Find out more about our courses at **www.londonlitlab.co.uk**

'Lily and Zoe offer teaching and coaching at the highest level. Their workshops have a reputation for encouraging excellence and creativity in a supportive environment. I am always recommending them.' Julia Bell, Course Convenor, MA Creative Writing, Birkbeck.

'Very clear, instructive and informative. The course opened my eyes to so many possibilities.' Mary, Continuing to Write.

Introduction

Welcome to the third edition of the *Indie Press Guide*.

It's now five years since we took on the daunting challenge of documenting each and every independent book publisher and literary magazine that we could find in these islands. The first edition of this Guide included 450 presses and magazines, and broke new ground in highlighting the extraordinary richness of this publishing sector – and its value to new, emerging and established writers alike. By the time we came to publish the second edition two years later, the number of presses had swelled to 590 as the success of the first edition brought yet more publishers to our attention. This third edition is bigger still – at nearly 640 entries.

But just as more independents are setting up shop and producing fascinating texts to delight and challenge us, others are throwing in the towel – as you might expect in such a cash-strapped sector. Around 20 per cent of the publishers listed in the second edition have either closed altogether, ceased publication temporarily, or withdrawn from an open submissions policy.

The majority of those fallen by the wayside are literary magazines. In some cases the reason is simply editorial burn out. But for others the reason is more positive, with editors and founders discovering that their own writing careers are taking off, or that running a small press has led to a dream job – aka a paid job – in Big Publishing. Happily, many of these magazines, particularly digital e-zines, have left behind an archive of published texts online – we're thinking in particular of publications like *Synaesthesia Magazine*, which has consistently turned out beautiful work.

The good news is that as fast as they are disappearing, more are appearing to take their place.

The indie press landscape is changing rapidly. An area of publishing that tended to be overlooked back in 2015 is becoming a watchword for quality. Titles from independent book publishers are appearing in increasing numbers on the longlists and shortlists of literary prizes. New magazines are launching with a level of digital-marketing know-how that earlier magazines couldn't hope to match. The indie press sector is gaining in power and status as the media, critics and readers sit up and take more notice of the writing and culture being produced outside the London bubble – because these nimble and infinitely various publishers spring up wherever their editors and founders live. And this means the indies are quintessentially local enterprises.

2016 saw the creation of the Northern Fiction Alliance, a consortium of publishers based in Manchester, Leeds, Liverpool, Sheffield, Salford, Newcastle, Hull and beyond, who have combined forces in an effort to compete with the Big Five London-based publishers in terms of marketing effort, sales deals and bookshop presence (www.northernfictionalliance. com). The indies are also developing a closer association with independent bookshops – another endangered species struggling to survive in the face of mighty Amazon – for launches, readings and promotions. And they're developing new and creative ways of staying afloat. Galley Beggar and Influx Press, for example, both now run a subscription service for their books.

The *Guardian*'s Not The Booker Prize and the Saboteur Awards also continue to do a huge amount of work to bring indie publications to the attention of readers who might not otherwise have encountered them – though both sets of awards have been criticised for being selected by crowd-choice as opposed to by a jury of experienced judges who are required to read every entry.

And, as we have pointed out before, the indies have the editorial passion, courage and freedom to publish material that does not always find favour in the risk-averse world of Big Publishing – and to find a market for it. Retreat West, for example, was publishing work about the climate crisis long before the rest of the publishing world jumped on board.

As we go to print with this third edition, the UK and the Republic of Ireland are caught up in political turmoil. However things work out – if they work out – it seems inevitable that the indie presses, who already exist on shoestrings and borrowed time, will struggle. Paper and postage costs are rising, and author tours and contracts may be affected by changes in the law, all adding to the challenges already faced by the sector.

So we're proud to support them, and, we hope, help you discover them: these publishers to which you can send the fictions, poems and essays you're writing about these troubled times; these are the publishers through which your voice might be heard, and through which you can hear others'.

We've divided the Guide into clear sections: book publishers, magazines and journals (including e-zines), and script publishers and producers who are prepared to look at submissions. Sub-sections divide the book publishers and magazines into those focusing on prose (including fiction, memoir, biography, etc.) and those focusing on poetry. Book publishers that produce both are listed in both sections, while magazines have been divided into poetry only, prose only and mixed form (prose, poetry, graphics and more).

Where a publisher didn't respond to our approaches, we checked to ensure they were still operating, and included them as a 'stub' entry, consisting of contact details and as much information as we could glean from their websites. Or, in the case of a press who has provided information in the past, we've checked the information we have is still up to date. We would add, though, that given the turbulent life of an indie press, you may still find that some included publishers are on hiatus, or have closed down since we printed this Guide.

Where we did received information from the publisher, we have generated entries that include much of the following information:

- The type of publications they produce. Please note that 'e-books' does not always mean *only* e-books – most also produce print books.
- Contact details (including where possible a postal address, a phone number, an email address and a website) and the name of the editor(s).
- The year the press was established (to give you some idea of their longevity), and where their publications are available (bookshops, online, or both) so that you, the writer, have an idea of where your work might end up. We've also tried to include details of any awards the press might have won.
- The genres published, where relevant.
- How to submit and where you can find further guidelines; any restrictions on eligibility; how long you can expect to wait for a response; whether the editor(s) can offer feedback – and the all-important payment policy.
- A ☆ symbol indicates that the press also runs one or more writing competitions – flip to the Competitions section on p301 for more information.

- References to any wider publishing activity – if a book publisher also runs a magazine, for example, we will direct you to the correct page.
- Some presses have also chosen to include an image – a logo or a sample book cover – and have taken the opportunity to describe their aims, aesthetics and the kind of writing they are looking for under 'They Say'.
- There is an Index at the end of the book if you want to look up a particular publisher (p317).

There is also a section entitled 'We Say' included with many of the entries, in which we provide our reviewers' perspective on the quality of production and what to expect from the press in question. In order to compile this, we asked publishers to provide a sample of their output: in print, as a PDF, or as an online link. Not every press was able to oblige, but where possible we've tried to fill in the gaps with our own research. If there is no 'We Say' under an entry for a poetry publisher, say, do check to see whether the press is listed in the prose section, where our review might be included.

Some presses state they they do not accept 'unsolicited submissions'. This does not necessarily mean their doors are closed to you. It usually means that the editors' policy is to approach writers whose work they have seen elsewhere, often in a literary magazine – another indication, if one were needed, of how important it is to get your work out there.

We hope this information will set you firmly on the way to being able to find an indie publisher or magazine that will be a good fit for your work. But remember, our 'We Say' opinion may not match yours, and guidelines may change – again! – so we *strongly* urge you to research the press yourself before sending your work. Visit their websites, check their backlist, buy a publication or two, or, better yet, subscribe!

Part 1:
Book publishers

FAHRENHEIT PRESS

"Part crime publisher, part international love cult."

"These guys scare me a little, but I like it..."

"The most unique, fearless and consistently innovative crime publisher in the world."

"The publishers your mother warned you about."

"There isn't another publisher like Fahrenheit Press and we need them now more than ever."

"...their t-shirts are pretty cool too."

IF YOU THINK YOU'VE GOT WHAT IT TAKES TO BECOME A FAHRENHEIT AUTHOR WE'D LOVE TO HEAR FROM YOU.

@FahrenheitPress   @69Crime   @FNoir13

www.Fahrenheit-Press.com

Indie publishers: an introduction

The indie publishing scene is thriving. Despite the closure of some presses – after 20 years or just a few months – for this third edition of the *Indie Press Guide*, we have identified more than 100 new publishers for you to send your work to.

There are pros and cons to approaching an indie. On the plus side, indie presses are often more willing to take a chance on experimental writing – indeed many were launched precisely because their founders were frustrated that work they admired was being ignored by big publishers.

An open submission policy is another major bonus; unlike with big publishers, you rarely need to have ensnared an agent before a small press editor is willing to consider your manuscript. And because editors are more personally invested and passionate about the books they publish, they have a reputation for working more closely with the authors they take on. That passionate risk-taking approach has certainly paid off: for example, books from Salt Publishing and Galley Beggar Press have been short and longlisted for the Booker Prize.

And if you're a fan of shorter forms, there's plenty of love for short stories and flash fiction amongst the indies, as well as cross-genre work. If your novel is in verse, or your novella is made up of flash fictions, there will be an indie press out there somewhere willing to consider it.

What about the cons? Well, there's the aforementioned higher risk of closure. And not surprisingly, small presses often lack the clout of the bigger publishers when it comes to marketing your book. So you might need to get involved in the marketing and publicity processes yourself.

The production values (design, proofing, paper quality, etc.) are also worth keeping an eye on – not because indie presses are lax, but because placing small orders means that it's not always possible to get the top-class materials they want at a price they can afford. If you can, examine other titles published by the press you're considering approaching, and make sure you're happy with their production values. In our 'We Say' comments we have tried to give you an idea of what to expect, but these are only an indication; standards may vary from year to year, even from title to title.

So here are some basic guidelines to follow when submitting:

- First, do your research. We've given you enough information to help you shortlist the right press for you, but you should also check the websites, research books they've published, and establish that your work is the kind of thing they are looking for. This will save a lot of heartache. It's a waste of your time and theirs if you send a sci-fi manuscript to a romance publisher.

- Second, make sure the publisher offers what you're looking for. You don't want your manuscript to be accepted only to discover that the look and feel of the resulting book is not how you envisioned your work appearing – or that you've been taken on by an e-book-only publisher when you harbour dreams of ink and clothbound covers.

- Third, though we have tried very hard to ensure that no vanity presses are listed here, do double check. It is incredibly exciting when a publisher is interested in your work, but keep your head. If a contract seems dodgy, do not sign it. Approach a body such as the Society of Authors (www.societyofauthors.org) for advice.

- Fourth, don't submit your manuscript until it is finished. This means you should have drafted and redrafted (and redrafted) and then polished it to a high gleam. No publisher wants to read three chapters of an unfinished book, or a hastily written first draft.

- Fifth, check your work is eligible. Several publishers in this section also run literary magazines, which can mean that any books they publish are compiled from work by authors who have submitted work to, or have been published in, the magazine.

- Sixth, follow the submission instructions. Most publishers have guidelines on their website, and they *will* all be slightly different from each other. You will irritate the editor if you don't follow the instructions carefully. Don't send more than the stated word limit; don't submit outside the submissions window if there is one; don't send your manuscript if they have asked for a query email first; don't email if they specify post, or post your only copy if they specify email. However good your work, we promise it's not good enough for you to ignore the guidelines.

- Finally, be patient. Most presses receive a lot of submissions, but won't have many people to assess them. Check in the Guide for their usual response time, and don't even think of chasing up your submission until that's elapsed. At that point, if you still haven't heard, check their website or social media to see if there's a reason for the delay. Then, and *only* then, send a *polite* reminder. To reiterate: *be polite*. These people are considering working closely with you, so any spikiness on your part will affect their decision. And bear in mind that the world of indie presses is small. If one publisher declines your work, move on. Do not reply in anger. Editors talk to each other, and they remember the writers who have been rude.

Good luck!

Being an independent press does not necessarily equate to being a small press. Bloodaxe Books, for example, have been established for decades, publish many titles every year, and have an enormous backlist.

But regardless of press size, most publishers of poetry collections will expect you to have a history of publication in magazines and anthologies. So if you don't yet have a track record for publishing single poems, skip to page p207 and check out the magazine listings.

Also listed in this section are a number of presses that publish both poetry and prose. In these cases we have indicated, where appropriate, what their dominant area of publishing is.

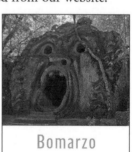

A3 PRESS, THE ☆

COLLECTIONS AND CHAPBOOKS/
PAMPHLETS
PO Box 65016, London N5 9BD
020 7193 7642
a3@writingmaps.com
www.thea3press.com
Editor: Shaun Levin

Established 2018. Mixed output, publishing fiction (see p91), poetry and art. Publications available direct from the publisher website.
GENRES: Poetry.
SUBMISSIONS: Open to all, during submissions windows. Submit via thea3review.submittable.com/ submit, where full guidelines are also available. A reading fee is charged. Usually responds in one to three months. Rejections do not include feedback unless paid for. Authors are paid a flat fee and receive copies of their book.
WE SAY: We considered the online sample of *The Abyss of the Other* by Cecilia Cavalieri, a soulful chapbook that explores an artist and mother's experience alone with her baby in exile, using words and images to bring the story to life. As with all of A3 Press' publications, it is printed on a single, folded A3 sheet of high quality paper.
**See also: *The A3 Review*
(mixed-form magazine) p213 and prose publishers p91**

AGENDA EDITIONS

COLLECTIONS
Harts Cottage, Stonehurst Lane, Five Ashes, Mayfield, East Sussex TN20 6LL
editor@agendapoetry.co.uk

www.agendapoetry.co.uk
Editor: Patricia McCarthy
Established 1959. By William Cookson and Ezra Pound.
SUBMISSIONS: This very small press does not take unsolicited manuscripts.
For a fuller description of this press, see *Agenda* (poetry magazine) p269

ALBA PUBLISHING

COLLECTIONS, ANTHOLOGIES AND CHAPBOOKS/PAMPHLETS
PO Box 266, Uxbridge UB9 5NX
01895 832444
info@albapublishing.com
www.albapublishing.com
Editor: Kim Richardson
Established 1990. Also publishes some prose (see p93). Publications available by post and email order, and from Amazon.
A title from Alba Publishing was shortlisted for the Haiku Foundation Touchstone Distinguished Book Award 2013.
GENRES: Spirituality and beliefs.
SUBMISSIONS: Publication history required. Submit by post (PO Box 266, Uxbridge UB9 5NX) or by email (info@albapublishing.com). Usually responds within four weeks, with submission feedback only if requested. Authors contribute to editorial/publication/marketing costs.
WE SAY: We looked at a PDF proof of *Initial Response* by Maeve O'Sullivan, a 33-page perfect-bound pamphlet. The cover has a striking red and black design of scribbled calligraphy, which will look lovely in print, and

16

the collection comprises 'an A-Z of haiku moments'. Each letter of the alphabet has a title ('A is for Autumn', 'B is for Birds & Berries', etc.) and a six-haiku poem across a double-page spread, with some black, splashed-ink illustrations on the second half of their spreads. It's an uncluttered, eye-catching design.

See also: prose publishers p93

ALLARDYCE, BARNETT, PUBLISHERS

COLLECTIONS, AND MIXED-FORM COLLECTIONS AND ANTHOLOGIES
14 Mount Street, Lewes, East Sussex
BN7 1HL
www.abar.net
Editor: Anthony Barnett
Also publishes prose (see p94).
Publications available direct from publisher website; by direct mail and email orders; from independent bookshops; from

AGAINST THE GRAIN POETRY PRESS

COLLECTIONS, CHAPBOOKS/ PAMPHLETS AND MIXED-FORM ANTHOLOGIES (ART AND POETRY)
againstthegrainpress@gmail.com
againstthegrainpoetrypress.
wordpress.com
Editors: Karen Dennison, Abegail Morley, Jessica Mookherjee

Established 2017. Primarily publishes poetry. Publications available direct from the publisher website; at events; and from PBS.
GENRES: Poetry.
SUBMISSIONS: Open to poets with a publication history, during submissions windows only – otherwise by invitation only. Submit by email to againstthegrainpress@ gmail.com. Guidelines at againstthegrainpoetrypress. wordpress.com/submissions. Usually responds in one to three months. Authors are paid royalties and receive free copies of their book.

THEY SAY

We aim to create books that are beautiful works of art from your poetry. We want words that lodge and dislodge, that create a friction to make poetry into art. We want to create beauty from pain, disorientation, defiance, love and dislocation. We create books that both look and feel beautiful. We care for the poets we choose and that choose us as we believe that poetry is being in a relationship with poets.

WE SAY: We viewed a PDF of *Metastatic* by Jane Lovell, a poetry collection that embodies nature and landscapes in thoughtful, meditative writing. Against The Grain's easy-to-navigate website promotes their collection of authors and their values of producing beautiful works of art. From here you can also learn about their publications, events and competitions, as well as their insightful online blog.

Amazon; and from SPD in the US.
SUBMISSIONS: By invitation only.
**See also: prose publisher p94
and Snow Lit Rev (mixed-form
magazine) p256**

AND OTHER STORIES
COLLECTIONS
Central Library, Surrey Street, Sheffield
S1 1XZ
nichola@andotherstories.org
www.andotherstories.org
Editors: Tara Tobler, Stefan Tobler
Established 2010. Mainly publishes
fiction (see p94). Publications
available in chain bookshops
nationwide; in independent
bookshops; at local literary
events; and from Amazon and
other bookshop websites. Plans
are in place for purchase direct
from the publisher. Also offers a
subscription: £22, £40 or £55 per
year for two, four or six books per
year.
And Other Stories was shortlisted
for the 2013 IPG Newcomer
Award. Its authors have also been
shortlisted for and won awards.
SUBMISSIONS: Open to all, but
submitters are required to show
proof of purchase from the press.
Submit by post to Central Library,
Surrey Street, Sheffield S1 1XZ.
Guidelines at www.andotherstories.
org/submissions. Usually responds
within one to three months. A
standard rejection may occasionally
include unsolicited feedback.
Author payment is an advance/fee
plus royalties.
**For a fuller description of this press,
see prose publishers p94**

ANIMA POETRY PRESS
COLLECTIONS, ANTHOLOGIES AND
CHAPBOOKS/PAMPHLETS
www.animapoetry.uk

Editor: Marcus Sly
Established 2014. Publications
available direct from publisher
website.
GENRES: Spirituality and beliefs.
SUBMISSIONS: Open to all. Submit
through Submittable at anima.
submittable.com/submit. Usually
responds within four to six months.
Rejection may occasionally include
unsolicited feedback. Authors
receive royalties.

AQUIFER BOOKS
COLLECTIONS AND ANTHOLOGIES
goodiebard2@googlemail.com
www.glasfrynproject.org.uk
Editor: Lyndon Davies
Established 2015. Publications
available direct from the publisher
website; and by direct mail and
email order.
GENRES: Literary; innovative and
experimental poetry.
SUBMISSIONS: Submissions by
invitation only. Authors receive
five free books and a discount
on further purchases of their
publication.
WE SAY: Aquifer Books publishes
a range of experimental, cutting
edge writing, that embraces those
precious moments of writing
found in our day-to-day lives. We
considered PDFs of *Floss* by Sarah
Crewe and *Poems for the Dance* by
Scott Thurston. These collections
present skilled writing on both
political and personal issues, with
equally bold and passionate voices.
**See also: *Junction Box* (mixed-form
magazine) p234**

ARACHNE PRESS
COLLECTIONS AND ANTHOLOGIES
100 Grierson Road, London SE23 1NX
020 8699 0206
www.arachnepress.com

Editor: Cherry Potts

Established 2012. Mainly publishes fiction (see p96) but also some poetry. Publications available direct from publisher website; by post and email order; at chain bookshops and independent bookshops nationwide; at local literary events; and from Amazon and other bookshop websites, including distributor inpressbooks.co.uk.

SUBMISSIONS: Particularly welcome from all women, disabled and D/deaf writers. During submissions windows, submit through Submittable at arachnepress.submittable.com/submit. Guidelines at arachnepress.com/submissions. Usually responds within one to three months. Authors receive royalties and free copies of the book.

WE SAY: We looked at the 96-page, less-than-A5 *With Paper for Feet* by Jennifer A McGowan. With white pages and a matte cover, McGowan's poetry collection considers folklore and frailties, often from a woman's perspective; most memorably in 'Lady Macbeth in palliative care', Shakespeare's antagonist did not die by her own hand, but slowly declines, pinning flies to the wall with her stainless hooks.

For a fuller description of this press, see prose publishers p96

ARC PUBLICATIONS

E-BOOKS, COLLECTIONS, ANTHOLOGIES AND CHAPBOOKS/ PAMPHLETS
Nanholme Mill, Shaw Wood Road, Todmorden OL14 6DA
01706 812338
info@arcpublications.co.uk
www.arcpublications.co.uk

Editors: Tony Ward, Angela Jarman

Established 1969. Publications available direct from publisher website; by post and email order; at chain and independent bookshops nationwide; at national and local literary events; and from Amazon and other bookshop websites.

Shortlisted for the Griffin Poetry Prize 2015.

SUBMISSIONS: Publication history required. Submit by email – check the guidelines at www.arcpublications.co.uk/submissions for details of where to send. Usually responds within four to six months. Rejections may occasionally include unsolicited feedback. Authors are paid an advance/fee plus royalties, and receive free copies of their book.

WE SAY: We looked at *Cold Spring in Winter* by Valerie Pouzeau, translated by Susan Wicks. This is part of Arc's 'Visible Poets' series, which is translated work, but includes the original text on the opposing pages. The materials used are high quality, with cream paper and plenty of space to display the poems. The collection also includes a preface from the translator sharing the joy and challenges of translating the work, and end notes giving literal translations of certain lines, where poetic licence was necessary for the translation.

ARETÉ BOOKS

E-BOOKS, COLLECTIONS
8 New College Lane, Oxford OX1 3BN
01865 289193
aretebooks@gmail.com
www.aretemagazine.com
Editor: Craig Raine
Book awards include *A Scattering*

by Christopher Reid winning the 2009 Costa Prize, which was also shortlisted for The Forward Prize and the T S Eliot prize in the same year. Writers receive royalties only. **For a fuller description of this press, see *Areté Magazine* (mixed-form magazine) p216**

ARLEN HOUSE
COLLECTIONS AND ANTHOLOGIES
42 Grange Abbey Road, Baldoyle, Dublin 13
arlenhouse@gmail.com
Editor: Alan Hayes
Established 1975, Ireland's oldest feminist publisher. Award-winning publisher, publishing poetry, prose and mixed poetry/prose anthologies (see p97). Publications available from chain and independent bookshops nationwide; at national and local literary events; and from Amazon and other online bookshops. International distribution by Syracuse University Press.
SUBMISSIONS: Submissions by invitation only. Author deals vary from book to book depending on funding and sales forecasts, but may pay an advance, royalties, and/or copies of the publication. Solicited work may receive a response in one to three months.
WE SAY: We looked at a PDF proof of Arlen House's recent publication, *Love, The Magician* by Medbh McGuckian. This collection of poems truly is extensive, offering over 50 delicately descriptive poems. This collection clearly holds strong personal influence from the author, making the writing both insightful and enjoyable to read. With its abstract cover design boasting colourful depictions of humans and nature, this collection is one from the heart.
See also: prose publishers p97

AS YET UNTITLED
ARTISTS' BOOKS
5 Veales Rd, Kingsbridge, Devon TQ7 1EX
ayupublishing@gmail.com
www.asyetuntitled.org
Editor: Rosie Sherwood
Established 2012. Mixed form: artists' books. As Yet Untitled specialises in limited edition, handmade book art and live events. Publications available direct from publisher website; from selected/local chain bookshops; from independent bookshops; at local literary events; and at Artists' Book Fairs (national), and the Small Publishers Fair.
SUBMISSIONS: As Yet Untitled does not take submissions. Artists and writers are invited to collaborate with the press.
See also: prose publishers p97

ASLS
COLLECTIONS
7 University Gardens, Glasgow G12 8QH
0141 330 5309
office@asls.org.uk
www.asls.org.uk
Established 1970. Publications available direct from publisher website; by post and email order; at chain bookshops; at independent bookshops; at national and local literary events; and from Amazon and other bookshop websites.
For a fuller description of this press, see *New Writing Scotland* (mixed-form magazine) p245 and prose publishers p97

AUGUR PRESS
COLLECTIONS AND ANTHOLOGIES
info@augurpress.com
www.augurpress.com
Established 2004. Books with an
emphasis on enabling the reader
'to reflect, and to look beyond
... that which is immediately
apparent'. Includes translated
collections.
See also: prose publishers p98

AWEN PUBLICATIONS
COLLECTIONS AND ANTHOLOGIES,
INCLUDING MIXED-FORM
12 Belle Vue Close, Stroud GL5 1ND
anthony@quintus1.plus.com
www.awenpublications.co.uk
Editor: Anthony Nanson
Established 2003. Publishes
both prose (see p99) and poetry.
Publications available direct from
the publisher website; by post
and email order; from chain and
independent bookshops; at local
literary events; and from Amazon
and other bookshop websites.
In 2013 Awen Publications won a
Storytelling World Award (honours).
SUBMISSIONS: Submissions by
invitation only. Authors are paid
royalties and receive free copies of
their book and a generous author
discount.
**For more information, including
what We Say, see also: prose
publishers p99**

BACKLASH PRESS
COLLECTIONS
www.backlashpress.com
Publisher: Gretchen Heffernan
Dedicated to releasing work that
'narrates a contemplated resistance
to obedience and trend'. Looks for
experimental, yet enduring poetry
collections.
See also: prose publishers p100 and

Backlash Journal (poetry magazine)
p270

BAD BETTY PRESS
COLLECTIONS, ANTHOLOGIES AND
CHAPBOOKS/PAMPHLETS
info@badbettypress.com
www.badbettypress.com
Editor: Amy Acre
Established 2017. Publications
available direct from the publisher
website; from independent
bookshops; at national and local
literary events; and from Amazon
and other bookshop websites.
Bad Betty Press was shortlisted for
the 2018 Michael Marks Publisher
Award.
SUBMISSIONS: Open to all, during
the biannual submissions windows.
Submitters are required to buy a
magazine/book from the press.
Submit by email to submissions.
badbettypress@gmail.com.
Guidelines at www.badbettypress.
com/subs. Responds within one
to three months. Writers will be
told if they were shortlisted for
publication ('there are always
more great manuscripts than we
have capacity to publish'). Authors
may be paid an advance fee
(dependent on ACE funding), and
receive free copies of their book.
WE SAY: We looked at PDFs
of anthology *The Dizziness of
Freedom* edited by Amy Acre and
Jake Wild Hall, and Anne Gill's
collection *Raft*, both of which
discuss mental health using bold
and unapologetic voices. With
their self-proclaimed love of
positively 'bad' poetry, Bad Betty
Press promote daring voices that
are carried by genuine human
experiences and emotions. Their
published works are particularly
invested in perspective and

platforming a variety of voices, whilst embracing risk-taking writers and styles.

BANIPAL PUBLISHING
COLLECTIONS
1 Gough Square, London EC4A 3DE
07979 540594
margaret@banipal.co.uk
www.banipal.co.uk
Editors: Margaret Obank and Samuel Shimon
Established 1997. Publishes translated poetry and prose (see p100) alongside *Banipal Magazine* (see p21). Publications available direct from the publisher website; at chain and independent bookshops; and from Amazon and other bookshop websites. Banipal Publishing won the 2016 Sheikh Hamad Award for Translation and International Understanding, Doha, Qatar.
GENRES: Literary.
SUBMISSIONS: Open to submissions, but because Banipal's publications are all translations (mainly from Arabic) the editors primarily select the works to translate and commission the translations. Submit by email to editor@banipal.co.uk. Guidelines at www.banipal.co.uk/submissions. Responds in over six months. No feedback is offered with rejections. Authors are paid a flat fee and royalties, and receive copies of their book.
See also: prose publishers p100 and *Banipal Magazine* (mixed-form magazine) p21

BANSHEE PRESS
COLLECTIONS
bansheelit@gmail.com
www.bansheelit.com
Editors: Laura Cassidy, Claire Hennessy, Eimear Ryan
Established 2019. Mixed form, publishing prose (see p100) and poetry. Publications available direct from publisher website; by post and email order; at major chain and independent bookshops; at national and local literary events; and from Amazon and other bookshop websites.
GENRES: Literary.
SUBMISSIONS: Does not accept unsolicited submissions – authors are found through literary magazine *Banshee* (see p217). Authors are paid an advance plus royalties.
See also: prose publishers p100 and *Banshee* (mixed-form magazine) p217

BARQUE PRESS
CHAPBOOKS AND COLLECTIONS
www.barquepress.com
Barque Press was founded by Andrea Brady and Keston Sutherland in 1995. Check the website for details of whether submissions are being accepted. Do read publications by the press before approaching.
See also: *Quid* (poetry magazine) p282

BIRLINN PRESS
COLLECTIONS AND ANTHOLOGIES
West Newington House, 10 Newington Road, Edinburgh EH9 1QS
info@birlinn.co.uk
www.birlinn.co.uk
Managing director: Hugh Andrews
Poetry published under the Polygon imprint. Mixed form: also publishes fiction and non-fiction.
See also: prose publishers p101

BLACK LIGHT ENGINE ROOM, THE
CHAPBOOKS
theblacklightenginedriver@hotmail.co.uk
Publishes at least four chapbooks
a year, with regular call-outs
given out on social media in the
Facebook group and Twitter
account (@BLERoom1_).

BLACK PEAR PRESS
COLLECTIONS AND ANTHOLOGIES
office@blackpear.net
www.blackpear.net
Editors: Rod Griffiths, Polly Robinson,
Tony Judge
Established 2013. Publications
available direct from publisher
website; by post and email order;
at local literary events; and from
Amazon and other bookshop
websites.
SUBMISSIONS: Usually by invitation
only, but with occasional short
submission windows open to
all, which are advertised on the
website. Usually responds within
one to three months. Rejections
may occasionally include
unsolicited feedback. Authors
receive royalties, plus discounted
copies of their books.
**For a fuller description of this press,
see prose publishers p102**

BLACKHEATH BOOKS
CHAPBOOKS/PAMPHLETS
grunt.blackheath@virgin.net
www.blackheathbooks.org.uk
'A home for literary outsiders.' A
very small press that hand-prints
books using vintage equipment.
Publications are limited print
runs, with signed and numbered
editions. Check the website for
details of whether submissions are
being accepted.
See also: prose publishers p103

BLOODAXE BOOKS
COLLECTION, ANTHOLOGIES,
E-BOOKS WITH AUDIO, BOOKS
WITH VIDEO DVDS AND AUDIO CDS
Eastburn, South Park, Hexham,
Northumberland NE46 1BS
01434 611581
publicity@bloodaxebooks.com
www.bloodaxebooks.com
Editor: Neil Astley
Established 1978. Publications
available direct from publisher
website; by post and email order;
from chain bookshops nationwide;
from independent bookshops; at
national literary events; and from
Amazon and other bookshop
websites.
Bloodaxe is a multi-award-winning
press: awards won by its poets
in the past ten years include the
Nobel Prize in Literature, T S
Eliot Prize, Griffin International
Poetry Prize, Queen's Gold Medal
for Poetry, Pulitzer Prize (USA),
National Book Award (USA),
Somerset Maugham Award,
Geoffrey Faber Memorial Prize,
Edwin Morgan Poetry Award,
Roland Mathias Poetry Award,
Wales Book of the Year Award,
Costa Poetry Award, Costa Book
of the Year Award, RSL Ondaatje
Prize, Corneliu M. Popescu Prize
for European Translation, Criticos
Prize, Bernard Shaw Prize, and
Cholmondeley Award – to name
just a few.
SUBMISSIONS: Publication history
required. Submit by post to
Submissions, Bloodaxe Books,
Eastburn, South Park, Hexham,
Northumberland NE46 1BS. A
sample of up to a dozen poems
is preferable to a full manuscript,
and don't forget to include return
postage. Usually responds within
three months. Usually no feedback

if rejected, but very occasionally a standard rejection may include unsolicited feedback. Authors receive an advance/fee, plus royalties.

WE SAY: We looked at *Inside the Wave*, the posthumous and award-winning collection by Helen Dunmore. As with all of Bloodaxe's publications, this is made of top quality materials and is perfect bound. The cover image is a clear and bright image of a wave curling onto a beach, with the title and author name unobtrusively in the lower part of the page. This modern classic collection highlights Bloodaxe's propensity for quality writing that feels accessible for even casual readers of poetry.

BLUE DIODE

COLLECTIONS AND ANTHOLOGIES
bluedioderob@gmail.com
www.bluediode.co.uk
Editor: Rob A Mackenzie
Established 2018. Publishes poetry. Publications available direct from the publisher website; from independent bookshops; at local literary events; and from Amazon. Blue Diode publication *Split* by Juana Adcock was the Poetry Book Society Choice for Winter 2019.

SUBMISSIONS: Submitting poets must have a publication history and should submit work only during open submissions windows. Submit by email to bluedioderob@gmail. com. Guidelines at www.bluediode. co.uk/single-post/2019/06/19/ Blue-Diode-Press-Poetry-Submissions. Usually responds in one to three months. No feedback offered with rejections. Authors are paid royalties and receive free copies of their book.

WE SAY: We looked at a PDF proof of anthology *Spark*, edited by Rob A Mackenzie and Louise Peterkin. This unique book contains poetry and art inspired by the novels of Muriel Spark, cleverly structured by pairing each work with the novel providing its influence. Through the individual writing styles of each contributor, this anthology emulates a community coming together to celebrate a beloved Scottish writer.

BLUE NIB, THE ☆

COLLECTIONS, ANTHOLOGIES AND CHAPBOOKS/PAMPHLETS
Ecklands, Carnhill, Loughshinny, Skerries, Co Dublin
+353 858 513 376
info@thebluenib.com
www.thebluenib.com
Editors: Shirley Bell (Poetry & EOC), Mimi Gladman (Fiction) and Dave Kavanagh (Online Editor)
Established 2016. Publishes poetry, short fiction, essays and reviews, including mixed-form anthologies (see p103). Available direct from the publisher website, from independent bookshops, and from Amazon.
The Blue Nib magazine (see p218) was longlisted for the 2018 Saboteur Awards Best Literary Magazine.

SUBMISSIONS: Submissions are open to all, during submissions windows. Guidelines at www. thebluenib.com/submission-guidelines. Usually responds in one to three months. Rejections may occasionally include unsolicited feedback. Unpaid, as The Blue Nib currently reinvests all funds into publishing work by emerging authors.

See also: prose publishers p103 and for more information, including

what We Say, *The Blue Nib* (mixed-form magazine) p218

BOATWHISTLE BOOKS
COLLECTIONS AND ANTHOLOGIES
www.boatwhistle.com
A London-based publisher of 'singular books for singular readers', Boatwhistle produces high quality poetry books, but no more than two books per year. Books are usually by writers the editors have solicited, but their submissions guidelines say they will still 'take a respectful look at anything sent to us'.

BOILER HOUSE PRESS
COLLECTIONS AND ANTHOLOGIES
www.boilerhouse.press
publishing@uea.ac.uk
Based at the University of East Anglia, Boiler House Press is a new publisher of fiction, non-fiction, poetry and everything in-between. The website states that they are 'passionate about writing that breaks the mould; that surprises; that plays with-and-between the creative and the critical'. If submitting, do so via their website and allow at least a month for a response.
See also: prose publishers p104

BOOK GUILD, THE
COLLECTIONS
www.bookguild.co.uk
info@bookguild.co.uk
Publishes poetry and prose (see p104). Looking for commercial work. May offer successful submissions either a traditional publishing model or a 'partnership' model (requiring a financial contribution from the author). Check www.bookguild.co.uk/publish-with-us.
See also: prose publishers p104

BROKEN SLEEP BOOKS
COLLECTIONS, ANTHOLOGIES, CHAPBOOKS/PAMPHLETS AND ART/PHOTO BOOKS
Carmarthenshire, Wales/Cornwall, England
brokensleepbooks@gmail.com
www.brokensleepbooks.com
Editor: Aaron Kent
Established 2018. Publishes poetry and art/photography. Publications available direct from the publisher website and from Amazon.
SUBMISSIONS: Submit during submissions windows only via www.brokensleepbooks.com. Guidelines at www.brokensleepbooks.com/about-us-submissions. Usually responds within four weeks. Rejections may occasionally include unsolicited feedback. Authors receive free copies of the book.
WE SAY: The *Broken Sleep Books Anthology 2018* is a 116-page perfect-bound paperback with a minimalist cover design containing five pieces of work from every author published in 2018 by Broken Sleep Books. The anthology is well put together, with a dedicated section for each author, and includes a handful of more experimental works including annotated poetry drafts and photographs.

BURNING EYE BOOKS
COLLECTIONS, ANTHOLOGIES AND CHAPBOOKS/PAMPHLETS
15 West Hill, Portishead, Bristol BS20 6LG
infodata@burningeye.co.uk
www.burningeye.co.uk
Editors: Jenn Hart, Clive Birnie
Established 2012. Publications available direct from publisher website and can be ordered to

bookstores internationally. Burning Eye Books won the Saboteur Award for Most Innovative Publisher 2016.

SUBMISSIONS: Submit only during submissions windows (via Submittable), otherwise by invitation only. Guidelines at burningeyebooks.wordpress.com/about/submit/. Sometimes charges a reading fee. Usually responds within one to three months. No feedback offered with rejection. Authors are paid royalties.

WE SAY: We had a peek at *Sex & Love & Rock&Roll* by Tony Walsh – an A5, perfect-bound paperback with a glossy cover. The poetry collection came with an accompanying CD, which was clever considering the author is renowned for his spoken word performances. The collection itself felt very accessible, featuring quotes and poetry with a lot of white space, which we personally love.

CANDLESTICK PRESS

COLLECTIONS, ANTHOLOGIES AND CHAPBOOKS/PAMPHLETS
Diversity House, 72 Nottingham Road, Arnold, Nottingham NG5 6LF
01159 674455
info@candlestickpress.co.uk
www.candlestickpress.co.uk
Editors: Di Slaney, Katharine Towers
Established 2008. Also publishes prose (see p105). Publications available direct from publisher website; by direct mail and email orders; from chain bookshops nationwide; from independent bookshops; at national and local literary events; and from Amazon and other bookshop websites.

GENRES: None specified.

SUBMISSIONS: By invitation only. Feedback not offered with rejections. Authors are paid a flat fee and receive free copies of the book.

WE SAY: Well-presented anthology chapbooks that can be sent as gifts, as Candlestick Press say, 'instead of a card'. The A5 chapbook comes complete with envelope, sticker and bookmark. We looked at *Ten Poems on the Telephone* (Candlestick covers many different topics): a quality product printed on thick textured paper with a bright cover and simple illustrations. Perfect as a light read for readers who enjoy quality over quantity.

See also: prose publishers p105

CARCANET PRESS

COLLECTIONS / ANTHOLOGIES / E-BOOKS
4th Floor Alliance House, 30 Cross Street, Manchester M2 7AQ
0161 834 8730
info@carcanet.co.uk
www.carcanet.co.uk
Editors: Michael Schmidt, Andrew Latimer
Established 1969. Publishes poetry, but also some fiction, non-fiction and mixed prose/poetry anthologies (see p106). Publications available direct from the publisher website; at chain and independent bookshops; at national and local literary events; and from Amazon and other bookshop websites.
In 2019, Carcanet Press won Northern Small Press of the Year at the 2019 British Book Awards. In 2018 it was made a finalist in the Manchester Culture Awards in the Outstanding Contribution category and shortlisted for Northern Publisher of the Year in the Northern Soul Awards. It

was also shortlisted for the IPG Alison Morrison Diversity Award for a fourth year. In 2017 Carcanet Press was shortlisted for the IPG Diversity Award and the Northern Soul Northern Publisher of the Year Award.

Carcanet celebrated its 50th anniversary from Autumn 2019 – Summer 2020.

SUBMISSIONS: Open to all. Guidelines at www.carcanet.co.uk/cgi-bin/scribe?showinfo=ip002. Rejections may occasionally include unsolicited feedback.

WE SAY: Carcanet is a heavy hitter in the indie world and their publication quality reflects their prestige. We looked at *Thousandfold* by Nina Bogin, an 88-page perfect-bound paperback collection printed on thick cream paper. The cover design is tasteful and the interior layout is clear and uncluttered, well-suited to the beautifully spare poems within.

See also: prose publishers p106 and *PN Review* (poetry magazine) p279

CB EDITIONS

COLLECTIONS
146 Percy Road, London W12 9QL
0208 7432467
info@cbeditions.com
www.cbeditions.com
Editor: Charles Boyle

Established 2007. Publishes poetry, and short fiction and other prose (see p107). Publications available direct from publisher website; at chain and independent bookshops nationwide; at national and local literary events; and from Amazon and other bookshop websites.

A multi-award-winning publisher: titles have won the Aldeburgh First Collection Prize (2009, 2011, 2013); the Scott Moncrieff Translation Prize (2014) and the McKitterick Prize (2008), as well as being shortlisted for the Goldsmiths Prize (2014) and the Guardian First Book Award (2014).

SUBMISSIONS: Currently publishing only a small number of titles; please email (info@cbeditions.com) before submitting. No feedback offered with rejection. Authors are paid an advance/fee plus royalties, and receive free copies of the book.

WE SAY: We looked at Dan O'Brien's *War Reporter*, a 134-page paperback, printed on high quality materials. The cover design adheres to the CB brand, which is a textured grey/brown background, with another single colour (red in this case) accenting the design. The text (long-line poems, based on interviews, conversations and transcripts) is well laid out.

See also: prose publishers p107

CINNAMON PRESS ☆

COLLECTIONS, ANTHOLOGIES, AND CHAPBOOKS/PAMPHLETS
Meirion House, Glan yr afon, Blaenau Ffestiniog, Gwynedd LL41 3SU
01766 832112
jan@cinnamonpress.com
www.cinnamonpress.com
Editors: Jan Fortune, Adam Craig

Established 2005. Mixed form: alongside poetry, also publishes novels, short stories and creative non-fiction (p109). Publications available direct from publisher website; at chain and independent bookshops nationwide; at local literary events; from Amazon and from Inpress Books.

Titles from Cinnamon Press have won Scottish Arts Best First Book of the Year; Wales Book of the Year; and Wales Book of the Year

Readers' Vote. Also shortlisted for Wales Book of the Year and the Forward Prize for Best First Collection and winner of the Saltire Scottish Book of the Year.
SUBMISSIONS: Submit only during submissions periods. See www.cinnamonpress.com/index.php/about-cinnamon-press/submissions for full details. Usually responds within one to three months. Submissions that came close to publication may receive some feedback with rejection. Authors are paid royalties only.
WE SAY: *Inland* by Kay Syrad features an earth-toned cover – a detail from Andrzej Jackowski's painting *Vigilant Dreamer 2* sits over a graphic design of the word 'inland', which looks like roots or foundations in the context of the page. Over this the book title and author name stand out in white text. We looked at a PDF of the inner pages. Filled with what is often rather dense, long-lined poetry with little opportunity for white space, the layout is, still, inviting rather than overwhelming.
For a fuller description of this press, including what They Say, see also: *Envoi Poetry Journal* **p272 and prose publishers p109**

CIRCAIDY GREGORY PRESS
COLLECTIONS
Creative Media Centre, 45 Robertson Street, Hastings, East Sussex TN34 1HL
sales@circaidygregory.co.uk
www.circaidygregory.co.uk
A mixed form 'independent publisher for independent readers'. As well as poetry, this press also publishes a range of prose (see p110).
See also: prose publishers p110

CLINIC
COLLECTIONS AND CHAPBOOKS/PAMPHLETS
clinicpresents@gmail.com
www.clinicpresents.com
Established 2009. Publishes pamphlets, anthologies, and occasionally on its website. Also runs popular poetry events.

CLUTAG PRESS
COLLECTIONS AND CHAPBOOKS/PAMPHLETS
PO Box 154, Thame OX9 3RQ
info@clutagpress.com
www.clutagpress.com
Publishes poetry and memoir with 'a marked but not exclusive interest in the margins and the marginal, in nature and place, in the British and Irish Archipelago'. Not currently accepting unsolicited manuscripts.
See also: *Archipelago Magazine* **(poetry magazine) p216**

COLUMBA PRESS
MIXED-FORM COLLECTIONS AND ANTHOLOGIES
23 Merrion Square North, Dublin 2, Ireland
garry@columba.ie
www.columba.ie
Editor: Garry O'Sullivan
Established 1985. Mainly publishes prose (see p110). Publications available direct from publisher website; by direct mail and email orders; from chain bookshops nationwide; from independent bookshops; at local literary events; and from Amazon and other bookshop websites.
SUBMISSIONS: Open to all. Submit by email to garry@columba.ie. Usually responds within four weeks. Rejections may occasionally include unsolicited feedback. Authors are paid an advance/

fee plus royalties and receive free copies of the book.
See also: prose publishers p110

COPY PRESS
COLLECTIONS
51 South Street, Ventnor, Isle of Wight
PO38 1NG
020 3 397 6575
info@copypress.co.uk
www.copypress.co.uk
Editors: Yve Lomax, Vit Hopley, Anne Tallentire, Kristen Kreider, Cecile Malaspina
Established 2012. Publishes contemporary writing (see p111) including poetry. Publications available by direct mail and email order; from chain and independent bookshops nationwide; and from Amazon and other bookshop websites.
SUBMISSIONS: Open to all. Submit by email to info@copypress.co.uk. Guidelines at www.copypress. co.uk/index/proposals. The press never charges a reading fee. Usually responds in one to three months. Rejections may occasionally include unsolicited feedback. Authors are paid royalties.
For more information, including what We Say, see also: prose publishers p111

CRATER PRESS, THE
E-BOOKS, COLLECTIONS, ANTHOLOGIES AND CHAPBOOKS/ PAMPHLETS
3 Kennington Park House, Kennington Park Place, London SE11 4JT
richie_fire@hotmail.com
www.craterpress.co.uk
Editor: Richard Parker
Established 2009. Offers a subscription of £55 for ten books. Publications available direct

from publisher website; from independent bookshops; and from Amazon.
In 2011 The Crater Press won the Michael Marks Publishers' Award for British poetry pamphlet publisher of the year.
SUBMISSIONS: By invitation only. Rejections may occasionally include unsolicited feedback. Authors receive free copies of the book.

CURRACH PRESS
ANTHOLOGIES AND MIXED-FORM COLLECTIONS AND ANTHOLOGIES
23 Merrion Square North, Dublin 2, Ireland
garry@columba.ie
www.currach.ie
Editor: Garry O'Sullivan
Established 2003. Mixed form: also publishes prose (see p113). Publications available direct from publisher website; by direct mail and email orders; from chain bookshops nationwide; from independent bookshops; at local literary events; and from Amazon and other bookshop websites.
SUBMISSIONS: Open to all. Submit by email to garry@columba.ie. Usually responds within four weeks. Rejections may occasionally include unsolicited feedback. Authors are paid an advance/ fee plus royalties and receive free copies of the book.
See also: prose publishers p113

DAHLIA PUBLISHING ☆
ANTHOLOGIES
shaikhf@hotmail.com
www.dahliapublishing.co.uk
Editor: Farhana Shaikh
Established 2010. Mainly publishes fiction (see p114). Publications available direct from publisher

website; by direct mail and email orders; from chain bookshops nationwide; and from independent bookshops.

SUBMISSIONS: Open to all. Submit by email (submissions@ dahliapublishing.co.uk) or by post (6 Samphire Close, Hamilton, Leicester LE5 1RW). Also accepts a Twitter pitch to @farhanashaikh. Guidelines at www.dahliapublishing. co.uk/submission-guidelines. Usually responds within four to six months. Rejections may occasionally include unsolicited feedback. Authors are paid royalties only and receive free copies of the book.

See also: prose publishers p114

DEDALUS PRESS

COLLECTIONS AND ANTHOLOGIES
13 Moyclare Road, Baldoyle, Dublin D13 K1C2, Ireland
+35 318 392034
www.dedaluspress.com
office@dedaluspress.com
Editor: Pat Boran
Established 1985. Publications are available direct from publisher website; chain bookshops nationwide; at independent bookshops; at local literary events; and from Amazon and other online booksellers.

GENRES: Poetry (mostly Irish, some translation).

SUBMISSIONS: Submissions open to all, but only during submission windows (see Submission Guidelines on website). Submissions via Submittable. com only. Usually responds within three months. Rejections may occasionally include feedback. Authors are paid royalties only, although an advance may be offered in particular cases.

WE SAY: The three books we looked at (*Geomantic* by Paula Meehan, *Clasp* by Doireann Ní Ghríofa and *Transmissions* by Elaine Cosgrove) all have a matte finish and illustrated cover – Meehan's showing stylised landscapes within a large white border, and Ni Ghríofa's featuring a green-toned scene of Eve reaching for the apple. However, the cover for Cosgrove's book is the most striking: it appears to be a purple flower on a black background, but on closer look, the image is made of geometric shapes. All three collections are under 100 pages. Meehan's poetry seems to have a more uniform style, while Ní Ghríofa and Cosgrove experiment with form slightly more.

DEMPSEY & WINDLE

COLLECTIONS, ANTHOLOGIES AND CHAPBOOKS/PAMPHLETS
01483 571164
dempseyandwindle@gmail.com
www.dempseyandwindle.com
Editor: Janice Dempsey
Publications sold direct from publisher website; at local literary events; on amazon.co.uk and by ordering through any bookshop.

SUBMISSIONS: Open to all, during submissions windows. Submit by email to dempseyandwindle@ gmail.com. Guidelines are posted on the website (www. dempseyandwindle.com). Usually responds within four weeks. Rejections may occasionally include feedback. Authors must contribute to production costs by agreeing to buy at least 60 copies of their book at 50% of RRP. Discounts are given to authors who agree to buy at least 100 copies of the initial print run. Authors sign an agreement setting out the rate of commission due to them from sales through publishers' distribution channels and a commitment to keep the books in print for five years.

WE SAY: We saw a copy of Imogen Russell Williams' *The Women Left Behind*, a 74-page paperback poetry collection with a glossy cover. Chris Riddell's sketches which accompany the poems are beautiful, and the poems themselves are laid out in a coherent way; however, the slightly low resolution of the cover image is a little at odds with the quality of the writing and illustration.

DIRT PIE PRESS

ANTHOLOGIES
editors@riptidejournal.co.uk
www.riptidejournal.co.uk
Editors: Dr Virginia Baily, Dr Sally Flint
Established 2006. Literary fiction (see p116) and poetry. Publications available direct from publisher website; by post and email order; from independent bookshops; and at local literary events. All stockists are listed on the website.

SUBMISSIONS: Open to all, guidelines on the website. Submit by email to editors@riptidejournal. co.uk. Usually responds within four to six months. No feedback offered with rejections. Contributors receive a flat fee.

See also: prose publishers p116, and, for a fuller description of this press, *Riptide Journal* (mixed-form magazine) p252

DOG HORN PUBLISHING ☆

COLLECTIONS, ANTHOLOGIES AND CHAPBOOKS/PAMPHLETS
45 Monk Ings, Birstall, Batley WF17 9HU
01924 466853
editor@doghornpublishing.com
www.doghornpublishing.com
Editor: Adam Lowe
Established 2005. Also publishes prose (short stories, non-fiction, novels), see p117. Publications available direct from publisher website; by post and email order; from chain bookshops nationwide; from independent bookshops; at national and local literary events; and from Amazon and other bookshop websites, including lulu.com.
Titles from Dog Horn have won the *Guardian* First Book Award (reader nomination); the Noble (not Nobel) Book Prize; and have had multiple honourable mentions in the Year's Best Horror.

SUBMISSIONS: Submissions by invitation only. If invited, submit by email to editor@ doghornpublishing.com. Guidelines at www. doghornpublishing.com/ wordpress/about. Usually responds in over six months. Rejections may occasionally include unsolicited feedback. Authors are paid royalties only and receive free copies of the book.

See also: prose publishers p117

DOIRE PRESS

COLLECTIONS AND ANTHOLOGIES
Aille, Inverin, County Galway, Ireland
+353 091 593290
www.doirepress.com
Editor: John Walsh
Established 2007. Publishes poetry and short stories equally (see p117). Publications available direct from publisher website; from independent bookshops; at national literary events; and from

Amazon and kennys.ie.
Doire Press title *Waiting for the Bullet* by Madeleine D'Arcy won the 2015 Edge Hill Readers' Prize and Breda Wall Ryan's *In a Hare's Eye* won the 2016 Shine/Strong Prize.
SUBMISSIONS: Only open to writers living in Ireland, and not actively seeking submissions (though open to being approached by writers familiar with Doire's books who are sure their work will be a good fit). Submit by post (Aille, Inverin, County Galway, Ireland) or by email (doirepress@gmail.com). Guidelines at www.doirepress.com/submissions. Usually responds within one to three months. No feedback offered with rejections. Book deals vary between poetry and short story collections, and between books published in the north or the Republic authors receive 15% royalties plus a fee – the deal depends on grant funding received.
WE SAY: *The Woman on the Other Side* by Stephanie Conn is an 80-page poetry collection. Perfect bound, with prize credentials proud on the cover above the title and set over the image of a snowy path. The book features pale blue end papers, which are a lovely touch, while the main block is made up of thick cream pages. The poetry, largely free verse, explores feelings of alienation in language, place and relationships. Well designed, with well-ordered poems that conduct the reader on a journey through the Netherlands.
See also: prose publishers p117

DOSTOYEVSKY WANNABE
COLLECTIONS, ANTHOLOGIES AND

CHAPBOOKS/PAMPHLETS
dostoyevskywannabe@gmail.com
www.dostoyevskywannabe.com
Editors: Victoria Brown, Richard Brammer
Established 2014. Also publishes prose and mixed-form anthologies (see p118). Publications available from Amazon and The Poetry Library, South Bank, London
SUBMISSIONS: Open to all. Submit by email to dostoyevskywannabe@gmail.com. Guidelines at www.dostoyevsky.com/submit. Usually responds within four weeks. Authors are given two choices regarding royalties which are outlined in the submission guidelines.
For more information, see also prose publishers p118 and *The All-New Swimmers Club* (mixed-form e-zine) p214

EARLYWORKS PRESS ☆
ANTHOLOGIES, INCLUDING MIXED-FORM ANTHOLOGIES
Creative Media Centre, 45 Robertson St, Hastings, TN34 1HL
kay@earlyworkspress.co.uk
www.earlyworkspress.co.uk
Editor: Kay Green
Established 2005. Mixed form. As well as poetry, Earlyworks publishes prose, as well as mixed-form anthologies (see p118). Most books are anthologies of work by authors from the publisher's competition shortlists. Publications available direct from publisher website; at independent bookshops; at local literary events; and online bookstores. Discounted books are available to club members and competition shortlisted authors.
GENRES: Any.
SUBMISSIONS: As Earlyworks Press is a club for authors and illustrators

– running writing competitions, producing winners' anthologies and some other books – please submit via competition initially (see p307). The press often invites shortlisted authors to join in other publishing projects.

WE SAY: We looked at Earlyworks Press' website, which promotes their writing competitions. These competitions are what in turn become their poetry and flash fiction collections, with shortlisted authors all featuring. Each collection is different from the next in both design and theme, also presenting a collaborative feel by grouping together successful competition entrants to form each title.

See also: prose publishers p118

EGG BOX PUBLISHING

COLLECTIONS, ANTHOLOGIES AND CHAPBOOKS/PAMPHLETS
ueapubsoc@gmail.com
www.eggboxpublishing.com
Advisor: Nathan Hamilton
Established 2006, working in partnership with UEA students. Publications available direct from publisher website; by post and email order; from chain bookshops nationwide; from independent bookshops; at national literary events; and from Amazon and other bookshop websites.

ENITHARMON PRESS

E-BOOKS, COLLECTIONS, ANTHOLOGIES, CHAPBOOKS/ PAMPHLETS, ART BOOKS
020 7430 0844
info@enitharmon.co.uk
www.enitharmon.co.uk
Established 1967. Publishes art, poetry and literary editions. Publications available direct from publisher website; by post and email order; from chain bookshops nationwide; from independent bookshops; and from Amazon.

SUBMISSIONS: Not accepted.

WE SAY: Enitharmon Press have 40 years of experience publishing poetry – longevity achieved by the production of first-rate publications. The quality of materials used remains high. Recent poetry collections favour bold, uncluttered graphic cover designs. We are particular fans of Maureen Duffy's *Pictures from an Exhibition*, which features different coloured eyes staring out from a dark blue background.

ERBACCE-PRESS

COLLECTIONS, ANTHOLOGIES AND CHAPBOOKS/PAMPHLETS
erbacce@blueyonder.co.uk
erbacce-press.com
Editor: Dr Alan Corkish
Co-Editor: Dr Andrew Taylor
Established 2004. Publications available direct from publisher website; by post and email order; from independent bookshops; at national and local literary events; and from Amazon. Note: erbacce is a cooperative. All profits are used exclusively to produce new books.

SUBMISSIONS: Open to all. Submit by post (Dr Andrew Taylor, 5 Farrell Close, Melling, Liverpool L31 1BU) or by email (erbacce@ hotmail.com). Guidelines are on the website. Usually responds within 48hrs. Authors are paid 20% royalties and receive free copies of the book and a discount on further copies.

WE SAY: The A5, 96-page perfect-bound collection we saw by Mudnakudu Chinnaswamy, *Before It Rains Again,* had a glossy cover

EMMA PRESS, THE

COLLECTIONS FOR CHILDREN,
ANTHOLOGIES AND CHAPBOOKS/
PAMPHLETS
16-26 Hylton Street, Jewellery Quarter,
Birmingham B18 6HQ
hello@theemmapress.com
www.theemmapress.com
Editor: Emma Wright

Established 2012. Also publishes
prose (see p120). Publications
available direct from publisher
website; from chain bookshops
nationwide; from independent
bookshops; at national and local
literary events; and from Amazon
and other bookshop websites.
In 2016, The Emma Press won the
Michael Marks award for Poetry
Pamphlet Publishers.
SUBMISSIONS: Open to all, during
submission windows. Submit
online at www.theemmapress.
com/about/submissions. Usually
responds within four to six months.
Rejections may occasionally
include unsolicited feedback.
Submitters are required to buy a
book from the press. Authors are
paid royalties only and receive free
copies of the book.
WE SAY: We looked at anthology
Slow Things, a slightly smaller than
A5 paperback, 53 pages long.
Made from quality materials, with
a lovely, quirky cover that has
an illustration of a sloth having a
picnic, and blue end papers. A
clean layout, plenty of biog space
and illustrated with sketches. Top
notch.
See also: prose publishers p120

THEY SAY

The Emma Press is an
independent publisher
dedicated to producing
beautiful, thought-provoking,
often illustrated books. The
founder, Emma Wright, caught
the publishing bug while
working at Orion Publishing
Group and originally started
the press to share the poetry
of Rachel Piercey. Seven years
later, the Emma Press has
retained its initial principles
of openness and accessibility
and published over 70 titles,
including 31 single-author
pamphlets and forays into
translated poetry, children's
poetry and prose. *Moon
Juice*, by Katie Wakeling,
with illustrations by Elīna
Braslina, won the 2017 CLiPPA,
the Centre for Literacy in
Primary Education's award for
children's poetry books.

showing a textured painting. Chinnaswamy, a prominent Dalit poet based in Bengaluru, India, was first being translated by Rowena Hill in 2002, before his collection was picked up by erbacce-press. *Before It Rains Again* explores the social mores of touch and taboo in Hinduism, digging into 2,000 years of history. **See also: *erbacce* (poetry magazine) p273**

ETRUSCAN BOOKS

COLLECTIONS AND ANTHOLOGIES
etruscanpublishing@gmail.com
etruscanbooks.cargo.site
Sussex-based publisher founded in 1996. Has published concrete, Gaelic and modernist poetry, 'with an ear for the lyric and the made up word'. Books are 'sewn on good papers', and sold at the LRB Bookshop. Their new website was being populated with more information as we went to press.

EYE FLASH POETRY

E-BOOKS / ANTHOLOGIES AND CHAPBOOKS/PAMPHLETS
7 Trevor Road, Newport, Isle of Wight PO30 5DZ
07827 447532
eyeflashpoetry@outlook.com
www.eyeflashpoetry.co.uk
Editor: Charlotte Begg
Established 2017. Publications available direct from the publisher website; from independent bookshops; at national literary events; from Southbank Poetry Library; and from Amazon and other bookshop websites.
GENRES: Contemporary mixed poetry.
SUBMISSIONS: Open to all. Submit by email to eyeflashpoetry@ outlook.com. Guidelines at www.

eyeflashpoetry.co.uk/?page_id=25. Usually responds within four weeks. Rejections may occasionally include unsolicited feedback. Authors are paid royalties.
WE SAY: We looked at PDF samples of two of Eye Flash Poetry's Pocket Poetry Collections, *The Heart* and *Dust*. Both collections display isolated graphics on their covers of a skull and a heart, embodying the poems' Gothic genre. This tone reflects the publication's style as a whole in their vein-struck eye logo, creating a consistent theme across the publications.
See also: *Eye Flash Poetry Magazine* (poetry magazine) p273

FAIR ACRE PRESS ☆

COLLECTIONS, ANTHOLOGIES AND CHAPBOOKS/PAMPHLETS
Primrose Cottage, Sweeney Mountain, Oswestry SY10 9EZ
01691 239466
fairacrepress@gmail.com
www.fairacrepress.co.uk
Editor: Nadia Kingsley
Established 2011. Also publishes prose (see p123). Publications available direct from publisher website; from chain bookshops nationwide; from independent bookshops; at local literary events; and from Amazon.
I Once Knew a Poem Who Wore a Hat, a Fair Acre Press children's poetry book by Emma Purshouse and Catherine Pascall Moore, won the Rubery Award for Poetry in 2016. *The Goldsmith's Apprentice* by Keith Chandler won the International Rubery Award for Poetry 2018. *#MeToo* Poetry Anthology edited by Deborah Alma won Saboteur's best anthology award 2018.

GENRES: Poetry; also nature writing, wildlife photography, cartoons, plays.
SUBMISSIONS: By invitation only. Guidelines at www.fairacrepress.co.uk/about. Authors are paid royalties only and receive free copies of the book.
WE SAY: Emma Purshouse's A5, 112-page perfect-bound collection of silly poems *I Once Knew a Poem Who Wore a Hat* isn't just for drawing kid's attention or making them laugh. Throughout the book, Figment (of the Imagination) pops up with suggestions for how to perform and memorise poetry. With fun illustrations by Catherine Pascall Moore, the collection won the Rubery Book Award in 2016.
See also: prose publishers p123

FINCHAM PRESS
ANTHOLOGIES
Department of English and Creative Writing, University of Roehampton, London SW15 5PH
finchampress@roehampton.ac.uk
www.fincham.press
Established 2013. Publishes prose (see p125) and poetry – primarily used to focus on publishing anthologies of work by Roehampton students, but now expanding its output. Publications available direct from the publisher website; from Amazon; and from Roehampton University e-store.
SUBMISSIONS: Submitters may only submit during submission windows, by email to finchampress@roehampton.ac.uk. Currently focused on work from the university, but with plans to extend this output in the future, so keep checking the guidelines at www.fincham.press/submissions. Responds within one to three

months. Authors and contributors are paid royalties only, and receive free copies of their book.
For more information, including what We Say, see prose publishers p125

FINE PRESS POETRY
COLLECTIONS
andrewmoorhouse@me.com
www.finepresspoetry.com
Editor: Andrew Moorhouse
Established 2014. Publications available direct from publisher website.
SUBMISSIONS: By invitation only. Submit by email to andrewmoorhouse@me.com. Usually responds within four weeks. Rejections include reason for decision and suggestions of alternative publishers. No feedback offered with rejections. Payment to author is individually arranged.
WE SAY: We were unable to see a full publication from Fine Press Poetry, but we did view some photos of the books, which are hard back and clothbound with plenty of texture. The title and author appear framed on white paper, embedded in the cover. The inner pages look delicate and well designed, featuring detailed ink drawings and a pleasing serif font, and the paper appears to be thick and textured.

FISH PUBLISHING ☆
ANTHOLOGIES
info@fishpublishing.com
www.fishpublishing.com
Editors: Clem Cairns, Jula Walton, Mary-Jane Holmes, Adam Wyeth, Tina Pisco, Simon Humphries, Paul MacMahon.
Established 1995. Mixed output – including mixed poetry and prose

anthologies. Publications available direct from the publisher website; by direct mail and email order; at chain and independent bookshops; and from Amazon and other bookshop websites.

SUBMISSIONS: Open to all. Submit by post (Fish Publishing, Durrus, Bantry, County Cork, Ireland), email (info@fishpublishing.com) or via the website at reader.fishpublishing. com/accounts/login/?next=/. Guidelines at www.fishpublishing. com/writing-contests. Submissions run as a competition, and so an entry fee is charged. Usually responds immediately when entries are made online. Fish publishes the winning submissions from its writing competitions and provides a feedback/critique for submissions for a fee. Contributors are paid a flat fee and receive free copies of the book.

For more information, including what We Say and what They Say, see prose publishers p127

FLAPJACK PRESS

PAPERBACKS, E-BOOKS, COLLECTIONS AND ANTHOLOGIES
6 Chiffon Way, Salford,
Greater Manchester M3 6AB
mail@flapjackpress.co.uk
www.flapjackpress.co.uk
Editor: Paul Neads

Established 2008. Publications available direct from publisher website; by post and email order; at independent bookshops; at local literary events; and from Amazon and other bookshop websites. Flapjack poets include Rosie Garland, Henry Normal, Janine Booth, Dominic Berry (Best Spoken Word Performer winner, Saboteur Awards), Jackie Hagan (Creative Future Literary Award winner & Best Spoken Word Show winner, Saboteur Awards), Anna Percy, Ben Mellor (BBC Radio 4 Slam Champion), Gerry Potter (formerly Chloe Poems) and Tony Walsh. Flapjack Press title *Selkie Singing at the Passing Place* by Sarah Miller and Melanie Rees was runner-up for Best Collaborative Work, Saboteur Awards 2015. Children's collection *We Are Poets!* by Helên Thomas won the Book of the Month Award from The Poetry Kit, 2008. Flapjack Press was shortlisted Best Northern Publisher in the Northern Soul Awards 2018.

SUBMISSIONS: Priority is for northwest-based performance poetry and début collections. Currently closed to unsolicited submissions. Usually responds within one to three months. No feedback offered with rejection. Authors receive a flat fee or advance plus royalties, and free copies of the book.

WE SAY: The less-than-A5 perfect-bound paperbacks we saw, *As in Judy* by Rosie Garland and *Travelling Second Class Through Hope* by Henry Normal, both featured pictures of the poets on the matte covers. Not all books by the press are so designed though, and the cover on Normal's collection differed as a French flap style. The final section of Garland's collection was inspired by the 1913 attack on paintings in Manchester Art Gallery by three suffragettes.

FLARESTACK POETS

CHAPBOOKS/PAMPHLETS
flarestackpoets@gmail.com
www.flarestackpoets.co.uk
Editors: Jacqui Rowe and Isabel Palmer

Established 2009. Publications available direct from publisher website; at independent bookshops; and at national and local literary events.

Flarestack Poets has won numerous awards, including Publisher of the Year and Pamphlet of the Year for Gaud by David Clarke in 2013.

SUBMISSIONS: Open to all, during submissions windows. Submit by email to flarestackpoets@gmail.com. Guidelines on the website. Usually responds within one to three months. No feedback offered with rejections. Authors receive free copies of the book, and are able to buy more copies at 33% discount. Pamphlets are promoted: sent to an extensive review list, plus a limited number of places nominated by the writer; submitted to PBS for Pamphlet Choice; and entered for the Michael Marks Award.

WE SAY: Wendy Pratt's A5-sized, saddle-stitched poetry pamphlet *Lapstrake* is bound in a thick, green cover, with pale pink inner covers. At the bottom of many of the cream-coloured pages are explanations of various references to Norse mythology; 'lapstrake' is a method of boat building where the edges of hull planks overlap, and as such the poems are interconnected. The collection considers the movement and what Pratt calls 'the changing emotions of the sea' in relation to loss.

FLIPPED EYE PUBLISHING

COLLECTIONS, ANTHOLOGIES AND CHAPBOOKS/PAMPHLETS
books@flippedeye.net
www.flippedeye.net
Established 2001. Predominantly publishes poetry, but also some fiction (see p128). Publications available direct from publisher website; from selected/local chain bookshops; from independent bookshops; from Amazon; and at book launches and readings.

Titles from Flipped Eye have won the PBS Pamphlet Choice award (2015) and been shortlisted for the Michael Marks Award (2014).

SUBMISSIONS: Submit by email to newwork@flippedeye.net. Guidelines at www.flippedeye.net/blog/2009/08/thesubs/. A response is not guaranteed, but may be sent within one to three months. Rejections may occasionally include unsolicited feedback. Authors are paid royalties only and receive free copies of the book.

See also: prose publishers p128

FLY ON THE WALL PRESS ☆

COLLECTIONS, ANTHOLOGIES AND CHAPBOOKS/PAMPHLETS
isabellekenyon@hotmail.co.uk
www.flyonthewallpoetry.co.uk
Editor: Isabelle Kenyon
Established 2018. Mainly publishes poetry, but also some prose and mixed-form anthologies (p128). Available direct from the publisher website, from selected chain and independent bookshops, at national literary events, and from Amazon and other online bookshops.

Fly on the Wall poetry anthology *Please Hear What I'm Not Saying* was shortlisted for the 2018 Saboteur Awards Best Anthology, and Fly on the Wall was longlisted for the 2019 Saboteur Awards Innovative Publisher category.

SUBMISSIONS: Submissions are open to all, during submissions windows. Submitters must buy a publication from the press. Submit by email to isabellekenyon@ hotmail.co.uk. Guidelines at www.flyonthewallpoetry.co.uk. Usually responds within four weeks, but for an optional fee, writers can receive an expedited response. Rejections may occasionally include unsolicited feedback. Authors are paid royalties and receive free copies of their book.

WE SAY: Looking at a PDF of Fly on the Wall's *Persona Non Grata* anthology, edited by Isabelle Kenyon, themes of displacement, human life and invisibility are clear. The simple monochromatic design, with few graphics, focuses the anthology entirely on the words and theme it embodies. Fly on the Wall clearly care for meaningful writing, with each section of the anthology introduced by an illustration denoting the human suffering that comes with displacement.

See also: prose publishers p128 and *Fly on the Wall Webzine* **(mixed-form magazine) p227**

FOR BOOKS' SAKE
ANTHOLOGIES
www.forbookssake.net
Mixed-form publisher. Publishes poetry, but also a lot of fiction and non-fiction prose (see page 129). Publications available direct from publisher website; from selected/ local chain bookshops; from independent bookshops; and at national and local literary events. For Book's Sake title *Furies: A Poetry Anthology of Women Warriors* was runner-up for the Best Anthology prize at the 2015 Saboteur Awards.

SUBMISSIONS: Open to self-identifying women, and especially encouraged from women of colour, disabled women, queer women, trans women and women from low-income backgrounds. Submit, during submissions windows only, via Submittable (forbookssake. submittable.com/submit – guidelines at same address). Usually responds within four weeks.

WE SAY: We checked out *Furies: A Poetry Anthology of Women Warriors*, which is one of a handful of For Books' Sake's cherry-picked titles. A perfect-bound hardcover with a sleek black and silver design, the collection has a luxurious feel – made edgy and current by the content itself. A fierce product for a fierce campaign: the collection raised money for the charity Rape Crisis. We approve.

See also: For Books' Sake (mixed-form e-zine p227 and prose publishers p129)

FOX SPIRIT BOOKS
COLLECTIONS AND MIXED-FORM ANTHOLOGIES
adele@foxspirit.co.uk
www.foxspirit.co.uk
Editor: Adele Wearing
Established 2012. Mainly fiction publisher (see p129), but does publish some poetry collections, and prose/poetry anthologies. Publications available from Amazon; and at select events. Fox Spirit Books won the 2015 British Fantasy Society award for Best Small Press.

SUBMISSIONS: Submit only during submissions windows. See submissions guidelines at www.foxspirit.co.uk/sample-page/ submissions for full instructions and details of author remuneration. Feedback not usually offered with rejections. Will try to provide

feedback on request, but this is not always possible.
See also: prose publishers p129

FOXTROT UNIFORM
CHAPBOOKS/PAMPHLETS
2 Sowell Street, Broadstairs, Kent CT10 2AT
foxtrotuniformpoetry@gmail.com
foxtrotuniformblog.wordpress.com
Editors: Joshua Cialis and Reece D Merrifield
Established 2017. Creative writing (poetry and prose, see p228, with visual art). Available direct from the publisher website, by direct mail and email order, from independent bookshops, and at local literary events.
GENRES: Literary; experimental; spontaneous; modern; political.
SUBMISSIONS: Open to all. Submit by email to foxtrotuniformpoetry@ gmail.com. Guidelines at foxtrotuniformblog.wordpress. com/2019/01/10/submissions-for-publication. Usually responds within four weeks. Rejections may occasionally include unsolicited feedback. Contributors receive free copies of the book, and profits are split between the publishers and the authors.
For more information, including what We Say, see also: *Foxtrot Uniform* (mixed-form magazine) p228

GALLERY PRESS, THE
COLLECTIONS
books@gallerypress.com
www.gallerypress.com
Established in 1970 to publish the work of young Irish poets, with many of those poets becoming established, leading figures, and continues to look for new poets. Submit hard copy only, and ensure you are familiar with previous publications.

GATEHOUSE PRESS
COLLECTIONS AND CHAPBOOKS/ PAMPHLETS
32 Grove Walk, Norwich NR1 2QG
admin@gatehousepress.com
www.gatehousepress.com
Editors: Meirion Jordan, Andrew McDonnell, Julia Webb
Established 2006. Mainly publishes poetry, but also some fiction (short stories and novellas – see p130). Publications available direct from publisher website; from selected/local chain bookshops; from independent bookshops; at national and local literary events; and from bookshop websites.
SUBMISSIONS: Submit during submissions windows. Usually responds within one to three months. No feedback offered with rejections. Writer payment/ remuneration varies according to publication.
For a fuller description of this press, see *Lighthouse* (mixed-form literary magazine) p237. See also: prose publishers p130

GIRASOL PRESS
COLLECTIONS, ANTHOLOGIES AND CHAPBOOKS/PAMPHLETS
girasolpressuk@gmail.com
girasolpress.wixsite.com/online
Editors: Leire Barrera Medrano and Daniel Eltringham
Established 2014. Primarily publishes poetry but also some mixed-form poetry/ prose anthologies. Publications available direct from the publisher website and from independent bookshops.
SUBMISSIONS: Submit by email to girasolpressuk@gmail.com.

40

Contributors and authors are currently unpaid.

GRAFT POETRY
COLLECTIONS, ANTHOLOGIES AND CHAPBOOKS/PAMPHLETS
Frizingley Hall, Frizinghall Road, Bradford BD9 4LD
01274 541015
info@graftpoetry.co.uk
www.graftpoetry.co.uk
Editor: Nicholas Bielby
Established 2008. Publishes individual poets. Publications available direct from the publisher website; by direct mail and email order; and from Amazon.
SUBMISSIONS: Submitters must have a history of publication, and must send a sample of six poems before a manuscript will be invited. Submit by post (Graft Poetry, Frizingley Hall, Frizinghall Road, Bradford BD9 4LD) or email (info@graftpoetry.co.uk). Guidelines available at www.graftpoetry.co.uk. Usually responds within four weeks. Feedback provided only at the discretion of the editor. Authors receive free copies of their book, and 50% of the profits once publication costs are covered.
WE SAY: We looked at a PDF of *The Insect Horizon* by Kevin Hanson, an extensive collection of poems by the author across multiple decades. With a simple cover image, this publication focuses primarily on the writing itself, including over 100 pages of poetry. Graft Poetry's website reinforces this passion for the writing itself, with a basic site providing information about their mission to publish previously under-recognised authors and increase accessibility to books by selling at affordable prices.

GREEN BOTTLE PRESS
COLLECTIONS AND CHAPBOOKS/PAMPHLETS
jennifer@greenbottlepress.com
www.greenbottlepress.com
Editor: Jennifer Grigg
Established 2014. Publications available direct from publisher website; from selected/local chain bookshops; and from independent bookshops.
SUBMISSIONS: During submissions windows. Publication history required – must have a record of publishing in magazines and journals. Submit by post to 83 Grove Avenue, London N10 2AL, or via the submissions form at www.greenbottlepress.com/submission-guidelines (guidelines at the same address). Usually responds within one to three months. The press will provide comments and feedback as part of rejection letters, but only on request. Authors are paid royalties only and receive free copies of the book.
WE SAY: Green Bottle Press arrived with a bang. The pamphlet *The Withering Room* by Sarah Sibley was named as the London Review of Books' pamphlet of the year. Containing 20 (mostly short) poems, this is a disconcerting collection, a feeling echoed in the beautiful cover image, which features lovely wallpaper with mould creeping across it. The layout is clear and uncluttered and the production values very high indeed. Any poet would be proud to have a pamphlet produced by this press.

GREY HEN PRESS
ANTHOLOGIES AND COLLECTIONS
info@greyhenpress.com

www.greyhenpress.com
Established in 2007, this Cumbrian press publishes poetry by older women, concentrating in the first instance on producing themed anthologies. Check the website for event and competition updates.

GRIST

MIXED-FORM ANTHOLOGIES
mhm.hud.ac.uk/grist/
Grist is the publishing branch of the University of Huddersfield, and produces acclaimed anthology Grist, which includes poetry and short prose. Submissions are through competitions. Also publishes some single-author books.
See also: prose publishers p132

GUILLEMOT PRESS

COLLECTION, ANTHOLOGIES AND CHAPBOOKS/PAMPHLETS
Cornwall
editor@guillemotpress.co.uk
www.guillemotpress.co.uk
Editors: Luke Thompson and Sarah Cave
Established 2016. Primarily publishes poetry, but also some short story collections (see p132). Publications available direct from the publisher website, and from independent bookshops. Guillemot Press won the 2018 Michael Marks Award for Publishers.
SUBMISSIONS: Open to all. Submit by email to editor@guillemotpress.co.uk. Usually responds in one to three months. Rejections may occasionally include unsolicited feedback.
See also: prose publisher p132

GUPPY BOOKS

BOOKS IN VERSE
Brackenhill, Cotswold Road, Oxford OX2 9JG

www.guppybooks.co.uk
bella@guppybooks.co.uk
Editor: Bella Pearson
Established 2018. Publishes children's fiction, up to age 18, including prose books (see p132). No non-fiction or picture books. Publications available from chain and independent bookshops nationwide; at national and local literary events; and from Amazon and other bookshop websites.
GENRES: Children's; middle-grade; young adult.
SUBMISSIONS: Submissions accepted from agents and from previously published writers. Open to unsolicited submissions during submissions window only. Guidelines at www.guppybooks.co.uk/contact-us. Usually responds in one to three months. Rejections may occasionally include unsolicited feedback. Authors are paid an advance fee and royalties.
See also: prose publishers p132

HAFAN BOOKS (REFUGEES WRITING IN WALES)

ANTHOLOGIES AND CHAPBOOKS/PAMPHLETS
c/o Tom Cheesman, Dept of Languages, Swansea University SA2 8PP
t.cheesman@swansea.ac.uk
lulu.com/hafan
sbassg.wordpress.com
Editors: Tom Cheesman, Jeni Williams
Established 2003. Mixed form: publishes poetry and prose, and various refugee-related books and booklets (see p133). Publications available direct from publisher website; by post and email order; at local literary events; and from Amazon.
SUBMISSIONS: By invitation only, depending on the publication.

Author contributions needed. Submit by email to t.cheesman@swansea.ac.uk. Usually responds within four weeks. Rejections may occasionally include unsolicited feedback. Authors receive free copies of the book; no fee or royalties.
See also: prose publishers p133

HALF MOON BOOKS ☆
COLLECTIONS, ANTHOLOGIES AND CHAPBOOKS/PAMPHLETS
Otley Courthouse, Courthouse Street, Otley, West Yorkshire LS21 3AN
info@halfmoonbooks.co.uk
www.halfmoonbooks.co.uk
Editors: Jane Kitsen, Peter R White, Rosalind Fairclough
Established 2014. Publications available direct from the publisher website; by post and email order; and at local literary events.
SUBMISSIONS: Pamphlet submissions open to poets within a 50-mile radius of Otley, during submissions windows only; collection submissions by invitation only; all others should be sent during submissions windows. Up-to-date guidelines at www.halfmoonbooks.co.uk/index.php/submissions. A submissions charge operated during the press' 2018/19 submissions window. For changes please see the website. Usually responds in one to three months. No feedback offered with rejections. Authors receive some free copies of their book (15 in 2019), then a 50% discount on further copies.

HAPPENSTANCE PRESS ☆
COLLECTIONS, ANTHOLOGIES AND CHAPBOOKS/PAMPHLETS
nell@happenstancepress.com
www.happenstancepress.com
Editor: Helena Nelson
Established 2005. Subscription available for £12.50 which includes one free pamphlet, discount on all titles and feedback on poems sent in during reading windows. Publications available direct from publisher website; by direct mail and email orders; from independent bookshops; at national and local literary events; and from Amazon. HappenStance Press was shortlisted in 2016 for the Michael Marks Award for Pamphlet Publishing.
SUBMISSIONS: During submission windows only; publication history required. Submit by post to 21 Hatton Green, Glenrothes, Fife KY7 4SD. Guidelines at www.happenstancepress.com/index.php/poetry-submission/submitting-to-happenstance. Usually responds within four weeks. Rejections include a personal letter with feedback. Authors receive at least 12 free copies of their book, plus ongoing support.
WE SAY: We saw Charlotte Gann's *Noir*, a slightly-larger-than-A5, 76-page collection featuring a cover with a matte finish. The title is displayed in a yellow text, inside a yellow box, which contrasts nicely with the black and grey cityscape that makes up the rest of the front. The pages feel thicker than normal, which makes the collection easy to peruse. *Noir* is a collection of prose poetry with a focus on darkness, obsession, and a sense of place – specifically, an urban setting.

HEARING EYE
COLLECTIONS
info@hearingeye.org
www.hearingeye.org

Editors: Susan John, Emily Johns, David Floyd

Established 1987 and publishes poetry ranging from haiku to epic translations. Its poets are often guest readers at Torriano Meeting House. Rarely publishes unsolicited collections.

HEDGEHOG PRESS

COLLECTIONS, ANTHOLOGIES AND PAMPHLETS/CHAPBOOKS
poetry@hedgehogpress.co.uk
www.hedgehogpress.co.uk
Established 2017, looking to build a list of 'great, modern collections'. This press also has a writers and readers club called The Cult of the Spiny Hog, members of which receive everything the press publishes for £25/three months. The press only accepts submissions for single poet collections via its competitions, which are run regularly. All other publications are by invitation only.

HENNINGHAM FAMILY PRESS

COLLECTIONS AND CHAPBOOKS/ PAMPHLETS
david@henninghamfamilypress.co.uk
www.henninghamfamilypress.co.uk
Editors: David and Ping Henningham
Established 2006. Primarily publishes fiction (see p135) but also non-fiction and poetry. Publications available direct from the publisher website; from chain and independent bookshops; at national literary events; and from hive.co.uk and other bookshop websites.
Henningham Family Press was shortlisted for The Republic of Consciousness Prize 2019, and was a Regional Finalist for Small Press of the Year in the The British Book Awards 2019.

GENRE: Literary.
SUBMISSIONS: Currently only open to women and BAME authors. Submit via email to david@henninghamfamilypress. co.uk. Guidelines at www. henninghamfamilypress.co.uk/ submissions. Usually responds within four weeks. Offers feedback where possible. Authors are paid an advance fee plus royalties, and receive free copies of their book.
For more information, including what We Say, see also: prose publisher p135

HERCULES EDITIONS

CHAPBOOKS/PAMPHLETS
07949 211740
tamar@herculeseditions.com
www.herculeseditions.com
Editor: Tamar Yoseloff
Established 2012. Publishes poetry combined with visual imagery. Publications sold direct from publisher website; at local literary events and from independent bookshops.
Their first publication, *Formerly*, was shortlisted for the Ted Hughes Award in 2012.
SUBMISSIONS: Accept very few unsolicited submissions. Please read submission guidelines beforehand: www.herculeseditions. com/submissions. Submit by email to tamar@herculeseditions.com. Usually responds within four weeks.
WE SAY: We looked at the available catalogue on the Hercules Edition website, where we found some very eye-catching books (Sean O'Brien's *Hammersmith* is particularly beautiful) which blend poetry and art together to create coffee-table-style collections. The site itself is very easy to use, and full of information without being

over cluttered – worth a browse to
see if Hercules is a fit for you.

HI VIS PRESS

COLLECTIONS AND ANTHOLOGIES
contact@hi-vispress.com
www.hi-vispress.com
Editors: Sophie Pitchford, Jim Gibson,
Ben Williams
Established 2016. Also publishes
prose (see p135). Publications
available direct from publisher
website; from selected/local chain
bookshops; from independent
bookshops; and at national literary
events.
SUBMISSIONS: During submission
windows only. Submit by email
to contact@hi-vispress.com.
Usually responds within one to
three months, with feedback only
if requested. Authors are paid
royalties only and receive free
copies of the book.
See also: prose publishers p135 and
Low Light Magazine **(mixed-form**
magazine) p239

HIGH WINDOW PRESS, THE

COLLECTIONS
submissions@thehighwindow.uk
www.thehighwindowpress.com/the-press
Editor: David Cooke
Established 2015.
GENRES: Contemporary verse.
SUBMISSIONS: Submitters
must have a publication history.
Usually responds within one to
three months. Rejections may
occasionally include unsolicited
feedback. Authors are expected
to buy some discounted copies of
their book. Further details found
on the Press Page: wordpress.com/
view/thehighwindowpress.com
For a fuller description of this press,
see also *The High Window* **(poetry**
magazine) p274

HOLLAND PARK PRESS ☆

COLLECTIONS AND ANTHOLOGIES
46 Baskerville, Malmesbury SN16 9BS
publishing@hollandparkpress.co.uk
www.hollandparkpress.co.uk
Established 2009. Mixed form:
also publishes prose (see p137).
Publications available direct from
publisher website; by direct mail
and email orders; from chain
bookshops nationwide; from
independent bookshops; at
national and local literary events;
and from Amazon. Holland Park
Press was the joint winner of the
Oxford-Weidenfeld Translation
Prize in 2016 and was shortlisted
for the Etisalat Prize for Literature
in 2013.
SUBMISSIONS: Open to all.
Submit by email to publishing@
hollandparkpress.co.uk. Guidelines
at www.hollandparkpress.co.uk/
submissions.php. Usually responds
within one to three months.
No feedback offered with
rejections. Authors are paid
royalties only and receive free
copies of the book.
For further information, including
what We Say and what They Say,
see also: prose publishers p137

HONEST PUBLISHING

E-BOOKS / COLLECTIONS /
MIXED-FORM ANTHOLOGIES
Unit 1B, Clapham North Arts Centre,
26-32 Voltaire Road, London SW4 6DH
info@honestpublishing.com
www.honestpublishing.com
Editors: Chris Greenhough, Daniel
Marsh
Established 2010. Mixed output –
also publishes prose and graphic
novels (see p138). Publications
available direct from publisher
website; from major chain and
independent bookshops; and

from Amazon and other bookshop websites.

SUBMISSIONS: Open to all, but only during submission windows. Submit by post (Unit 1B, Clapham North Arts Centre, 26-32 Voltaire Road, London SW4 6DH) or by email (info@honestpublishing. com). Guidelines at www. honestpublishing.com/submissions. Usually responds within one to three months. No feedback offered with rejection. Authors are paid royalties and receive free copies of the book.
See also: prose publishers p138

HURST STREET PRESS
COLLECTIONS, ANTHOLOGIES AND CHAPBOOKS/PAMPHLETS
OVADA,14a Osney Lane, Oxford OX1 1NJ
general@hurststreetpress.co.uk
www.hurststreetpress.co.uk
Editors: Beth Sparks, Shoshana Kessler
Established 2015. Mixed form. As well as poetry, Hurst Street Press also publishes short story collections and anthologies, non-fiction books and mixed-form anthologies (see p140). Publications available direct from publisher website; from selected/ local chain bookshops and from independent bookshops.
SUBMISSIONS: Open to all. Submit by post (Studio 1, OVADA, 14a Osney Lane, Oxford OX1 1NJ) or by email (general@hurststreetpress. co.uk). Usually responds within one to three months. Rejections may occasionally include unsolicited feedback. Authors are paid royalties only.
See also: prose publisher p140 and IRIS (mixed-form magazine) p233

IF A LEAF FALLS PRESS
CHAPBOOKS/PAMPHLETS
www.samriviere.com/index.php?/ together/if-a-leaf-falls-press/
Editor: Sam Riviere
Established 2015. Over 50 works published from an international list of writers. Publications available direct from the publisher website. Subscription information available on request.
GENRES: Procedural writing; conceptual writing; appropriation.
SUBMISSIONS: Submission guidelines are available at samriviere.com/index.php?/ together/if-a-leaf-falls-press.

IF P THEN Q
COLLECTIONS, CHAPBOOKS/ PAMPHLETS AND ARTISTS' BOOKS
41 Fulford Street, Old Trafford, Manchester M16 9PX
mail@ifpthenq.co.uk
www.ifpthenq.co.uk
Editor: James Davies
Established 2008. Poetry publisher, also published mixed-form (prose and poetry) anthologies. Publications available direct from the publisher website; by post and email order; chain bookshops; Amazon; and Lulu.
If p then q publication *A Field Guide to Lost Things* by Peter Jaeger was nominated for the *Guardian* Not The Booker Prize in 2015.
GENRES: Minimalism; conceptualism.
SUBMISSIONS: Collections are solicited by the editor. Check www.ifpthenq.co.uk/contact for information on whether the press is open to submissions.
WE SAY: We considered digital versions of several publications, including *The Unbearable Contact*

INDIGO DREAMS ☆

COLLECTIONS, ANTHOLOGIES
AND CHAPBOOKS/PAMPHLETS
24 Forest Houses, Halwill, Beaworthy,
Devon EX21 5UU
publishing@indigodreams.co.uk
www.indigodreams.co.uk
Editors: Ronnie Goodyer, Dawn
Bauling

Established 2005 (ltd company
2010). Publications available
direct from publisher website; by
post and email order; from chain
bookshops and independent
bookshops nationwide; and from
Amazon.
Indigo Dreams won the Most
Innovative Publisher 2017 category
at the annual Saboteur Awards
for publishing and literature, and
came second in 2016 and 2018.
The Indigo Dreams editors won
the Ted Slade Award for Services
to Poetry (2015), organised by
Poetry Kit. They were the first joint
winners.
SUBMISSIONS: Open to all, but
only during their submission
window, usually September each
year (see website). Authors are
paid royalties and receive free
copies of the book.
WE SAY: How Time Is In Fields by
Jean Atkin has a perfect-bound
gloss cover featuring an abstract
cover image; a detail of a painting
evoking cornfields. The back cover
includes the poet biography,
plus praise for the collection
from David Morley and Elisabeth
Sennitt Clough. As with all of
IDP's publications, the production
quality is very high, with the poems
carefully presented.

HOW TIME IS IN FIELDS
Jean Atkin

THEY SAY

We consider work from
new and established poets,
publishing around 30 poetry
collections/pamphlets
annually, plus Reach Poetry,
Sarasvati and The Dawntreader
magazines. Further publishing
opportunities are available
through various competitions.
We won the Most Innovative
Publisher 2017 award in the
Saboteur Awards and The Ted
Slade Award for Services to
Poetry (yay!) with a respected
newspaper calling us 'shining
examples' of presses who
'keep the doors open for
different kinds of voices
and experiences.' We have a
reputation for high production
qualities and enjoy excellent
working relationships with our
poets. 'Pleasure, not pressure'
all the way!

**See also: magazines Reach Poetry
p282, Sarasvati p253 and The
Dawntreader p223**

with Poets by Derek Beaulieu and *Midamble* by Peter Jaeger. Both texts show the experimental nature of this publisher's publications, playing with form, structure and typeface to add another dimension to their respective stories.

INK SWEAT & TEARS PRESS ☆
ANTHOLOGIES AND PAMPHLET COMPETITION WINNERS
www.inksweatandtears.co.uk
Editors: Kate Birch and Helen Ivory
Established 2013. Publications available direct at www.inksweatandtears.co.uk/pages/?page_id=5711 or from Amazon.
SUBMISSIONS: Currently publishing winners of the Ink Sweat & Tears/Café Writers Pamphlet Commission Competition only (see p309).
For a fuller description of this press, see *Ink Sweat & Tears* (mixed-form e-zine) p233

IRON PRESS
E-BOOKS / COLLECTIONS, ANTHOLOGIES AND CHAPBOOKS/ PAMPHLETS
5 Marden Terrace, Cullercoats, North Shields NE30 4PD
0191 253 1901
ironpress@blueyonder.co.uk
www.ironpress.co.uk
Editor: Peter Mortimer
Established 1973. Primarily publishes poetry, but also releases some prose (fiction, drama etc) – see p142. Publications available direct from publisher website; by post and email order; from selected/local chain bookshops; from independent bookshops; and via Inpress Ltd.
Iron Press' 2014 Iron Age Literary Festival won Best Event: Tyneside in The Journal Culture Awards.

GENRES: All poetry including haiku.
SUBMISSIONS: Contact the press before submitting work: see the website for guidelines. Submit by post (5 Marden Terrace, Cullercoats, North Shields NE30 4PD) or by email (ironpress@blueyonder.co.uk). Usually responds within one to three months. Rejections may occasionally include unsolicited feedback. Authors are paid a flat fee.
WE SAY: We saw *Connectomics* by Alison Calder, a 54-page perfect-bound A5 collection of poetry inspired by science and the brain. Though the poems could stand alone, the notes included at the bottom of each enhance the reading; for example, one piece references research into Alzheimer's conducted by splicing firefly genes into mice and utilising the resultant florescences of the brain to conduct neural mapping.
See also: prose publishers p142

KATABASIS
COLLECTIONS AND ANTHOLOGIES
020 7485 3830
10 St Martin's Close, London NW1 0HR
katabasis@katabasis.co.uk
www.katabasis.co.uk
Editor: Dinah Livingstone
Established 1967. Primarily publishes English and Latin American poetry, but also some non-fiction and mixed poetry/prose anthologies (see p144). Publications available direct from the publisher website; by direct mail and email order; from chain and independent bookshops nationwide; at national and local literary events; and from Amazon.

48

SUBMISSIONS: Submissions by invitation only. Solicited work may receive a response within four weeks. No feedback offered with rejections.

WE SAY: Katabasis provided us with a link to their website. The cover of every book in their catalogue is displayed on the homepage, giving instant insight as to the brightness of their designs. They seem to favour paintings or illustration over photography, with serif fonts for titles. We note in particular that there is a certain amount of branding for individual authors: for example, Dinah Livingston's books all seem to have covers taken from the same painting, or at least provided by the same artist.

See also: prose publishers p144

KHIDR COLLECTIVE
POETRY ANTHOLOGIES
69 Uxbridge Road, Shepherds Bush, London W12 8NR
07852 337369
khidrcollective@googlemail.com
www.khidrcollective.co.uk
Editors: Zain Dada, Raeesah Akhtar, Zainab Rahim and Nishat Alam
Established 2017. Publishes both poetry and prose anthologies (see p144). Publications available direct from the publisher; by direct mail and e-mail orders; from independent bookshops; and at local literary events.

GENRE: Literary.

SUBMISSIONS: Open to all. Submit by email to khidrcollective@googlemail.com. Guidelines at www.khidrcollective.co.uk. Usually responds in one to three months. No feedback offered with rejections. Contributors are paid a flat fee.

See also: prose publishers p144 and for further information, including what We Say, see Khidr Collective Zine (mixed-form magazine) p235

KNIGHT ERRANT PRESS
COLLECTIONS, ANTHOLOGIES AND CHAPBOOKS/PAMPHLETS
knighterrantpress@outlook.com
www.knighterrantpress.com
Editors: Nathaniel Kunitsky and Rhiannon Tate
Established 2017. Publishes poetry and prose (see p144). Publications available direct from the publisher website; from independent bookshops; and at local literary events.

GENRES: Literary.

SUBMISSIONS: Open to all during submissions windows, otherwise by invitation only. Submit by email to knighterrantpress@outlook.com. Guidelines at www.knighterrantpress.com/page. Responds within one to three months. Rejections include feedback only if requested. Authors are paid an advance fee plus royalties, and receive free copies of their book. Some crowdfunding required.

See also: prose publishers p144

KNIVES FORKS AND SPOONS
E-BOOKS, COLLECTIONS, ANTHOLOGIES AND CHAPBOOKS/PAMPHLETS
theknivesforksandspoonspress@hotmail.com
www.knivesforksandspoonspress.co.uk
Editor: Alec Newman
Established 2010. Publications available direct from publisher website; by post and email order; from chain bookshops and independent bookshops nationwide; at national and local

literary events; and from Amazon and other bookshop websites. Some online content (videos and audio) is also freely available to all. Knives Forks and Spoons was shortlisted for the Michael Marks Publisher of the Year Award (2010). **SUBMISSIONS:** During submissions windows, submit by email to theknivesforksandspoonspress@hotmail.com. Usually responds in over six months. No feedback offered with rejections. Authors receive free copies of the book.

WE SAY: We saw *Oh-Zones* by Elizabeth-Jane Burnett, a 20-page pamphlet. The cover design, which prominently features tree bark, appears ambiguous until you've read the pamphlet, at which point it's revealed as simple yet effective. Contemporary environmental poetry with an urban edge.

LAGAN PRESS
COLLECTIONS
info@laganpress.co
www.laganpress.co
Mixed form: also publishes non-fiction and novels (see p145). Looks for work of 'literary, artistic, social and cultural importance to the north of Ireland'. Irish and Ulster-Scots language work also welcomed.
See also: prose publishers p145

LAPWING PUBLICATIONS
COLLECTIONS AND CHAPBOOKS/PAMPHLETS, E-BOOKS
1 Ballysillan Drive, Belfast BT14 8HQ
lapwing.poetry@ntlworld.com
www.lapwingpoetry.com
Editor: Dennis Greig
Established 1988. Primarily a poetry publisher, but does occasionally produce autobiographical memoirs and novellas. Publications available direct from publisher website; by post and email order and at author events, self-organised or in partnership. Any five PDF books available for requested £5 donation.

SUBMISSIONS: Open to all within Western Europe (due to logistical costs). Submit by email to lapwing.poetry@ntlworld.com, ideally using Word doc or docx format. Guidelines at www.lapwingpoetry.com/submissiondetails.htm. Usually responds within four weeks. Rejections may occasionally include unsolicited feedback. Authors receive ten free copies of their book.

WE SAY: We looked at several collections, all in digital format. These A5 publications maintained a cohesive design, with covers featuring a photo or piece of artwork framed by the title and author's name, though sometimes only text, on a white background. Digital versions are available as PDFs, rather than HTML-based e-books, to maintain the house style. Hard copies also sold.

LAUDANUM
ANTHOLOGIES AND CHAPBOOKS/PAMPHLETS
37 Hartham Road, London N7 9JQ
editor@laudanumpublishing.co.uk
www.laudanumpublishing.co.uk
Editor: Tiffany Anne Tondut
Established 2016. Publications available direct from publisher website; from independent bookshops; and at local and national literary events.
SUBMISSIONS: Submissions for anthologies open to all, during submission windows; submissions for chapbooks are currently by

invitation only. Submit by email to anthology@laudanumpublishing. co.uk. Guidelines at www. laudanumpublishing.co.uk/about. Usually responds within four weeks. Rejections may occasionally include unsolicited feedback. Authors receive free copies of the book.

WE SAY: The perfect-bound paperback anthologies are slightly thinner than A5 size, with matte covers adorned with eye-catching art. We especially liked the 50-page *Chapbook Anthology: Volume One*, which continued the theme of the cover art's colourful vegetation by including a pattern of apples and flowers at the beginning of each new section. Laudanum has taken the chapbook, often a brief and economically produced piece, and increased its design quality by presenting anthologies of three per volume. We also saw *Asterism*, a 64-page anthology of poems inspired by punctuation.

LAWRENCE AND WISHART
MIXED POETRY/PROSE ANTHOLOGIES
Central Books Building, Freshwater Road, Chadwell Heath RM8 1RX
020 8597 0090
office@lwbooks.co.uk
www.lwbooks.co.uk
Editor: Katharine Fletcher
Established 1936. As well as non-fiction (see also p146) and mixed poetry/prose anthologies, they also publish six different journals, with between two and four issues each year for each title, including *Soundings* (see p257). Publishes short fiction in a book-length literary magazine (see also p146). Publications available direct from

the publisher website; at chain and independent bookshops; and from Amazon and other bookshop websites.

GENRES: Political history; political analysis; philosophy; cultural theory and analysis; biography; poetry.
SUBMISSIONS: Open to all, submit by email (submissions@lwbooks. co.uk) or post (Lawrence and Wishart, Central Books Building, Freshwater Road, Chadwell Heath RM8 1RX). Guidelines at www. lwbooks.co.uk/about-us#authors. Usually responds in one to three months. Rejections may occasionally include unsolicited feedback. Contributors are paid royalties only and receive free copies of their book.
See also: prose publishers p146 and *Soundings* (prose magazine) p257

LEAFE PRESS
COLLECTIONS AND CHAPBOOKS/ PAMPHLETS
leafepress@hotmail.com
www.leafepress.com
Editor: Alan Baker
Established 2000. Publications available direct from publisher website; by post and email order; from chain bookshops nationwide; from independent bookshops; at national and local literary events; and from Amazon and other bookshop websites.
SUBMISSIONS: Submissions currently by invitation only. Usually responds within four weeks. No feedback offered with rejections. Authors receive free copies of the book.
For a fuller description of this press, see *Litter Magazine* (poetry magazine) p275

51

LIBERTIES PRESS
COLLECTIONS AND ANTHOLOGIES
+353 86 853 8793
sean@libertiespress.com
www.libertiespress.com
Editor: Seán O'Keeffe
Established 2003. Publishes both prose (fiction and non-fiction, see p148) and poetry. Publications available direct from the publisher website; at chain and independent bookshops; and from Amazon and other bookshop websites. Liberties Press publication *Setting the Truth Free: The Inside Story of the Bloody Sunday Justice Campaign* won the 2012 Christopher Ewart-Biggs Memorial Prize.
SUBMISSIONS: Open to all. Submit by email to sean@libertiespress.com. Guidelines at www.libertiespress.com/submissions/. Liberties Press charges a fee to consider a manuscript for publication (currently €495 for fiction, €295 for non-fiction/poetry, incl VAT). For this it prepares a report, covering the content/structure, literary quality, and marketability of the work, and can then arrange a meeting to discuss next steps. Aims to respond to enquiries within 24 hours, and, if the author decides to go ahead, aims to complete the report within six weeks. Contributors are paid a flat fee and royalties, and receive free copies of their book. Authors also contribute to marketing and publishing costs.
WE SAY: Neat and whimsical, the collection we reviewed – *The Goose Tree* by Moyra Donaldson – is a slim, A5, perfect-bound volume printed on plain cream paper, with no-fuss fonts and a quirky, illustrated feather-themed cover. All the key components of a classy collection with no frills. Conversely, the hardback edition of *Clearing the Hurdles* by J B McGowan was weighty and authoritative, with soft matte pages interspersed with glossy colour photographs. A publisher with many strings to their bow.
See also: prose publishers p148

LITERARY POCKET BOOK, THE
CHAPBOOKS/PAMPHLETS
hitchinssteven@gmail.com
literarypocketblog.wordpress.com
Editor: Steven Hitchins
Established 2007. Publications available by direct mail and e-mail orders.
GENRES: Experimental; innovative; performative; conceptual.
SUBMISSIONS: Open to all, but please look at the sorts of books published by the press before submitting your work. Submit via email (hitchinssteven@gmail.com). Usually responds within one to three months, with a personal email to each submission. Accepted poets receive free copies of their publication, and any further copies at half price.

LITTLE ISLAND BOOKS
COLLECTIONS AND ANTHOLOGIES
7 Kenilworth Park, Dublin 6W, Republic of Ireland
siobhan.parkinson@littleisland.ie
www.littleisland.ie
Editors: Siobhán Parkinson and Matthew Parkinson-Bennett
Established 2010. Publishes both prose (see p150) and poetry for children. Publications available direct from the publisher website; by post and email order; from chain and independent bookshops; at national and local literary events; and from Amazon.

Little Island Books won the Bookseller Award for Irish Small Press of the Year in 2019, and the Special Award of the Reading Association of Ireland in 2011. Several of its authors have also won awards, including the Lollies award in 2017.

GENRES: Poetry for children.

SUBMISSIONS: Open to all, when publishing lists are not full. Submit via the website at www.littleisland. ie/submissions, where guidelines are also available. Usually responds in one to three months. The press gives feedback if editors feel a book has potential, even if it is not for them, and will occasionally explain why they can't consider a book. Authors are paid an advance fee plus royalties, and receive free copies of their book.

For more information, including what We Say, see also prose publishers p150

LONELY PRESS, THE

COLLECTIONS AND MIXED-FORM ANTHOLOGIES
62 Kings Road, Cardiff CF11 9DD
johnlavin@thelonelycrowd.org
www.thelonelycrowd.org
Editor: John Lavin

Established 2015. Publishes poetry and prose, including book-sized mixed-form journal *The Lonely Crowd* (p238). Publications available direct from the publisher website; from independent bookshops; and at local literary events.

GENRES: Literary.

SUBMISSIONS: When open, submissions are open to all – but please note The Lonely Press is not currently open to submissions of full poetry collections. Usually responds to submissions in four to six months. No feedback is offered with rejections. Authors receive free copies of their book.

See *The Lonely Crowd* (p238) for how to submit work to anthologies.

See also: prose publishers p151. For more information, including what We Say, see *The Lonely Crowd* (mixed-form magazine) p238

LUATH PRESS

COLLECTIONS AND ANTHOLOGIES
www.luath.co.uk
sales@luath.co.uk

Edinburgh-based Luath Press publishes across a wide range of genres, including literary, children's, biography, travel (see p151), poetry and more. Most of its books have a Scottish connection, but editors 'are always looking out for new and innovative books and authors, whatever the background'. Postal submissions only.

See also: prose publishers p151

MAGIC OXYGEN ☆

POETRY ANTHOLOGIES / MIXED-FORM ANTHOLOGIES
simon@magicoxygen.co.uk
www.magicoxygen.co.uk
Editor: Simon West

Established 2012. Mainly publishes fiction (see p152). Publications available direct from publisher website; from major chain and independent bookshops; at local literary events; and from Amazon and other bookshop websites.

SUBMISSIONS: Submissions are usually by invitation only. Work should be sent to editor@ magicoxygen.co.uk. Usually responds within one to three months. Rejections may include occasional unsolicited feedback. Authors receive royalties.

For more information, see also: prose publishers p152

53

MARISCAT PRESS

COLLECTIONS, ANTHOLOGIES AND
CHAPBOOKS/PAMPHLETS
10 Bell Place, Edinburgh EH3 5HT
0131 332 3451
hamish.whyte@btinternet.com
www.mariscatpress.com
Editors: Hamish Whyte, Diana Hendry
Established 1982. Publications
available direct from publisher
website; by post and email
order; from selected/local chain
bookshops; from independent
bookshops; and at local literary
events.
In 2015 Mariscat Press won both
the Callum Macdonald Memorial
Award for poetry pamphlet
publishing and the Michael Marks
Publishers Award for poetry
pamphlet publishing.
SUBMISSIONS: Open to all. Submit
preferably by post (10 Bell Place,
Edinburgh EH3 5HT) or by email
(hamish.whyte@btinternet.com).
Usually responds within one to
three months. Rejections may
occasionally include unsolicited
feedback. Authors are paid
royalties only, or an advance/fee
plus royalties.
WE SAY: We looked at two of
Mariscat's books: *Alphabet Poems*
by Mary Robinson and *Sykkel
Saga* by Vicki Husband. Both are
well-designed and professionally
typeset with a clear, uncluttered
layout. The cover designs are
simple but attractive and the paper
stock is of a high quality. We also
love Mariscat's grumpy little cat
logo.

MELOS PRESS

COLLECTIONS AND CHAPBOOKS/
PAMPHLETS
melos.press@btinternet.com
www.melospress.blogspot.co.uk

Editor: William Palmer
Established 2007. Publications
available direct from publisher
website; by post and email order;
in chain bookshops nationwide;
in independent bookshops; and
on Amazon and other bookshop
websites. Strictly poetry only.
SUBMISSIONS: Publication history
required. Submit by email to
melos.press@btinternet.com.
Usually responds within one to
three months. Rejections may
occasionally include unsolicited
feedback. Authors receive free
copies of their book.
WE SAY: Saddle-stitched
pamphlets with plain card covers
and white printer paper inside. We
flicked through *Black and Blue*,
a sequence of sonnets by Cathy
Galvin, which was clean and clear –
focusing on the words themselves
as opposed to the aesthetic. A
glance at the website, though,
shows that there are more colourful
designs being released.

MICA PRESS

COLLECTIONS, PAMPHLETS,
ANTHOLOGIES, E-BOOKS
47 Belle Vue Rd, Wivenhoe,
Colchester, Essex CO7 9LD
07894 210147
info@micapress.co.uk
www.micapress.co.uk
Editor: Les Bell
Established 2012. Publications
available by post and email order;
from chain and independent
bookshops; and from Amazon.
SUBMISSIONS: Open to all.
Submit by post (47 Belle Vue Rd,
Wivenhoe, Colchester, Essex CO7
9LD) or by email (info@micapress.
co.uk). Usually responds within one
to three months. Rejections may
occasionally include unsolicited

feedback. Authors receive royalties on sales; free copies of the book; and additional copies at a discount rate.

WE SAY: We looked at a digital copy of *Certain Roses* by Angela Livingstone. The collection features a purple cover, with a photograph of a bay window overlooking a brick wall. The prose-poetry inside is given a good amount of space on the page to breathe, which suits the contemplative writing style. The back cover features a very sweet blurb, where the author and publisher discuss the themes of the collection.

MONSTROUS REGIMENT PUBLISHING

MIXED-FORM COLLECTIONS/ ANTHOLOGIES
editor@monstrous-regiment.com
www.monstrous-regiment.com
Editors: Lauren Nickodemus, Ellen Desmond
Established 2017. Also publishes prose (see p155). Publications available direct from publisher website; by direct mail and email orders; and at local literary events.
SUBMISSIONS: Open to all, during submission windows. Submit by email (editor@monstrous-regiment. com) or online (www.monstrous-regiment.com/contact). Guidelines at www.monstrous-regiment.com/ submissions. Usually responds within four weeks, with feedback only if requested. Authors are paid a flat fee.
For more information, including what They Say, see also: prose publishers p155 and *Monstrous Regiment* (mixed-form magazine) p242

MOORMAID PRESS

CHAPBOOKS/PAMPHLETS
397 Park Lane, Macclesfield SK11 8JR
hello@moormaidpress.co.uk
www.moormaidpress.co.uk
Editor: Ailsa Holland
Established 2013. Publications available direct from publisher website; by direct mail and email orders; and at local literary events.
SUBMISSIONS: By invitation only. Submit by email to hello@ moormaidpress.co.uk. Usually responds within four weeks. Feedback provided with all solicited submissions.
WE SAY: The digital version of the prose-poetry collection *Mermaids and Other Devices* by Nell Farrell features a black cover with a photo manipulated image of winged girls, flying away from a figure in the foreground. The work is divided into two halves; the first having poetry that flows together to form a loose narrative, the other being a more traditional anthology of poetry. The back cover has three quotes in praise of the book, and the author's bio and photo.

MORBID BOOKS

COLLECTIONS AND ANTHOLOGIES
www.morbidbooks.net
info@morbidbooks.net
Based in South London, Morbid Books claims to be 'a Temple of Surrealist Literature'. It publishes books in limited editions of up to 500 and is open to proposals all year round.
See also: prose publishers p155 and *A Void* (mixed-form magazine) p214

MOTHER'S MILK BOOKS ☆

COLLECTIONS, ANTHOLOGIES AND CHAPBOOKS/PAMPHLETS
teika@mothersmilkbooks.com

www.mothersmilkbooks.com
Editor: Dr Teika Bellamy
Established 2011. Mixed form: also publishes prose (see p154). Publications available direct from publisher website; from independent bookshops; at national and local literary events; and from Amazon.
Mother's Milk Books has won numerous awards. Founder Teika Bellamy received the Women in Publishing's New Venture Award for pioneering work on behalf of under-represented groups in society. Mother's Milk Books title *Baby X* won the Commercial Fiction category of the Eric Hoffer Award in 2017. The poetry duets pamphlet *Inheritance*, by Ruth Stacey and Katy Wareham Morris, won Best Collaborative Work in the 2018 Saboteur Awards.
SUBMISSIONS: During submission windows only. Submit by email to submissions@mothersmilkbooks.com. Guidelines at www.mothersmilkbooks.com/index.php/submissions. Submitters are required to buy a book from the press. Usually responds within one to three months. Rejections may occasionally include unsolicited feedback. Authors are paid an advance/fee plus royalties and receive free copies of the book.
For more information, including what We Say and what They Say, see also: prose publishers p154

MUDFOG PRESS
COLLECTIONS AND ANTHOLOGIES
c/o Beacon Guest, Chop Gate, Stokesley TS9 7JS
contact@mudfog.co.uk
www.mudfog.co.uk
Editors: Pauline Plummer, Jo Heather,

David Lynch, Adrienne Silcock, Geoff Strange
Established 1993. Mixed form: also publishes prose (see p155). Publications available direct from the publisher website.
GENRES: All considered.
SUBMISSIONS: Favours writers in the Tees Valley, stretching from Whitby to Sunderland, west to Darlington. However also occasionally publishes writers outside this area. Submit by post (Beacon Guest, Chop Gate, Stokesley TS9 7JS) or by email (contact@mudfog.co.uk). Guidelines at www.mudfog.co.uk/submissions. Usually responds within one to three months. Rejections may occasionally include unsolicited feedback. Authors are able to buy a number of their books at cost-price and sell them at sales price.
WE SAY: The PDF proof of *Vamoose* by Lesley Mountain that we looked at had a dramatic, bright-red cover with a negative print image of a horse and rider jumping or falling into flames. The blurb on the back includes reviews by Pippa Little and Ellen Phethean. The collection spans 44 pages, with a page-long biography, plus two pages of Acknowledgements, and the layout is clean, with wide margins and well-sized font giving the shapes of the poems plenty of room to shine.
For more information, see also: prose publishers p155

MUDPRESS
ANTHOLOGIES
www.mudpress.co.uk
info@mudpress.co.uk
Editor: Georgina Wilding
Mud Press aims to 'celebrate the work of a vivacious variety of poets

and poetic styles', presented in books they describe as 'part anthology, part magazine, part portfolio'. They announce calls for submissions on themes. As we went to press, they were in the process of relaunching their website, but can be found on Facebook at www.facebook.com/mudpoetry.

MULFRAN PRESS
COLLECTIONS AND CHAPBOOKS/PAMPHLETS
queries@mulfran.co.uk
www.mulfran.co.uk
As well as poetry, Mulfran also publishes essay pamphlets on topics in poetics. The editors read widely and like contemporary poetry from the 20th and 21st Centuries, as well as poetry from earlier periods and translated poetry. See the website for examples.

NEON BOOKS
COLLECTIONS, ANTHOLOGIES AND CHAPBOOKS/PAMPHLETS
info@neonbooks.org.uk
www.neonbooks.org.uk
Editor: Krishan Coupland
Established 2006. Also publishes prose (see p158). Publications available direct from publisher website; by direct mail and email orders; from independent bookshops; at national literary events; and from Amazon and other bookshop websites.
Neon Books title *The Mesmerist's Daughter* won the 2015 Best Novellas Saboteur Award.
SUBMISSIONS: Open to all, during submission windows. Submit by email to info@neonbooks.org.uk. Guidelines at www.neonbooks.org.uk/guidelines. Usually responds

within one to three months. Rejections may occasionally include unsolicited feedback for a fee. Submissions hold a tip-jar option, but this does not affect publisher's decision. Authors are paid royalties only and receive free copies of the book.
See also: prose publishers p158. For more information, including what We Say, see *Neon Literary Magazine* (mixed-form magazine) p243

NEW ISLAND
COLLECTIONS
info@newisland.ie
www.newisland.ie
New Island started out as Raven Arts Press In the 1980s and continues to commit to publishing 'exceptional literature'. Mixed form, it also publishes drama, fiction and Irish-focused non-fiction.
See also: prose publishers p158

NEW WALK EDITIONS
PAMPHLETS
c/o Dr Rory Waterman, Department of English, Philosophy and Communications, Mary Ann Evans Building, Nottingham Trent University, Clifton Campus, Clifton Lane, Nottingham NG11 8NS
newwalkmagazine@gmail.com
www.newwalkmagazine.com
Editors: Rory Waterman, Nick Everett
Established 2010 as New Walk Magazine; turned to pamphlet publication Autumn 2017. 18-month subscription (four pamphlets per year) £19.95. Available direct from publisher website; from independent bookshops; and at national and local literary events.
SUBMISSIONS: Open to all. Submit 12-20 pages of poems

by email to newwalkmagazine@
gmail.com. Guidelines at www.
newwalkmagazine.com/purchase-
submit. Usually responds within
two months. Only successful
submissions receive a response.

NEWCON PRESS
COLLECTIONS
41 Wheatsheaf Road, Alconbury
Weston, Cambridgeshire PE28 4LF
finiang@aol.com
www.newconpress.co.uk
Editor: Ian Whates
Established 2006. Mainly publishes
fiction (see p159). Publications
available direct from publisher
website; from chain bookshops
nationwide; from Amazon; and at
genre-themed literary events.
Jaine Fenn's short story 'Liberty
Bird' from NewCon Press
anthology *Now We Are Ten* won
the BSFA Award for best short
fiction in 2017.
SUBMISSIONS: Submissions by
invitation only. Author payment
varies depending on the published
work.
See also: prose publishers p159

NINE ARCHES PRESS ☆
E-BOOKS, COLLECTIONS AND
ANTHOLOGIES
mail@ninearchespress.com
www.ninearchespress.com
Editors: Jane Commane
Established 2008. Publications
available direct from publisher
website; by post and email
order; from chain bookshops
and independent bookshops
nationwide; at national and local
literary events; and from Amazon
and other bookshop websites.
Nine Arches Press won the
2014 Saboteur Award for Most
Innovative Publisher.

SUBMISSIONS: Open to all,
during submissions windows.
Submit through Submittable at
ninearchespress.submittable.
com/submit. Guidelines at
ninearchespress.com/submissions.
html. Usually responds within one
to three months. No feedback
offered with rejections. Contracts
vary.
WE SAY: Nine Arches produce
excellent books. *Kith* by Jo Bell
is a perfect-bound, 74-page
publication complete with a
high-quality dust-cover. It has
an abstract artistic cover design
that lends itself well to the title:
the more you read, the more you
understand. Made from quality
materials and containing engaging
poetry inspired by Bell's community
and friends. Ideal for readers who
wish to be immersed in various
poetry techniques.
**See also: *Under the Radar* (poetry
magazine) p263**

OFFA'S PRESS
COLLECTIONS AND ANTHOLOGIES
info@offaspress.co.uk
www.offaspress.co.uk
Publishes and promotes
contemporary poetry by West
Midland poets. 'Eclectic' in range,
it focuses on both the performance
and publication merit of the work
it publishes. Its watchword is 'good
on the page and good on the
stage'.

OFFORD ROAD BOOKS
COLLECTIONS, ANTHOLOGIES AND
CHAPBOOKS/PAMPHLETS
offordroadbooks@gmail.com
www.twitter.com/offordroadbooks
Editors: Martha Sprackland, Patrick
Davidson Roberts
Established 2017. Also publishes

58

prose (see p161). Publications available by direct mail and email orders; from selected/local chain bookshops; from independent bookshops; at local literary events; and from Amazon.

SUBMISSIONS: Open to all. Submit by post (29a Womersley Road, Crouch End, London N8 9AP) or by email (offordroadbooks@gmail.com). Usually responds within four weeks. Rejections may occasionally include unsolicited feedback. Authors receive a small fee.

WE SAY: We saw the PDF proof of Melissa Houghton's *Cumshot in D Minor*, and the not-yet-typeset MS of James Brookes' *Spoils*. This press does not print poetry to comfort the reader. With no opening poem title and no warning, *Cumshot in D Minor* plunges the reader into prose poetry like an angry stream of consciousness, leaping from moment to explicit moment. This writing challenges and jolts the reader right out of their comfort zone from the first. *Spoils*, while less caustic, is just as merciless in its own way. No chicken soup for the soul here, but unrelenting realism.

See also: prose publishers p161

ONSLAUGHT PRESS, THE
COLLECTIONS AND ANTHOLOGIES
www.onslaughtpress.com
onslaughtpress@gmail.com
Based in East Oxford, publishing about ten books per year. Specialises in poetry books and haiku but also publishes picture books, which range from illustrated prose stories to graphic novels (p162). Publishes in a variety of languages including Irish, Scots, Scottish Gaelic, Cornish, French,

Japanese and English.
See also: prose publishers p162

ORIGINAL PLUS
COLLECTIONS AND CHAPBOOKS/PAMPHLETS
38 Pwllcarn Terrace, Blaengarw, Bridgend, South Wales CF32 8AS
asamsmith@hotmail.com
sites.google.com/site/samsmiththejournal
Editor: Sam Smith
Established 1996. Publications available direct from publisher website; and by post and email order.

SUBMISSIONS: Poets should preferably have some history of publication in *The Journal* (see p275). Submit by post (38 Pwllcarn Terrace, Blaengarw, Bridgend, South Wales CF32 8AS) or by email (asamsmith@hotmail.com). Usually responds within four weeks. Rejections may occasionally include unsolicited feedback. Writers can buy copies of their publication for resale at 33% discount.

WE SAY: We looked at a digital version of *Catch Ourselves in Glass* by Samantha Roden and *West Abutment Mirror Image* by Geoffrey Winch, which are also available in print. Although both poetry collections are subjectively different, both are well crafted, with great variety of poems and poetic voices that are raw and refreshing. The covers of both are stylistically eye-catching and their websites is clear and easy to navigate.

See also: *The Journal* (poetry magazine) p275

OTTER-BARRY BOOKS
CHILDREN'S COLLECTIONS AND ANTHOLOGIES

info@otterbarrybooks.com
www.otterbarrybooks.com
A children's book publisher
producing high quality picture
books and picture information
books, as well as poetry for children.
Two of Otter-Barry's publications
were shortlisted for the CLiPPA
Prize in 2019. Their work addresses
big themes for young minds. Best
approached through an agent.
See also: prose publishers p163

OUT-SPOKEN PRESS
COLLECTIONS, ANTHOLOGIES
AND CHAPBOOKS/PAMPHLETS /
E-BOOKS
Future Studio, 237 Hackney Road,
London E2 8NA
press@outspokenldn.com
www.outspokenldn.com/press
Editor: Anthony Anaxagorou
Established 2015. Primarily
publishes poetry, but also
some non-fiction (see p164).
Publications available direct from
the publisher website; from chain
and independent bookshops; at
national and local literary events;
and from Amazon.
GENRES: Poetry.
SUBMISSIONS: Authors are paid
royalties and receive free copies of
their book.
WE SAY: We saw a copy of The
Neighbourhood by Hannah
Lowe, a 20-page perfect-bound
pamphlet. Some of the pages are
illustrated with simple graphics
– circles and intersecting lines –
which ties in nicely with the theme
of connection explored throughout
the pamphlet. One of the poems
features white text on a black
background, which made it a little
difficult to read, but overall this is a
professional, stylish little book.
See also: prose publishers p164

OVERSTEPS BOOKS LTD
COLLECTIONS
6 Halwell House, South Pool, nr
Kingsbridge, Devon TQ7 2RX
01548 531969
alwynmarriage@overstepsbooks.com
www.overstepsbooks.com
Editor: Alwyn Marriage
Established 1992. Publications
available direct from publisher
website; by post and email order;
independent bookshops; at
national and local literary events;
and from bookshop websites.
SUBMISSIONS: Publication history
required. Guidelines at www.
overstepsbooks.com/submissions.
Usually responds within one to
three months. Authors receive free
copies of the book.
WE SAY: We looked at digital
proofs of Another Life by Fokkina
McDonnell. This 58-page collection
is split into three parts, showing
a clear journey: 'Still casting a
shadow', 'Trying' and 'Another
life'. There is a lengthy page
of acknowledgements, noting
where the poems have previously
been published and won prizes –
testament to the quality of poetry
Oversteps prints. The layout is
clean – one poem per page, in a
reasonable sized font. The cover of
the book is eye catching – bright
blue, with an abstract picture of
sailboats against a sunset on the
front, a small picture of the poet
on the back, and praise for the
collection.

OYSTERCATCHER PRESS
CHAPBOOKS/PAMPHLETS
Cynefin, Coed y Parc, Bethesda,
Bangor LL57 4YW
oystercatcherpress@gmail.com
www.oystercatcherpress.com
Editor: Peter Hughes

Established 2007. Publications available direct from publisher website, and by post and email order. All online content is available to all. Offers an annual subscription of £25 for six pamphlets.
Oystercatcher Press won the 2008 Michael Marks Award for Outstanding UK Publisher of Poetry in Pamphlet Form.
SUBMISSIONS: Submissions by invitation only. Authors receive initial free copies of the book, plus a discount on all further copies.

PAEKAKARIKI PRESS
COLLECTIONS, ANTHOLOGIES AND CHAPBOOKS/PAMPHLETS
4 Mitre Ave, Greenleaf Road, London E17 6QG
020 8509 8175 / 07836 785505
matt@paekakarikipress.com
www.paekakarikipress.com
Editor: Matt McKenzie
Established 2010. Publishes poetry. Publications available direct from the publisher website and from Amazon.
SUBMISSIONS: Open to all, preferably only from poets based in the UK. Submit by email to poetry@paekakarikipress.com. Usually responds within one to three months. Rejections may occasionally include unsolicited feedback. Authors receive some free copies of their book, and discounted copies thereafter.
WE SAY: This publisher is immediately eye-catching through its revival of letterpress printing. Each publication is produced using traditional letterpress, which can be seen through fascinating images on their website. We looked at their poetry collections *Reflections in a Well* by Rumiana Ebert and Tzveta Sofronieva, and upcoming title *Serenade* by Isabel Bermudez and Simon Turvey, both written simply in black and white, with occasional images, to accommodate the letterpress process. Paekakariki Press is a publisher bringing writing back to its roots.

PALEWELL PRESS LTD
COLLECTIONS, ANTHOLOGIES AND CHAPBOOKS/PAMPHLETS
enquiries@palewellpress.co.uk
www.palewellpress.co.uk
Editor: Camilla Reeve
Established 2016. Mixed form: also publishes prose (see p164). Publications available direct from publisher website; at local literary events; and from Amazon and other bookshop websites.
SUBMISSIONS: Open to all, but must relate to subject areas of human rights, history, environment, or wellbeing methodology. Submit by email (enquiries@palewellpress.co.uk) or by post (384 Upper Richmond Road West, London SW14 7JU). Usually responds within four weeks. Rejections may occasionally include unsolicited feedback. Authors are paid royalties only and receive free copies of the book. For authors in mainland UK, publisher shares cost of launch.
For more information, see also: prose publishers p164

PAPER SWANS PRESS ☆
COLLECTIONS, ANTHOLOGIES AND CHAPBOOKS/PAMPHLETS
77 Cambrian Road, Tunbridge Wells, Kent TN4 9HJ
sarah@paperswans.co.uk
www.paperswans.co.uk
Editor: Sarah Miles
Established 2014. Publications

available direct from the publisher website; from Amazon; and at national and local literary events. Paper Swans Press was shortlisted for the award for Best Anthology in the Saboteur Awards 2016 and 2017 and their pamphlet *Glass,* by Elisabeth Sennitt Clough, won Best Pamphlet in the 2017 awards. Her collection *At or Below Sea Level,* also published by Paper Swans, was selected as a Poetry Book Society choice.

SUBMISSIONS: Open to all, during submission windows. Submit via submissions page on website. Guidelines at www.paperswans. co.uk/submissions. Reading fee applies only for single-author pamphlet and single-poem competition. Usually responds within one to three months. Rejections may occasionally include unsolicited feedback. Authors receive free copies of the book.

WE SAY: We considered a PDF of *At or Below Sea Level* by Elisabeth Sennitt Clough, a dark and menacing poetry collection that attaches itself firmly to the painful side of the human and often specifically female experience. With experimental structures, including the use of different typefaces and style to heighten the sense that we are listening to numerous conflicting voices, this collection is disturbingly captivating.

PAPILLOTE PRESS

COLLECTIONS
23 Rozel Road, London SW4 0EY
info@papillotepress.co.uk
www.papillotepress.co.uk
Editor: Polly Pattullo
Established 2004. Books from the Caribbean. Mainly publishes fiction (p165), but occasionally poetry. Publications available via the publisher's website; from chain and independent bookshops; and from Amazon.

SUBMISSIONS: Open to all. Submit by post (23 Rozel Road, London SW4 0EY) or email (info@ papillotepress.co.uk). Usually responds within four weeks. Rejections may occasionally include unsolicited feedback. Authors are usually paid an advance fee and royalties. An alternative model, which is sometimes available, is for author to pay for publication costs and to take all income from sales. **For more information, including what We Say and what They Say, see also prose publishers p165**

PARALLEL UNIVERSE PUBLICATIONS

COLLECTIONS
130 Union Road, Oswaldtwistle, Lancashire BB5 3DR
paralleluniversepublications@gmx.co.uk
www.parallelpublications.blogspot. co.uk
Editors: David A. Riley, Linden Riley
Established 2012. Mainly publishes prose (see p166). Publications available direct from publisher website; by direct mail and email orders; from chain bookshops nationwide; from independent bookshops; and from Amazon and other bookshop websites.

SUBMISSIONS: Open to all. Submit by post (Parallel Universe Publications, 130 Union Road, Oswaldtwistle, Lancashire BB5 3DR) or by email (paralleluniversepublications@ gmx.co.uk). Guidelines at www. parallelpublications.blogspot. co.uk/p/submissions.html.

Usually responds within one to three months. Rejections may occasionally include unsolicited feedback. Authors are paid royalties only.

For more information, including what We Say, see also prose publishers p166

PATRICIAN PRESS

COLLECTIONS AND CHAPBOOKS/ PAMPHLETS

12 Lushington Road, Manningtree CO11 1EF

07968 288651

patricia@patricianpress.com

editorial@patricianpress.com

www.patricianpress.com

Editor: Mark Brayley

Established 2012. Publishes mainly fiction (see p167), but also some poetry books and poetry-and-prose anthologies. Publications available direct from publisher website; from selected/local chain bookshops; from independent bookshops; at local literary events; and from Amazon and other bookshop websites, including The Great British Bookshop website.

SUBMISSIONS: Open to new and unpublished writers without agents. Please submit only during submissions windows via the form at www.patricianpress.com/ submissions (guidelines at the same address). Usually responds within one to three months. Rejections may occasionally include unsolicited feedback. Authors are paid royalties only.

PB PRESS

COLLECTIONS AND CHAPBOOKS/ PAMPHLETS

Co. Wicklow, Éire

+353 4022 3556

buspoems@gmail.com

thepoetrybusmag.wixsite.com/change

Editors: Peadar and Collette O'Donoghue

Established 2013. Publications available direct from publisher website; by post and email order; and at independent bookshops.

SUBMISSIONS: Open to all. During submissions windows, submit by email to buspoems@gmail.com. Usually responds within one to three months. Rejections may occasionally include unsolicited feedback. Authors receive free copies of their book.

For more information, including what We Say, see also: *PB Mag* **(poetry magazine) p277**

PEEPAL TREE PRESS

COLLECTIONS, ANTHOLOGIES AND CHAPBOOKS/PAMPHLETS

contact@peepaltreepress.com

www.peepaltreepress.com

Editors: Jeremy Poynting, Kwame Dawes, Jacob Ross, Kadija Sesay

Established 1986. Mixed form: also publishes short stories and novels (see p167). Specialises in Caribbean and Black British writing. Publications available direct from publisher website; by post and email order; from chain bookshops and independent bookshops nationwide; at national and local literary events; and from Amazon and other bookshop websites. Peepal Tree title *Sounding Ground* by Vladimir Lucien was overall winner for The OCM Bocas Prize for Caribbean Literature 2015.

SUBMISSIONS: Open to all, specialising in Caribbean and Black British writing. Submit through Submittable at peepaltreepress. submittable.com (guidelines at same address). Usually responds within four to six months.

Rejections may occasionally include unsolicited feedback, and some manuscripts by UK-based authors are offered a (free) in-depth reader report through the press' Inscribe Writer Development Programme Authors are paid royalties only.
WE SAY: A prolific publisher of exclusively Caribbean and Black British writing with over 300 titles to its name, from memoir and fiction to historical studies and literary criticism. We looked at *Unknown Soldier*, a poetry collection by Seni Seneviratne. It is a Poetry Book Society Recommendation. Inspired by a bundle of photographs of Seneviratne's late father, the collection is formatted beautifully and includes the photos in a 30-page 'album' after the poems. The cover also features one of these pictures. As well as the blurb, the back cover includes a biography and a small photo of the poet.
See also: prose publishers p167

PENNED IN THE MARGINS
COLLECTIONS AND ANTHOLOGIES
Toynbee Studios, 28 Commercial Street, London E1 6AB
020 7375 0121
info@pennedinthemargins.co.uk
www.pennedinthemargins.co.uk
Editor: Tom Chivers
Established 2006. Mixed form: also publishes prose (see p169). Publications available direct from publisher website; by post and email order; from selected/local chain bookshops; from independent bookshops; at local literary events; and from Amazon. In 2017 Penned in the Margins titles were shortlisted for the Costa Poetry Award, Ted Hughes Award and Dylan Thomas Prize.

SUBMISSIONS: Submit by email to submissions@pennedinthemargins.co.uk. Guidelines on website. Usually responds within one to three months. Rejections may occasionally include unsolicited feedback. Authors are paid royalties only.
WE SAY: We saw a copy of Melissa Lee-Houghton's 88-page collection *Sunshine*, which features a bubble-gum pink cover, with a dropped ice cream cone in the centre. This cover was simple, but the use of both imagery and colour were very effective. The work inside is mostly prose poetry, with acknowledgements, notes on the text, and quotes after the contents page. The tone is sensual, with a focus on both emotion and the female body – a really fascinating read.
See also: prose publishers p169

PLATYPUS PRESS
COLLECTIONS, ANTHOLOGIES AND CHAPBOOKS/PAMPHLETS
enquiries@platypuspress.co.uk
www.platypuspress.co.uk
Editors: Michelle Tudor, Peter Barnfather
Established 2015. Also publishes prose (see p170). Publications available direct from publisher website; at local literary events; and from Amazon and other bookshop websites.
GENRES: Literary.
SUBMISSIONS: Open to all. Submit by email to submissions@platypuspress.co.uk. Guidelines at www.platypuspress.co.uk/submit. Usually responds within four weeks. No feedback offered with rejections. Authors are paid royalties only and receive free copies of the book.

See also: prose publishers p170 and *Wildness* (mixed-form magazine) p265

POETRY IRELAND ☆
MIXED-FORM AND POETRY
ANTHOLOGIES / E-BOOKS

PINDROP PRESS

COLLECTIONS
Gardoussel, 30940 St Andre de
Valborgne, France
editor@pindroppress.com
www.pindroppress.com
Editor: Sharon Black

Established 2010. Publications available direct from publisher website; from independent bookshops; at national and local literary events; and from Amazon. Though a UK press, Pindrop Press founding editor Jo Hemmant passed the reins to France-based Sharon Black in early 2016.
SUBMISSIONS: Publication history required. Submit by email to editor@pindroppress.com. Usually responds within one month. No feedback offered with rejections. Authors receive free copies of the book.
WE SAY: We looked at digital editions of *Sightings* by Elisabeth Sennitt Clough and *Oysterlight* by Cheryl Pearson. The covers of both feature striking artwork, with *Sightings* using stylised artwork of two peacocks, while *Oysterlight* shows some sheer material lit with very soft, pale light. Each collection features a blurb at the top, and quotes about the work from prize-winning poets such as Helen Mort and Mona Arshi. The layout of the poetry is clean and uncrowded.

THEY SAY

We publish poetry that is exciting, well-crafted and fresh. We select books we feel passionate about, and create collections that are not only beautiful to read but also to handle. Authors include Alicia Stubbersfield, Abegail Morley, Graham Burchell, Kiran Millwood Hargrave and Jeremy Page. We operate no submissions windows at present so authors are invited to send a sample of ten poems from a full collection of at least 60 poems via the website at any time. We publish four collections a year and welcome work from début as well as established poets.

11 Parnell Square, Dublin 1, Ireland
+353 1 6789815
publications@poetryireland.ie
www.poetryireland.ie
Editors: various
Established 1999. Mainly publishes
poetry, though some mixed-form
anthologies. Publications available
direct from publisher website; by
post and email order; at chain
and independent bookshops
nationwide; at literary events; and
from Amazon and other bookshop
websites.
Poetry Ireland was shortlisted for
two categories at the 2016 Irish
Book Awards: The Ryan Tubridy
Listeners' Choice Award, and Best
Irish Published Book of the Year.
GENRE: Literary.
SUBMISSIONS: Open to all. Submit
by post to Poetry Ireland, 11
Parnell Square, Dublin 1, Ireland.
Usually responds within four to six
months. Rejection may occasionally
include unsolicited feedback.
Authors receive a flat fee and free
copies of the book.
**For more information, including
what We Say, see also: *Poetry
Ireland Review* (poetry magazine)
p280**

POETRY SPACE ☆
COLLECTIONS, ANTHOLOGIES AND
CHAPBOOKS/PAMPHLETS
www.poetryspace.co.uk
Editor: Susan Sims
Publications available direct
from publisher website and from
Amazon.
SUBMISSIONS: Open to all.
Submit by email to susan@
poetryspace.co.uk. Guidelines at
www.poetryspace.co.uk/about/.
Usually responds within one to
three months. Rejections may
occasionally include unsolicited

feedback. Authors receive free
copies of the book.
**For more information, see *Poetry
Space Showcase* (poetry e-zine)
p281**

PROLEBOOKS ☆
COLLECTIONS, ANTHOLOGIES AND
CHAPBOOKS/PAMPHLETS
01204 497726
admin@prolebooks.co.uk
www.prolebooks.co.uk
Editors: Brett Evans, Phil Robertson
Established 2010. Primarily a
poetry press, but does also publish
prose in mixed-form collections
and anthologies (see p171).
Publications available direct from
publisher website and by direct
mail and email orders.
SUBMISSIONS: Work for anthology
and collection publication is usually
selected from competition entries.
Authors are paid royalties only.
**See also: prose publishers p171 and
Prole (mixed-form magazine) p249**

PROTOTYPE
COLLECTIONS AND ANTHOLOGIES
71 Oriel Road, London E9 5SG
admin@prototypepublishing.co.uk
www. prototypepublishing.co.uk
Editor: Jess Chandler
Established 2019. Also publishes
fiction and interdisciplinary projects
(see p172). Publications available
direct from publisher website; via
distributor NBN International; from
a selection of independent and
chain bookshops nationwide; and at
local literary events and book fairs.
SUBMISSIONS: Open year-round.
Submit by post (71 Oriel Road,
London E9 5SG) or by email
(admin@prototypepublishing.
co.uk). Guidelines at www.
prototypepublishing.co.uk/
submissions. Responses within

three months. Authors are paid in royalties.

WE SAY: We looked at a PDF of the anthology *Try To Be Better*, edited by Sam Buchan-Watts and Lavinia Singer. This is an experimental publication in every sense. The two-page introduction text is in red, and the contents (printed in black text on a yellow background) and index of prompts (red on white) book end the work. Biographies and poems are on yellow backgrounds, while artwork shines on a white background, and prompts and work are linked to each other via footnotes. The work really does come first here – the names of the writers and even the titles are relegated to the footer of each page. The overall impression is one of a press not afraid to break the rules – and to great effect.

See also: prose publishers p172 and mixed-form magazine p249

PS PUBLISHING

COLLECTIONS, ANTHOLOGIES AND CHAPBOOKS/PAMPHLETS
Grosvenor House, 1 New Road, Hornsea, East Yorkshire
01964 537575
nickycrowther@pspublishing.co.uk
www.pspublishing.co.uk
Editor: Nicky Crowther
Established 1991. Mainly publishes fiction (see p172), but also some poetry. Publications available direct from publisher website; from Amazon and other bookshop websites; and at the British Science Fiction Convention and British Fantasy Convention.
PS Publishing won the Karl Edward Wagner Award at the British Fantasy Awards 2012.

SUBMISSIONS: Submissions welcome by invitation only or from agents, during submissions windows. Submit by email to nickycrowther@pspublishing. co.uk. Usually responds within one to three months. Rejections may occasionally include unsolicited feedback. Authors may receive a flat fee; royalties only; an advance/ fee plus royalties; and/or free copies of the book (depending on agreement).

See also: prose publishers p172

PUBLISHING PROJECT, THE

COLLECTIONS AND ANTHOLOGIES
www.ueapublishingproject.com
publishing@uea.ac.uk
Based at the University of East Anglia, The Publishing Project encourages writers to get in touch to discuss the best means, method or form of publication for work. Along with its imprints Boiler House Press and Strangers Press they publish a wide variety of fiction, poetry, life-writing, journalism, audio/visual work, literary translations and experimental approaches to all modes and forms of writing.

See also: prose publishers p172

PUSHING OUT THE BOAT

MIXED-FORM ANTHOLOGIES WITH VISUAL ART
info@pushingouttheboat.co.uk
www.pushingouttheboat.co.uk
Established 2000. Creative writing (poetry and prose, see p173, with visual art). Available direct from the publisher website; by direct mail and email; from chain and independent bookshops; at local literary events; and at local galleries/coffee houses, etc.

SUBMISSIONS: Submissions are open to all, during submissions windows only. To

submit follow the instructions at www.pushingouttheboat.co.uk/instructions, with additional guidelines at www.pushingouttheboat.co.uk/hints-and-tips. Usually responds in four to six months, with the selection decision made available to writers in their web-record on the online submission system. Contributors receive free copies of the book.
See also: prose publishers (p173) and for more information, including what We Say, *Pushing Out The Boat* (mixed-form magazine) p251

RACK PRESS

CHAPBOOKS/PAMPHLETS
The Rack, Kinnerton, Presteigne, Powys, Wales LD8 2PF
07817 424560
rackpress@nicholasmurray.co.uk
www.rackpress.blogspot.com
Editor: Nicholas Murray
Established 2005. Primarily publishes poetry, but also publishes some criticism (see 173). Publications available direct from publisher website; by post and email order; from chain bookshops and independent bookshops nationwide; at national and local literary events; and from bookshop websites.
Rack Press won the 2014 Michael Marks Award for Publisher of the Year.
SUBMISSIONS: Open to all. Submit by post (The Rack, Kinnerton, Presteigne, Powys, Wales LD8 2PF) or by email (rackpress@nicholasmurray.co.uk). Guidelines at www.nicholasmurray.co.uk/About_Rack_Press.html. Please check the publisher's website to confirm whether submissions are currently being accepted. Usually responds within four weeks.

Rejections may occasionally include unsolicited feedback. Authors receive free copies of the book, plus other copies at discount price for sale at readings etc.
WE SAY: Rack Press pamphlets are part of the Rack Press Editions imprint 'Little Green Books'. They are simple affairs, with clean, cream covers, and a bold font for the title and poet name. The name of the press takes a backseat in the branding, as they focus on the poetry. However, the press does also sell limited sets of the pamphlets, signed by the poets and numbered accordingly, which we think adds a 'must read now' edge.
See also: prose publishers p173

RED CEILINGS PRESS, THE

CHAPBOOKS/PAMPHLETS
53 High Street, New Mills, High Peak, Derbyshire SK22 4BR
theredceilings@gmail.com
www.theredceilingspress.co.uk
Editor: Mark Cobley
Publications available direct from publisher website and from the poets themselves.
SUBMISSIONS: Chapbooks from UK poets only. Publication history required. Submit by email to theredceilings@gmail.com. Guidelines on the website. Author contributions needed. Usually responds within one to three months. No feedback offered with rejections. Authors receive at least ten copies of the book.
WE SAY: We looked at a digital version of *anyone for anymore* by Rufo Quintavalle. A simple design with an abstract photograph on the cover, reflecting its content. The publication is modern and experimental, the poem building

68

up by one word, and one line per page to begin with. An experimental piece that challenges conventional poetry and is smartly presented. A press that's ideal for poets whose work doesn't fit the traditional mould.

RED PRESS
COLLECTIONS AND MIXED-FORM ANTHOLOGIES / E-BOOKS
info@redpress.co.uk
www.redpress.co.uk
Editor: Katherine Knotts, FRSA
Established 2017. Publishes big ideas in social justice, in whichever form is appropriate, including nonfiction, some fiction and photography (see p174), as well as poetry and mixed prose/poetry anthologies. Publications available direct from the publisher website; from chain and independent bookshops; and from Amazon and other bookshop websites.
Red Press was recognised as one of the Top 100 Changemakers in the UK by the *Big Issue*.
SUBMISSIONS: Open to all. Submit by email to submissions@redpress.co.uk. Usually responds within four weeks. Rejections may occasionally include unsolicited feedback. Author deals vary, and may include a flat rate for the author, an advance plus royalties, free copies of the book, crowdfunding, or the author contributing to editorial/publication/marketing costs.
For more information, including what We Say, see also: prose publishers p174

RED SQUIRREL PRESS
COLLECTIONS, ANTHOLOGIES AND CHAPBOOKS/PAMPHLETS
Briery Hill Cottage, Stannington, Morpeth NE61 6ES

info@redsquirrelpress.com
www.redsquirrelpress.com
Editor: Sheila Wakefield
Established 2006. Mainly publishes poetry, but also some prose (see p174). Publications available direct from publisher website; by post and email order; from chain bookshops nationwide; from independent bookshops; at national and local literary events; from Amazon and other bookshop websites; and from Inpress.com.
Red Squirrel was shortlisted for the Callum Macdonald Memorial Award 2015.
SUBMISSIONS: Open to all. Submit by post to Briery Hill Cottage, Stannington, Morpeth NE61 6ES. Guidelines at www.redsquirrelpress.com/submissions. Usually responds in over six months. No feedback offered with rejections. Authors receive free copies of the book.
WE SAY: Red Squirrel press has a reputation for promoting its poets well, and working with local groups to create events. Its print output doesn't have a strong branded feel – title design varies from book to book – but the formatting is well done and the materials good quality.
See also: prose publishers p174

RIALTO, THE/BRIDGE PAMPHLETS ☆
PAMPHLETS/CHAPBOOKS
c/o 74 Britannia Road, Norwich NR1 4HS
info@therialto.co.uk
www.therialto.co.uk
Editor: Michael Mackmin
Established 1984. Publications available direct from publisher website; from selected/local chain bookshops; and from independent

bookshops. Rialto title *What I Saw* by Laura Scott won the 2014 Michael Marks Pamphlet Award.
SUBMISSIONS: Currently by invitation only, but with plans to open a submission programme for pamphlets. Please keep checking the website, www.therialto.co.uk. Chapbook authors receive all profits.
WE SAY: We looked at *What I Saw* by Laura Scott. Printed on quality cream paper, with a line sketch of the Thames and London skyline on the cover. A light, but compelling look that matches a light but compelling selection of poems. Stapled spine and lovely texture to the paper.
See also: *The Rialto* (poetry magazine) p282

ROCKINGHAM PRESS
COLLECTIONS
11 Musley Lane, Ware, Herts SG12 7EN
01920 467 868
rockpress@ntlworld.com
www.rockinghampress.co.uk
Editor: David Perman
Established 1991. Primarily publishes poetry, but also some non-fiction on Hertfordshire local history. Publications available by post and email order; at local literary events; from Amazon; and from www.inpressbooks.co.uk.
SUBMISSIONS: Submissions by invitation only, to rockpress@ntlworld.com. Usually responds within one to three months. Authors are paid royalties only.
WE SAY: *More new and collected poems* by Lotte Kramer is a perfect-bound 411-page poetry publication with a simple design. Plain cover, with a photo of the poet, and plenty of blurb on the back. This collection is a nostalgic tour of Germany and England, with poems focusing on family and nature within both countries. The book includes a good introduction, some marketing of other titles and well-formatted poems.

ROUTE PUBLISHING LTD
COLLECTIONS
01977 793442
info@route-online.com
www.route-online.com
Editor: Ian Daley
Established 2000. Primarily publishes non-fiction above other prose (see p176) and poetry. Publications available direct from publisher website; by post and email order; from chain bookshops nationwide; from independent bookshops; at national and local literary events; and from Amazon and other bookshop websites. Route has been shortlisted for the Pen/Ackerley Prize (2008); the James Tait Black Memorial Prize for Fiction (2011); NME Book of the Year (2015); and the Penderyn Prize (Music Book of the Year) (2015).
GENRES: Literary fiction; biography and true stories; music, stage and screen; and sports and leisure.
SUBMISSIONS: Guidelines at www.route-online.com/submissions. Usually responds within four to six months, with feedback only if an SAE is provided. No feedback offered with rejections. Authors receive a flat fee, or royalties only, or an advance/fee plus royalties.
For more information, see also: prose publishers p176

SACRISTY PRESS
COLLECTIONS AND ANTHOLOGIES
PO Box 612, Durham DH1 9HT
01913 038313

enquiries@sacristy.co.uk
www.sacristy.co.uk
Editor: Natalie Wilson
Established 2011. Primarily
publishes non-fiction (see p177).
Publications available direct
from publisher website; from
independent bookshops; and
from Amazon and other bookshop
websites.
GENRES: History; theology;
religious poetry.
SUBMISSIONS: Open to all.
Guidelines at www.sacristy.co.uk/
info/authors. Usually responds
within one to three months.
Rejections may occasionally
include unsolicited feedback.
Authors contribute to editorial/
publication/marketing costs and
are paid royalties only.
WE SAY: We looked at a digital
edition *Hope in Dark Places* by
David Grieve: a collection of
'poems about depression and
the Christian'. It contains a well-
considered introduction by Chris
Cook looking at the difficulties of
maintaining faith while struggling
with depression. The poems
themselves are simply arranged
in alphabetical order and offered
as a 'resource' for people needing
the companionship of Christ while
depressed. The poems are laid
out with an eye to use of space,
and we found the writing quietly
buoying, even for those readers
who aren't religious.
See also: prose publishers p177

SAD PRESS

COLLECTIONS, ANTHOLOGIES AND
CHAPBOOKS/PAMPHLETS
c/o Samantha Walton, Bath Spa
University, Newton Park, Bath
BA2 9BN
franciscrot@gmail.com
www.sadpresspoetry.wordpress.com
Editors: Jo Lindsay Walton, Samantha
Walton
Established 2009. Look for
experimental and linguistically
innovative poetry as well as
eco-poetry. £33 for bundle of
six books. Publications available
direct from publisher website; from
independent bookshops; and at
local literary events.
SUBMISSIONS: Open to all during
occasional submission windows.
Submit by email to franciscrot@
gmail.com. Usually responds within
one to three months. Rejections
may include reasons for decision
and suggestions of alternative
publishers. Authors receive free
copies of the book.
WE SAY: Although some
collections, such as *Landscaping
Change* edited by Samantha
Walton, conform to a standard
e-book style, Sad Press does
focus on experimental writing.
Chapbooks such as Nick-E
Melville's eclectic *Alert Stage is
Heightened* clearly reflect this,
with mixed styles of blocks of text
and sparse collections of lines;
a brightly coloured background
featuring only the words 'Spend
Happy'; a scan of a letter from
Jobseeker's or Barclays; etc.

SALMON POETRY

COLLECTIONS, ANTHOLOGIES AND
LITERARY CRITICISM
Knockeven, Cliffs of Moher, County
Clare, Ireland
jessie@salmonpoetry.com
www.salmonpoetry.com
Editor: Jessie Lendennie
Established 1981. Publications
available direct from publisher
website; by post and email
order; from chain bookshops

and independent bookshops nationwide; at national and local literary events; and from Amazon and other bookshop websites. Salmon Poetry was one of five finalists for the 2015 Association of Writers and Writing Programs (AWP) Small Press Publisher Award.
SUBMISSIONS: Publication history required. Submit by email to jessie@salmonpoetry.com. Usually responds within two to six months. Authors are paid royalties only and receive a certain number of free copies of the book.
WE SAY: The 80-page A5 collection by Millicent Borges Accardi we saw, *Only More So*, had a vibrant purple matte cover featuring a mandala design. Accardi's poetry varies from the atrocities of war to tender moments between brothers, such as in 'Buying Sleep' when the elder brother offers to sell the other 'a cocoon of sleep', which he tucks in around the boy.

SALÒ PRESS
COLLECTIONS, ANTHOLOGIES AND CHAPBOOKS/PAMPHLETS
editorsalopress@gmail.com
www.salopress.weebly.com
Editor: Sophie Essex
Established 2015. Primarily publishes poetry but also some prose (see p178). Publications available direct from the publisher website.
GENRES: Experimental; literary.
SUBMISSIONS: Open to all. Submit by post (85 Gertrude Road, Norwich NR3 4SG) or by email (editorsalopress@gmail. com). Guidelines at www.salopress. weebly.com. Usually responds in one to three months. No feedback offered with rejection. Authors and contributors are paid royalties.

WE SAY: We considered *They Are Really Molluscs* by Anna Cathenka, a poetry collection that explores themes of nature and the ocean in an experimental, observational and sometimes humorous style. Whilst this collection presents a consistent and comforting theme, Salò Press describe themselves as passionate about writing of a weird and surreal nature that isn't afraid to break away from the boundaries of traditional writing, and indeed the poems presented here are in a range of free-written styles including fragments and prose poems, laid out cleanly.
See also: prose publishers p178 and *Fur-lined Ghettos* (mixed-form magazine) p229

SALT PUBLISHING LTD
E-BOOKS / NOVELS / SHORT STORY COLLECTIONS AND ANTHOLOGIES
12 Norwich Rd, Cromer NR27 0AX
01263 511011
jen@saltpublishing.com
www.saltpublishing.com
Editors: Jen Hamilton-Emery, Nicholas Royle
Established 1999. Publishes literary fiction (see p178) and poetry. Publications available direct from publisher website; by post and email order; from chain bookshops nationwide; from independent bookshops; at national and local literary events; and from Amazon and other bookshop websites.
SUBMISSIONS: Agent submissions only. Guidelines at www. saltpublishing.com/pages/ submissions. Usually responds within four to six months. Authors are paid royalties only, or an advance/fee plus royalties, and receive free copies of the book.
For more information, including

what We Say, see also: prose
publishers p178

SAQI BOOKS
MIXED-FORM COLLECTIONS AND
ANTHOLOGIES
26 Westbourne Grove, London
W2 5RH
020 7221 9347
elizabeth@saqibooks.com
www.saqibooks.com
Publisher and Managing Director:
Lynn Gaspard
Editor: Elizabeth Briggs
Established 1983. Primarily
publishes prose (see p179), and
widely publishes work from and
about the Middle East and North
Africa. Publications available from
chain bookshops nationwide;
from independent bookshops; at
national and local literary events;
and from Amazon and other
bookshop websites.
Saqi Books won the IPG Diversity
Award in 2013, the Arab British
Culture and Society Award in
2008 and the British Book Industry
Award for Diversity in Literature in
2009.
SUBMISSIONS: Open to all.
Guidelines at www.saqibooks.
com/contact/submissions.
Usually responds within one to
three months. Rejections may
occasionally include unsolicited
feedback. Authors are paid an
advance/fee plus royalties.
See also: prose publishers p179

SCOTLAND STREET PRESS
COLLECTIONS / VERSE NOVELS
scotlandstreetpress@gmail.com
www.scotlandstreetpress.com
Publishing a range of prose work
including non-fiction, memoir, YA,
children's (see p180) as well as
poetry in the form of collections

and verse novels, this Edinburgh-
based press seeks to promote
Scotland as a distinctive creative
voice in the world, and redress
the balance of women's voices in
Scottish literature. The press was a
regional finalist for Small Press of
the Year, British Book Awards 2019.
See also: prose publishers p180

SEREN BOOKS
COLLECTIONS, ANTHOLOGIES AND
CHAPBOOKS/PAMPHLETS
57 Nolton Street, Bridgend, Wales
CF31 3AE
01656 663018
seren@serenbooks.com
www.serenbooks.com
Editor: Amy Wack
Established 1963. Mixed form:
also publishes fiction and non-
fiction (see p181). Publications
available direct from publisher
website; by post and email order;
from chain bookshops nationwide;
from independent bookshops; at
national and local literary events;
and from Amazon.
Winner of the Costa Poetry Award
2014.
SUBMISSIONS: Open to all. Submit
by post to 57 Nolton Street,
Bridgend CF31 3AE. Guidelines
at www.serenbooks.com/seren/
submissions-policy. Usually
responds within one to three
months. Rejections may occasionally
include unsolicited feedback.
Authors are paid an advance/
fee plus royalties and receive free
copies of the book, as well as other
copies at a discount price.
WE SAY: Seren is one of the most
established and respected poetry
publishing houses, and certainly
one for poets to aspire to. *My
Family and Other Superheroes* by
Jonathan Edwards is a 72-page

award-winning publication with an artistic design, available in both print and digital format. Provides nostalgia and naivety through the poet's voice. Various poetic forms are used throughout, including free-verse; ideal for readers who wish to escape into a good book. **See also: *Poetry Wales* (poetry magazine) p281 and prose publishers p181**

SHEARSMAN BOOKS LTD
COLLECTIONS, ANTHOLOGIES AND CHAPBOOKS/PAMPHLETS
50 Westons Hill Drive, Emersons Green, Bristol BS16 7DF
editor@shearsman.com
www.shearsman.com
Editor: Tony Frazer

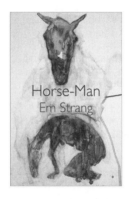

Established 1982. Publications available direct from publisher website; by post and email order; from selected/local chain bookshops; from independent bookshops; and from Amazon and other bookshop websites. Shearman Books is a multi-award-nominated press, and has been nominated for the Forward Prize for Best First Collection (2011, 2012); the Forward Prize for Best Collection (2012, 2015); Jerwood Aldeburgh First Collection Prize (2007); the Popescu Translation Prize (2009, 2011, 2013); the Michael Murphy Award for First Collections (2015) and the Michael Marks Awards for Pamphlets (Publisher Award) (2013, 2014). Publications from the press have won the Ledbury Award for best second collection (2017) and the Saltire Award for best Scottish Poetry Book of the Year (2017), and regularly receives recommendations from the Poetry Book Society.

SUBMISSIONS: Publication history required. Submit by post (Shearsman Books Ltd, 50 Westons Hill Drive, Emersons Green, Bristol BS16 7DF) or via the online PDF submissions portal (www.shearsman.com/how-to-contact-shearsman-books). Please read the guidelines at www.shearsman.com/shearsman-book-submissions. Usually responds within four to six months. No feedback offered with rejections. Authors are paid royalties only and receive ten free copies of the book.
For more information, see *Shearsman Magazine* (poetry magazine) p283

SHOESTRING PRESS

COLLECTIONS, ANTHOLOGIES AND
CHAPBOOKS/PAMPHLETS
19 Devonshire Avenue, Beeston,
Nottingham NG9 1BS
info@shoestring-press.com
www.shoestring-press.com
Editor: John Lucas
Mainly publishes poetry, but
also some prose (see p182).
Publications available direct from
publisher website; by post and
email order; from independent
bookshops; at national and local
literary events; and from Amazon.
Shoestring titles have been
shortlisted for Vondel Prize for
Translation and for the Cricket Club
Writers Book of the Year.
SUBMISSIONS: Submit by invitation
only.
WE SAY: A stalwart of poetry
publishing, Shoestring have
moved with the times in terms
of production. Its designs are
modern and clean, with clear
formatting that looks stylish on
the page (we looked at *A Night of
Islands* by Angus Martin). This is a
press widely acknowledged to be
publishing important work, and
doing it well.
See also: prose publishers p182

SIDEKICK BOOKS

ANTHOLOGIES, CHAPBOOKS/
PAMPHLETS, POETRY-BASED MIXED
CONTENT
hello@sidekickbooks.com
www.sidekickbooks.com
Editors: Kirsten Irving, Jon Stone
Established 2009. Primarily
publishes poetry, with mixed
content including poems with
essays, poets teamed with
illustrators, poetry comics etc.
Publications available direct
from publisher website; from
independent bookshops; and
at local literary events. All
online content is available to
all.
Sidekick title *Riotous* won Best
Collaboration at the Saboteur
Awards 2014, and *Finders Keepers*
(poems by Harry Man, illustrations
by Sophie Gainsley) was shortlisted
for the Ted Hughes Award.
SUBMISSIONS: Open during
submissions windows (check the
website). Usually responds within
four to six months. Rejections may
occasionally include unsolicited
feedback. Writers receive a flat fee
and free copies of the book.
WE SAY: We looked at *Birdbook:
Farmland, Heathland, Mountain,
Moorland*, in which poets 'poemify'
birds of Britain. The book is printed
on high quality materials with a
striking silhouette image cover,
and filled with glorious illustrations
and poems in a range of styles.
Sidekick is a particularly creative
press, and this really shines
through here.

SILKWORMS INK

E-BOOKS / CHAPBOOKS
www.silkwormsink.com
Established in 2010, Silkworms Ink
is 'a digital publisher of eclectica, a
purveyor of literary mixtapes, and
a weekly-themed quasi-magazine.'
They are interested in poetry
which is 'new, thoughtful, exciting,
enjoyable and crafted.'
**See also: prose publishers p182 and
mixed-form magazines p255**

SINE WAVE PEAK

COLLECTIONS, ANTHOLOGIES AND
CHAPBOOKS/PAMPHLETS
114 Sandy Lane, Cholton, Manchester
M21 8TZ
www.sinewavepeak.com

Managing Editor: Valgerður
Þóroddsdóttir
Established 2011. Poetry and
philosophy/criticism. Available
direct from publisher website and
at independent bookshops.
Winner of the Creative Futures
Award, NALD, 2012.
GENRES: Emphasis on philosophy
and typography.
SUBMISSIONS: Open to all. Submit
by email (luke@sinewavepeak.
com). Usually responds within
four weeks. A rejection may
occasionally include unsolicited
feedback. Authors receive copies
of the book.
WE SAY: Extremely high quality
publications. Both hardcover
and paperback have very simple,
white designs on the cover, with
folded flaps. The paper is thick
and textured, and the formatting
clean and sophisticated, with light
illustration on occasion.

SINGING APPLE PRESS
COLLECTIONS AND CHAPBOOKS/
PAMPHLETS
info@singingapplepress.com
www.singingapplepress.com
Editor: Camilla A. Nelson
Established 2014. Also publish
book art, hand-made books,
bookworks and text art.
Publications available direct from
publisher website; by direct mail
and email orders; and at local and
national literary events.
SUBMISSIONS: Accepts occasional
unsolicited submissions.
Usually responds within one to
three months. Rejections may
occasionally include unsolicited
feedback. Authors receive free
copies of the book.
WE SAY: This unique press is
charming and fascinating in its

endeavour to blend writing with
nature. Singing Apple Press'
website displays their projects,
which include using a letterpress
on natural elements such as leaves
to explore the nature of language.
These delicate pieces of art
accompany the publisher's carefully
crafted poetry in unique, limited
edition prints.

SMITH|DOORSTOP BOOKS ☆
E-BOOKS, COLLECTIONS,
ANTHOLOGIES AND CHAPBOOKS/
PAMPHLETS
The Poetry Business, Bank Street Arts,
32-40 Bank Street, Sheffield S1 2DS
0114 346 3037
office@poetrybusiness.co.uk
www.poetrybusiness.co.uk
Editors: Ann Sansom, Peter Sansom
Established 1986. Publications
available direct from publisher
website; by post and email order;
online at Newsstand; at Salts
Mill (Shipley), Heffer's Bookshop
(Cambridge), Five Leaves
Bookshop (Nottingham), Magazine
(Brighton), and Blackwell's
Bookshop.
smithldoorstop won the 2012
Michael Marks publisher award.
SUBMISSIONS: Open to all, during
submissions windows.
Submit by post to The Poetry
Business, Bank Street Arts,
32-40 Bank Street, Sheffield
S1 2DS. Online submissions
accepted only from overseas
writers (see www.poetrybusiness.
co.uk/north-menu/international-
submissions). Full guidelines
at www.poetrybusiness.co.uk/
north-menu/submissions. Usually
responds within one to three
months. No feedback offered with
rejection. Authors receive free
copies of their books. Only book

authors (not pamphlet) receive royalties.

WE SAY: We looked at a digital version this 35-page poetry bundle, which contains a range of poems from Geraldine Clarkson. Although complementing illustrations would have worked well here, the plain design also holds up as simple and fitting. The left aligned text in the middle of the page and the variations of poems make for a pleasant whole.

See also: *The North Magazine* **(poetry magazine) p277**

SMITHEREENS PRESS
ONLINE CHAPBOOKS
smithereens.press@gmail.com
www.smithereenspress.com
Editor: Kenneth Keating
Established 2013. Publishes online-only poetry chapbooks. Publications available direct from the publisher website.

SUBMISSIONS: Open to all. Submit by email to smithereens. press@gmail.com. Guidelines at www.smithereenspress.com/submissions/submissions.html. Usually responds in one to three months. Rejections may occasionally include unsolicited feedback. Unpaid.

WE SAY: Free to read via the Smithereens website, we looked at a few chapbooks. The cover design is consistent – a large photograph or illustration takes up much of the front, with header and footer banners in complementing colours, and the title and poet in the top banner. It's an effective and professional look. The inner pages are in a good-sized font for online reading, sans serif, with wide margins. The poet's

biography is featured on the back cover.

See also: *Smithereens Literary Magazine* **(poetry magazine) p284**

SMOKESTACK BOOKS
COLLECTIONS AND ANTHOLOGIES
1 Lake Terrace, Grewelthorpe, Ripon, North Yorkshire HG4 3BU
01765 658917
info@smokestack-books.co.uk
www.smokestack-books.co.uk
Editor: Andy Croft
Established 2003. Publications available direct from publisher website; by post and email order; at chain bookshops and independent bookshops nationwide; at national and local literary events; and from Amazon and other bookshop websites. Shortlisted for the British Book Awards Small Press of the Year 2019. Smokestack poet Steve Ely's collection, *Oswald's Book of Hours*, was shortlisted for the 2013 Forward Best First Collection and shortlisted for the 2014 Ted Hughes Award. David Cain's *Truth Street* was shortlisted for the 2019 Forward Best First Collection.

SUBMISSIONS: Publication history required. Submit by post (1 Lake Terrace, Grewelthorpe, Ripon, North Yorkshire HG4 3BU) or by email (info@smokestack-books. co.uk). Guidelines at smokestack-books.co.uk/publish.php. Usually responds within four weeks. Rejections may occasionally include unsolicited feedback. Author payment in the form of free copies of the book.

WE SAY: The paperback titles we saw (*Little Blue Hut* by Nancy Charley, *Articles of War* by Marilyn Longstaff and *Liberties* by Victoria Bean) featured a cohesive matte cover design of an image bordered by two light grey bands, and a bright red spine. Victoria Bean's collection is about trouble – those who cause it, are looking for it, or have found it.

SOUNDSWRITE PRESS
COLLECTIONS, ANTHOLOGIES AND CHAPBOOKS/PAMPHLETS
52 Holmfield Road, Leicester LE2 1SA
01162 702661
soundswritepoetry@gmail.com
www.soundswritepress.co.uk
Women's poetry press established 2005. Publications available direct from publisher website and from Amazon.
SUBMISSIONS: See website.
WE SAY: We saw a copy of *Take Three: Soundswrite Press New Poets Volume 1*, a perfect-bound volume featuring the work of three women poets from the East Midlands. The cover has a bright and attractive design, and French flaps lend the collection a sense of quality. The poems are printed on cream paper with a dedicated contents page for each poet featured.

SOUTHWORD EDITIONS ☆
CHAPBOOKS/PAMPHLETS
Munster Literature Centre, Frank O'Connor House, 84 Douglas Street, Cork, Ireland
+353 21 431 2955
munsterlit@eircom.net
www.munsterlit.ie
Editor: Patrick Cotter
Established 2001. Publishes poetry and fiction chapbooks (p184). Publications available direct from publisher website; by post and email order; at national and local literary events; and from Amazon.
SUBMISSIONS: Open to all, during submissions windows – chapbook publication comes as part of the Fool for Poetry competition. Guidelines at www.munsterlit.ie/Fool%20for%20Poetry.html. Usually responds within one to three months. No feedback offered with rejections. Authors are paid a flat fee and receive free copies of the book.
See also: prose publishers p184 and *Southword Journal* **(mixed-form magazine) p258**

SPECULATIVE BOOKS
COLLECTIONS, ANTHOLOGIES AND PAMPHLETS/CHAPBOOKS
www.speculativebooks.net
mail@speculativebooks.net
Offer a subscription service to readers – subscribers receive a new book every month. Glasgow-based publisher offering poetry, fiction (see p184), and mixed poetry/prose collections, as well as an annual anthology.
See also: prose publishers p184

STAIRWELL BOOKS
COLLECTIONS AND ANTHOLOGIES
161 Lowther Street, York YO31 7LZ
01904 733767
rose@stairwellbooks.com
www.stairwellbooks.co.uk
Editors: Rose Drew, Alan Gillott, and assorted guest editors
Established 2005. Publishes prose (see p185) and poetry, including poetry-and-prose anthologies – with a slight preference towards novels. Publications available direct from the publisher website; by direct mail and email order; at local and national literary events; and from bookshop websites including Gardners and Neilson.
Stairwell authors have won Saboteur Awards including

performance poet, 2015, and publication *Pressed by Unseen Feet* was shortlisted for 2012 Saboteur Awards: Best Anthology. Tim Ellis' poetry collection *Gringo on the Chicken Bus* placed number 11 in the Purple Patch Top 20 collections of 2011.

GENRES: Literary fiction; genre fiction including sci-fi, speculative fiction and fantasy; memoirs; children's literature

SUBMISSIONS: Send synopsis and 30 pages (prose) or ten poems to rose@stairwellbooks.com. Full guidelines at www.stairwellbooks. co.uk. The press publishes 15-20 books per year, but receives hundreds of submissions. It helps if they are familiar with your work, so they suggest also submitting work to *Dream Catcher Magazine* (see p225). 'If you purchase a book, that can create a virtuous circle. Some day someone might purchase yours.' Responds to submissions within one to three months. Rejections include feedback, often with detailed criticism and a few pages edited. Authors are paid royalties and receive free copies of their book.

WE SAY: We considered a PDF of *Northern Lights* by Harry Gallagher, a soulful collection exploring the author's life growing up in Teesside and the communities that inhabited it. This is reflected in the cover design, which includes a dark red back, and an almost ethereal photograph of a Sunderland factory lit by shafts of light on the front, the title embossed on the page in grey. The attention to home and our communities is a theme embodied by its publisher; Stairwell Books particularly publishes writers from in and around Yorkshire.

See also: prose publishers p185 and *Dream Catcher* (mixed-form magazine) p225

STEWED RHUBARB PRESS

COLLECTIONS, ANTHOLOGIES AND CHAPBOOKS/PAMPHLETS
james@stewedrhubarb.org
www.stewedrhubarb.org
Editor: James T Harding
Established 2012. Publications available direct from the publisher website; from independent bookshops; at national and local literary events; and direct from the poet. Stewed Rhubarb Press won the Callum MacDonald Memorial Award in 2013 and was nominated for the Emerging Publisher Saltire Award in 2018.

GENRES: Spoken word.

SUBMISSIONS: Submissions by invitation only, during submissions windows, to subs@stewedrhubarb.org. Guidelines at www.stewedrhubarb.org/contact/submissions. Usually responds in one to three months. Rejections may occasionally include unsolicited feedback. Authors contribute to editorial/publication/marketing costs.

STONEWOOD PRESS

COLLECTIONS, ANTHOLOGIES AND CHAPBOOKS/PAMPHLETS
Diversity House, 72 Nottingham Road, Arnold, Nottingham NG5 6LF
0845 456 4838
stonewoodpress@gmail.com
www.stonewoodpress.co.uk
Editor: Martin Parker
Established 2011. Publications available direct from publisher website; from chain bookshops and independent bookshops nationwide; and from Amazon and

other bookshop websites.
SUBMISSIONS: See guidelines at www.stonewoodpress.co.uk/about/submissions. Usually responds within four months. Rejections may occasionally include unsolicited feedback. Authors are paid royalties only and receive free copies of the book.
WE SAY: A boutique publisher with a petite catalogue of a dozen titles. *Small Grass*, the special edition poetry collection we pored over, was a perfect-bound, A6 hardcover in a striking slipcase. The vivid orange cover with silver title and grass graphic was incredibly eye-catching, and the short poetry inside, paired with black and white illustrations, was dainty and satisfying. Exceptionally well presented.
See also: prose publishers p186

STONY THURSDAY POETRY BOOK, THE

ANTHOLOGIES
Limerick City and County Council, Merchant's Quay, Limerick V94 EH90, Ireland
+353 61 556370
artsoffice@limerick.ie
www.limerick.ie
Editors: Limerick Culture and Arts Office
Established 1975. Publishes one annual poetry book, as part of a single series. Publications available direct from the publisher website; by direct mail and email order; from selected chain bookshops; and at local libraries.
SUBMISSIONS: Open to all. Submit by post (Culture & Arts Office, Limerick City and County Council, Merchant's Quay, Limerick, Ireland) or email (artsoffice@limerick.ie). Guidelines at www.limerick.ie/

council/services/community-and-leisure/culture-and-arts/stony-thursday-book-poetry-call-out. Usually responds in up to three months. No feedback offered with rejections. Contributors receive a free copy of the book.

STRANGER PRESS

COLLECTIONS, CHAPBOOK/PAMPHLETS AND BROADSIDES
strangerpress@gmail.com
www.strangerpress.com
'Modern innovative poetry'. Interested in publishing new and innovative, experimental poetry and writing. Check the website to find out whether submissions are being accepted.

STRUCTO PRESS

CHAPBOOKS/PAMPHLETS
editor@structomagazine.co.uk
www.structomagazine.co.uk
Editor: Euan Monaghan
Established 2015. Mixed form: also publishes fiction (see p187). Publications available direct from publisher website.
GENRES: All
SUBMISSIONS: Open only to poets previously published in *Structo* (see p261).
WE SAY: We looked at a digital version of David Russomano's chapbook (*Reasons for) Moving*. The cover features a blue and white geometric illustration by the poet, which wraps around the book. Russomano's biography and praise for the work are on the back cover. Acknowledgements, rights and thanks are within the first few pages, after which the 19 poems, set in a serif font, are left to sing out without interruption. The poems themselves move

from location to location around the world, a sense of unrest throughout.

For more information see also: *Structo* **(mixed-form magazine) p261 and prose publishers p187**

TALL-LIGHTHOUSE
COLLECTIONS, ANTHOLOGIES AND CHAPBOOKS/PAMPHLETS
104 Woodyates Road, London SE12 9JL
tall.lighthouse@yahoo.com
Editor: Les Robinson
Established 2001. Publications available direct from the publisher website; by direct mail and email order; and from independent bookshops.
SUBMISSIONS: By invitation only. Authors are paid royalties only, and receive free copies of their book. Usually responds within four weeks. Rejections may occasionally include unsolicited feedback.
WE SAY: We looked at a PDF of poetry collection *Where, the Mile End* by Julie Morrissy. A simple yet vibrant cover encapsulates a collection of poems that play with structure and perspective, delving into both the ordinary and the weird of human experiences. On tall-lighthouse's website, the editors provide extensive information about their publications.

TANGERINE PRESS
COLLECTIONS AND CHAPBOOKS/ PAMPHLETS
Unit 18 Riverside Rd, Garratt Business Park, London SW17 0BA
info@thetangerinepress.com
www.thetangerinepress.com
Editor: Michael Curran
Established 2006. Mainly publishes fiction (see p189). Publications

available direct from publisher website; by post and email order; from major chain and independent bookshops; and at local literary events.
SUBMISSIONS: No feedback offered with rejections.
See also: prose publishers p189

TAPSALTEERIE
COLLECTIONS, ANTHOLOGIES AND CHAPBOOKS/PAMPHLETS
9 Anderson Terrace, Tarland, Aberdeenshire
info@tapsalteerie.co.uk
www.tapsalteerie.co.uk
Editors: Duncan Lockerbie, Eddie Gibbons, Christie Williamson, Rebecca Parker
Established 2013. Publications available direct from publisher website; by direct mail and email orders; and from the Scottish Poetry Library shop.
Tapsalteerie pamphlet *Nae Flooers* by Ann Mackinnon was shortlisted for the 2016 Callum Macdonald Memorial Award for Best Scottish Poetry Pamphlet, and pamphlet *tilt-shift* by Kate Tough was runner up in the 2017 Callum Macdonald Memorial Award for Best Scottish Poetry Pamphlet. Tapsalteerie were shortlisted for the 2018 Michael Marks Poetry Publisher of the Year award.
SUBMISSIONS: Month-long submissions windows open once or twice a year. Submit by email to submissions@tapsalteerie.co.uk. Guidelines at www.tapsalteerie. co.uk/submissions. Usually responds within one to three months. Rejections include explanation of reason for decision. Authors receive free copies of the book.
WE SAY: We looked at PDFs of *Refuge* by Marjorie Lofti Gill,

Stitch by Samuel Tongue, and *An Offering* by Stewart Sanderson. These poetry pamphlets all feature animal-themed covers in calming colours and gentle fonts, whilst other Tapsalteerie titles are bolder in their design. Other than their passion for publishing in all Scottish languages, including Scots, Gaelic and English, Tapsalteerie's publications are varied in their output, embracing all themes and ideas.

TEMPLAR POETRY
COLLECTIONS, ANTHOLOGIES AND CHAPBOOKS/PAMPHLETS
info@templarpoetry.com
www.templarpoetry.com
Originally founded in Scotland in 2005. A modern poetry list, with the press' poets having received recognition in major book awards and in national and international competitions. Regular pamphlet publication as part of their Templar Quarterly Portfolio awards, with launches at Keats House.
See also: *Iota Poetry* (poetry magazine) p275

TUBA PRESS
COLLECTIONS AND CHAPBOOKS/ PAMPHLETS
Tunley Cottage, Tunley, Sapperton, Nr Cirencester, Gloucester GL7 6LW
01285 760424
tubapoetry@icloud.com
www.tubapress.eu
Partners: Charles Graham, Susan Clydesdale-Cotter, Margaret Hannigan Popp, Peter Ellson
Established 1976. Publications available direct from the publisher website; by post and email order; and at local and national literary events.
GENRES: Literary.

SUBMISSIONS: Open to all. Submit by email to tubapoetry@icloud.com, initially with five poems, or six A4 pages maximum. The press will ask for more if interested. Work can be posted by ordinary mail (to Route des Vans, La Republique, 30160 Bordezac, France) but unfortunately cannot be returned. Usually responds in one to three months. Rejections may occasionally include unsolicited feedback. Authors are paid royalties and receive six free copies of their publication.

TURAS PRESS
COLLECTIONS
6-9 Trinity Street, Dublin D02 EY47
+353 1 818 3176
admin@turaspress.ie
www.turaspress.ie
Editor: Liz McSkeane
Established 2016. Primarily publishes poetry, but also some fiction (see p195). Publications available direct from the publisher website, and from independent bookshops.
SUBMISSIONS: Open to all, within specified submissions windows twice a year. Submit by email to admin@turaspress.ie. Guidelines at www.turaspress.ie/submissions. Usually responds in one to three months. Rejections may very occasionally include a small amount of feedback. Authors are paid an advance/fee plus royalties, and receive free copies of the book.
See also: prose publishers p195

UNBOUND
E-BOOKS, COLLECTIONS AND ANTHOLOGIES
Unit 18, Waterside, 44-48 Wharf Road, London N1 7UX

020 7253 4230
www.unbound.co.uk
Established 2011. Mixed form:
also publishes prose (see p195).
Publications available direct
from publisher website; by
post and email order; at chain
and independent bookshops
nationwide; at national and local
literary events; and through
Amazon and other bookshop
websites. Publications are
subsidised by crowdfunding.
Multi-award-winning: Unbound title
The Wake won Book of the Year
at the 2015 Bookseller Industry
Awards and the 2014 Gordon Burn
Prize; was shortlisted for the 2014
Goldsmiths Prize; and longlisted
for the Man Booker Prize 2014, the
Desmond Elliott Prize 2014, and
The Folio Prize 2014. Unbound
won Best Publisher Website 2014
at the FutureBook Innovation
Awards and British Book Design
and Production Awards, and Best
Start-Up at the 2011 FutureBook
Innovation Awards. The press also
won the Literature Award 2013, for
26 Treasures, at the British Book
Design and Production Awards.
SUBMISSIONS: Open to all. Submit
via the online form at unbound.
co.uk/authors/work-with-us.
Guidelines at the same address.
Usually responds within one to
three months. Rejections may
occasionally include unsolicited
feedback. Authors are paid
royalties: a 50/50 profit share from
crowdfunding.
**For more information, including
what We Say, see also: prose
publishers p195**

UNIFORMBOOKS
COLLECTIONS
info@uniformbooks.co.uk

www.uniformbooks.co.uk
Editor: Colin Sackett
Established 2011. Primarily
publishes non-fiction (see p196).
Publications available direct from
publisher website; by direct mail
and email orders; from chain
bookshops nationwide; from
independent bookshops; and from
Amazon.
SUBMISSIONS: Open to all. Submit
by email to info@uniformbooks.
co.uk. Usually responds within four
weeks. Rejections may occasionally
include unsolicited feedback.
Authors are paid royalties only and
receive free copies of the book.
See also: prose publishers p196

V. PRESS
COLLECTIONS, ANTHOLOGIES AND
CHAPBOOKS/PAMPHLETS
vpresspoetry@hotmail.com
vpresspoetry.blogspot.co.uk
Editor: Sarah Leavesley
Established 2013. Publishes poetry
and flash fiction. Publications
available direct from publisher
website; at national and local
literary events; and from Amazon.
SUBMISSIONS: Submit by email
to vpresspoetry@hotmail.com,
but only when the submissions
window is open. Guidelines at
vpresspoetry.blogspot.co.uk/p/
submissions.html. Usually responds
within three months. Rejections
may occasionally include feedback.
Authors receive initial free copies
of the book, followed by copies at
a discount rate.
WE SAY: As with their prose entry
(p197) V. Press shared a favourite
poem with us, but were careful
to remind us that their tastes
are eclectic. 'Chromosomes'
comes from Romelyn Ante's first
collection, *Rice and Rain*, which has

a plain pale green cover featuring a line-drawing of rice 'dripping' from a drooping plant. It's a rich poem, painting the collapse of a marriage through a series of snapshot imagery.
See also: prose publishers p197

VAGABOND VOICES
COLLECTIONS AND ANTHOLOGIES
www.vagabondvoices.co.uk
info@vagabondvoices.co.uk
Glasgow-based press publishing novels, poems and polemics. They are committed to introducing new titles from Scottish authors and translating fiction from other languages. They only accept submissions during their open submission window.
See also: prose publishers p198

VALLEY PRESS
COLLECTIONS, ANTHOLOGIES AND CHAPBOOKS/PAMPHLETS
Woodend, The Crescent, Scarborough YO11 2PW
07806 765524
jo@valleypressuk.com
www.valleypressuk.com
Editor: Jamie McGarry
Established 2008. Also publishes prose (see p198). Publications available direct from publisher website; from chain bookshops nationwide; from independent bookshops; at national and local literary events; and from Amazon and other bookshop websites. In 2017, Valley Press title *Remembering Oluwale* won the Saboteur Award for Best Anthology.
SUBMISSIONS: Open to all. Submit online at www.valleypressuk.com/submissions. Usually responds within one to three months. Rejections may occasionally

include unsolicited feedback. Submitters are required to buy a magazine/book from the press. Authors are paid a flat fee and royalties only and receive free copies of the book.
See also: prose publishers p198

VANE WOMEN PRESS
COLLECTIONS, ANTHOLOGIES AND PAMPHLETS
low.down@vanewomen.co.uk
www.vanewomen.co.uk
Editors: SJ Litherland, Marilyn Longstaff (assistant editor), Pat Maycroft (art editor)
Established 1993. Mainly publishes poetry, but also short stories (see p198). Publications available direct from publisher website; by post and email order; at local literary events; and at Vane Women events and workshops.
Vane Women title *The Spar Box* by Pippa Little was the 2006 Poetry Book Society Pamphlet choice.
SUBMISSIONS: Open to previously unpublished women in North East England. Contact by email (submissions@vanewomen.co.uk) in the first instance, and a postal address to send poems and short stories to will be provided if appropriate. Full submission guidelines at www.vanewomen.co.uk/submissions.html. Usually responds in up to six months. Rejections may occasionally include unsolicited feedback. Authors receive free copies of their book.
WE SAY: We looked at a PDF proof of *The Ship Owner's House* by Judi Sutherland. The cover design features a near-collapsing house in the middle of a body of water, with sea birds perched on the roof. The water continues onto the

84

back cover where a playful 'here be dragons'-style sea monster frolics. The collections open with acknowledgements before the reader launches into some 30 carefully crafted poems about displacement, exile and belonging. A timely and well-produced collection.
See also: prose publishers p198

VANGUARD EDITIONS
COLLECTIONS, ANTHOLOGIES AND CHAPBOOKS/PAMPHLETS
Apt 18, Triangle Court, 315 Camberwell New Road, London SE5 0AT
vanguardeditions@gmail.com
richardskinner.weebly.com/vanguard-editions
Editor: Richard Skinner
Established 2014. Mixed form: also publishes short stories (see p199). Publications available direct from publisher website; by post and email order; from independent bookshops; and at local literary events.
SUBMISSIONS: Submissions by invitation only to vanguardeditions@gmail.com. Usually responds within four weeks. Rejections may occasionally include unsolicited feedback. Authors receive free copies of the book.
See also: prose publishers p199

VICTORINA PRESS
COLLECTIONS AND ANTHOLOGIES
victorinapress@gmail.com
www.victorinapress.com
Established in 2017, Victorina Press is based in Staffordshire, and rooted strongly in Chilean and British cultures courtesy of founder Consuelo Rivera-Fuentes. The press is focused on bibliodiversity

– which is to say it looks for books engaging with society in a range of styles and genres rather than for books fitting a certain brand. Submissions guidelines are available on the website.
See also: prose publishers p200

VOIDERY APERTURE, THE
COLLECTIONS
information@thevoideryaperture.com
www.thevoideryaperture.com
Editor: Christopher Pickard
Established 2016. Mixed form: also publishes prose (see p200). Publications available from chain bookshops nationwide; from independent bookshops; on Amazon; and from other bookshop websites.
SUBMISSIONS: Submissions by invitation only. Rejections may occasionally include unsolicited feedback. Authors are paid royalties only.
For more information, including what We Say, see also: prose publishers p200

WARD WOOD PUBLISHING
COLLECTIONS / MIXED-FORM ANTHOLOGIES / E-BOOKS
6 The Drive, Golders Green, London NW11 9SR
07504 863024
adele@wardwoodpublishing.co.uk
www.wardwoodpublishing.co.uk
Editor: Adele Ward
Established 2010. Mixed output – also publishes prose (see p201), as well as the Bedford Square MA Anthology from from Royal Holloway, University of London, with work by graduates of the poetry and fiction courses. Publications available direct from publisher website; from major chain and independent bookshops;

at literary events; and from Amazon and other bookshop websites.

SUBMISSIONS: By invitation only, to adele@wardwoodpublishing. co.uk. Please check www. wardwoodpublishing.co.uk/ manuscripts.htm for submissions information. Usually responds within one to three months. Rejections may occasionally include unsolicited feedback. Authors are paid royalties.

WE SAY: Three weathered dolls stare out from the matte cover of Ann Alexander's A5-sized book, *Old Things*. The off-white, perfect-bound pages have a pleasing, slight texture. Poems included in the collection vary from witnessing the age of an elderly parent; the shift from treating a pet as familiar to an object after death; to the comparison of a midwife to a gardener.

See also: prose publishers p201

WAYWISER PRESS

COLLECTIONS

Christmas Cottage, Church Enstone, Oxfordshire OX7 4NN

01608 677492

info@waywiser-press.com

www.waywiser-press.com

Editors: Philip Hoy, Joseph Harrison, Dora Malech, V Penelope Pelizzon, Eric McHenry, Greg Williamson, Clive Watkins, Matthew Yorke

Established 2001. Publications available direct from publisher website; by post and email order; at chain bookshops and independent bookshops nationwide; and from Amazon and other bookshop websites, including Inpress Books.

SUBMISSIONS: Poetry may only be submitted to annual Anthony Hecht Poetry Prize during August-December submission windows.

WE SAY: We looked at a PDF of *How to Avoid Speaking* by Jaimee Hills, a 96-page publication with a simple cover design (slightly unpolished – the title runs close to the edge) and clean layout. The collection won the Anthony Hecht award, and includes a foreword from prize judge Anthony Thwaite. Includes both contemporary free poetry and more traditional forms, all experimenting with and confronting language.

See also: prose publishers p201

WORPLE PRESS

COLLECTIONS

theworpleco@aol.com

www.worplepress.com

Co-directors: Peter Carpenter, Amanda Carpenter

Mainly publishes poetry, but also translations, anthologies, arts essays and writing other than poetry. Looks for excellence and diversity of format and approach. Check the site to find out when submissions are open.

WRECKING BALL PRESS ☆

COLLECTIONS, ANTHOLOGIES AND CHAPBOOKS/PAMPHLETS

5 Theatre Mews, Egginton Street, Hull HU2 8DL

01482 211499

editor@wreckingballpress.com

www.wreckingballpress.com

Editors: Shane Rhodes, Russ Litten

Established 1997. Also publishes prose (see p202). Publications available direct from publisher website; by post and email order; at chain and independent bookshops nationwide; at literary events; and from amazon.co.uk. Some online content available to all.

Wrecking Ball Press title *The Scene*

of My Former Triumph by Matthew Caley was nominated for Best First Collection, The Forward Prize 2005.
SUBMISSIONS: Open to all. Submit by post (Wrecking Ball Press, 5 Theatre Mews, Egginton Street, Hull HU2 8DL) or by email (editor@wreckingballpress.com). Guidelines on the website. Usually responds within one to three months. Rejection may occasionally include unsolicited feedback. Authors receive royalties and free copies of the book.
See also: prose publishers p202

WUNDOR EDITIONS
COLLECTIONS
www.wundoreditions.com
enquiries@wundoreditions.com
Publishing fiction, non-fiction (see p203), art and poetry, London-based Wundor primarily welcomes fiction submissions. They are 'committed to publishing innovative and challenging literature and images, working with new and established writers'.
See also: prose publishers p203

YEW TREE PRESS
COLLECTIONS, ANTHOLOGIES AND CHAPBOOKS/PAMPHLETS
Yew Tree Cottages, The Lagger, Randwick, Stroud GL6 6HP
yewtreepress@gmail.com
www.yewtreepress.co.uk
Editor: Philip Rush
Established 2012. Publications available direct from publisher website and from Amazon.
SUBMISSIONS: By invitation only, although local poets are welcome to contact. Submit by email to yewtreepress@gmail.com. Usually responds within four weeks. Rejections may occasionally include unsolicited feedback. Authors receive free copies of the book.
WE SAY: We looked at four pamphlets from Yew Tree Press: three from their Stroud Poets series (which each contain work by three local poets), and *Skinny White Kids* by Mark Husband. A little smaller than A5, the pamphlets all have staple spines and cardboard covers (in bright colours for the Stroud Poets and cream for Husband), and all are neatly printed, with no feeling of cramped text. The poets each have their own title pages with biographies, and the poetry is a pleasure to read. The Stroud pamphlets also have a growing list of other pamphlets in the Stroud series on their back covers. It's a small touch, but a really nice one.

ZENOPRESS
COLLECTIONS AND ANTHOLOGIES
zenopress.info@gmail.com
www.zenopress.com
Editor: Christian Patracchini
Established 2017. Mixed form: also publishes prose, including mixed prose/poetry anthologies (see p204). Publications available direct from the publisher website.
GENRES: Literary fiction.
SUBMISSIONS: Open to all. A reading fee may apply. Submit by email to zenopress.info@gmail.com. Guidelines at www.zenopress.com/submissions. Usually responds in one to three months. No feedback offered with rejection. Authors receive free copies of the book.
WE SAY: We looked at PDFs of Zeno Press' anthologies *Millets* and *Felt*, as well as writing project *Knots* by Christian Patracchini. With a minimalist white format,

Millets and Felt both present a collection of deeply philosophical, explorative and experimental writing. Even more experimental is Patracchini's Knots; an extensive collection of aphorisms, one-line verses and fragments. All of these texts clearly conceptualise Zeno Press as a publisher favouring avant-garde work with a deep consciousness.

See also: prose publishers p204

ZIMZALLA

COLLECTIONS AND CHAPBOOKS/ PAMPHLETS
mail@zimzalla.co.uk
www.zimzalla.co.uk
Editor: Tom Jenks
Established 2009. Publications available direct from publisher website.
SUBMISSIONS: Open to all. Submit by email to mail@zimzalla.co.uk. Guidelines at www.zimzalla.co.uk/about. Usually responds within four weeks. Rejections may occasionally include unsolicited feedback. Authors receive free copies of the book.
WE SAY: This is a publisher looking at the world askew, and we love it. Emma Hammond's Waves on a Beach is the most 'traditional' of the samples we looked at. It's slim, perfect-bound poetry; gloss cover featuring a photo image – but no title. That's on the first page with the author name and publisher details, but there are no page numbers and barely any poem titles. Chaingrass by Catherine Vidler is all concrete poetry, all constructed by repetitions of the word 'chaingrass'. It is spiro-bound, and both the back and front have poems on. Our favourite was 'Piotr Kalisz' Flags of the Countries' from Space, filled with line-drawing designs for the flags of the 270 planets with symptoms of life. If you think your work is too out there to be published, try here.

Listed in this section are publishers of every kind of prose, including full-length fiction, short stories, non-fiction, essays, memoir and other types of creative non-fiction, as well as a few graphic novel publishers. There are more fiction than non-fiction publishers, but many of the presses cover a range of prose publishing.

Remember that, particularly with indie presses, and particularly with regards to short story collections, it helps to have a publication history in journals and magazines, so don't forget to check out the prose (p287) and mixed-form magazines (p211).

Also listed in this section are a number of presses that publish both prose and poetry. In these cases we have indicated, where appropriate, what their dominant area of publishing is.

404 INK

E-BOOKS / NOVELS / SHORT STORY COLLECTIONS AND ANTHOLOGIES / NON-FICTION
hello@404ink.com
www.404ink.com
Editors: Heather McDaid, Laura Jones
Established 2016. Mixed form: alongside short stories, novels and non-fiction, it also publishes some poetry, including mixed prose/poetry anthologies (see p213). Publications available direct from publisher website; by post and email order; from chain bookshops nationwide; from independent bookshops; at national and local literary events; and from Amazon.
GENRES: Contemporary fiction; literary fiction; experimental fiction; social and political commentary (non-fiction); humour.
SUBMISSIONS: Open to all. Submit by email to submissions@404ink.com. Guidelines are available www.404ink.com/submissions. Usually responds in one to three months. Rejections may occasionally include unsolicited feedback. Authors are paid an advance and royalties, and receive free copies of the book.
WE SAY: We considered a PDF proof of *Animals Eat Each Other* by Elle Nash, a hair-raising exploration of obsession, sex, and the wild fragility of our teenage years. With tantalising language and gripping turns, Nash writes with vigour and ambition. 404 Ink's website declares their appreciation for unheard voices and for publishing writing that is unapologetically loud; a description certainly met by Nash's novel.
See also: *404 Ink* **(mixed-form magazine) p213**

A3 PRESS, THE ☆

SHORT STORY COLLECTIONS / CHAPBOOKS
PO Box 65016, London N5 9BD
020 7193 7642
a3@writingmaps.com
www.thea3press.com
Editor: Shaun Levin
Established 2017. Mixed output, publishing fiction, poetry (see p15) and art. Publications available direct from the publisher website.
GENRES: Literary fiction; graphic art; comics.
SUBMISSIONS: Open to all, during submissions windows. Submit via thea3review.submittable.com/submit, where full guidelines are also available. A reading fee is charged. Usually responds in one to three months. Rejections do not include feedback unless paid for. Authors are paid a flat fee and receive copies of their chapbook.
WE SAY: We looked at the online sample of *MASH* by Lena Ziegler, a chapbook that invites the reader to choose their own path in this lyrical, free-flowing narrative. As with all of A3 Press' publications, it is printed on a single, folded A3 sheet of high quality paper. Its unique structure and absence of colourful graphics make it an adventurous dip into the possibility that words bring, playfully creating an interactive reading journey. Written in the second person, this

text is inviting and reader-driven, focusing on themes of obsession, sex, and writing.
See also: *The A3 Review* **(mixed-form magazine) p213 and poetry publishers p15**

ABADDON BOOKS
NOVELS / SHORT STORY COLLECTIONS AND ANTHOLOGIES / NON-FICTION / E-BOOKS
Riverside House, Osney Mead
01865 792201
www.abaddonbooks.com
Editor: David Thomas Moore
Established 2005. Publications available direct from the publisher website; from chain and independent bookshops; and on Amazon and other bookshops websites.
GENRES: Science fiction; fantasy; horror.
SUBMISSIONS: Submit only during submissions windows. Usually responds in one to three months. Rejections may occasionally include unsolicited feedback. Authors are paid a flat fee.
WE SAY: As imprints of international games development company and publisher Rebellion, Solaris (see p183) and Abaddon Books house a vast collection of science-fiction, fantasy and horror, and have been publishing for over ten years. Their website is easy to navigate and clearly presents the titles published by each of these imprints as well as their parent publisher. Overall, they pride themselves on stepping away from airy-fairy fantasy and into clear-cut and captivating writing.
See also: prose publisher *Solaris* **(p183)**

ACCENT PRESS
NOVELS / NON-FICTION
Tŷ Cynon House, Navigation Park, Abercynon CF45 4SN
029 2000 2880
info@accentpress.co.uk
www.accentpress.co.uk
Managing director: Hazel Cushion
Editors: Rebecca Lloyd, Greg Rees, Alex Davies
Established 2003. Award-winning independent publisher, now a major name in trade publishing. Includes imprints Xcite and Cariad. Named Specialist Publisher of the Year and shortlisted for Independent Publisher of the Year at the IPG Awards.
GENRES: Commercial fiction, including women's fiction, romance, historical, crime and fantasy; non-fiction including self-help, memoirs, biography and humour. Strictly no short stories, poetry or children's books.
SUBMISSIONS: Open to all, during submissions windows. Guidelines at www.accentpress.co.uk/submission-guidelines.

AD HOC FICTION ☆
E-BOOKS / SHORT STORY COLLECTIONS AND ANTHOLOGIES / NOVELLAS-IN-FLASH
helpdesk@adhocfiction.com
www.adhocfiction.com
Editor: John O'Shea
Established 2015. Publications available direct from publisher website; by direct mail and email orders; from independent bookshops; and at national and local literary events.
Ad Hoc Fiction was longlisted for the Saboteur Awards in 2016 and 2017 in the Wild Card Category.
GENRES: Flash/micro fiction; hybrid form (prose poetry/flash fiction/art);

creative non-fiction.
SUBMISSIONS: By invitation only. Usually responds within four weeks. Authors are paid a flat fee and receive free copies of the book.
WE SAY: We looked at two Ad Hoc anthologies: *How to Make a Window Snake* (three novellas-in-flash), and *To Carry Her Home* (Volume 1 of the Bath Flash Fiction anthologies). Both books are brightly bound, using a frame effect around the title text, against a backdrop of bold colour. Quality paper and a tidy layout all reinforce the professionalism.
See also: prose magazines p289

AESTHETICA MAGAZINE ☆
ANTHOLOGIES
PO Box 371, York YO23 1WL
01904 629 137
info@aestheticamagazine.com
www.aestheticamagazine.com
Editor: Cherie Federico
Established 2003. Stunning anthology resulting from the Aesthetica Creative Writing Award. Publications available direct from publisher website and at chain bookshops nationwide.

ALANNA MAX
CHILDREN'S BOOKS / PICTURE BOOKS
fay@alannamax.com
www.alannamax.com
Editor: Maria Pembroke
Established 2006. Publications available from chain bookshops nationwide; from independent bookshops; at national literary events; from other bookshop websites; and from inclusive book clubs like Letterbox Library. Alanna Max was shortlisted by the Independent Publishers Guild

for Diversity Publisher of the Year 2016.
GENRES: Picture books; board books and cards for babies and toddlers.
SUBMISSIONS: Open to all. Submit online at www.alannamax.com submissions page. Responds to successful submissions only. No response/feedback offered with rejections. Authors are paid an advance plus royalties.
WE SAY: Alanna Max's fun, playful website hosts a wide range of children's books, including the Lulu Series and the Zeki Series, as well as individual books in varied formats. Alanna Max believe firmly in there being a story out there for every child, as well as prioritising diversity and inclusion in their books to ensure all children feel they can relate to characters' experiences.

ALBA PUBLISHING
SHORT STORY COLLECTIONS AND ANTHOLOGIES / NON-FICTION
PO Box 266, Uxbridge UB9 5NX
01895 832444
info@albapublishing.com
www.albapublishing.com
Editor: Kim Richardson
Established 1990. Mainly publishes poetry (see p15). Publications available by post and email order; and from Amazon.
A title from Alba Publishing was shortlisted for the Haiku Foundation Touchstone Distinguished Book Award 2013.
GENRES: Spirituality and beliefs.
SUBMISSIONS: Publication history required. Submit by post (PO Box 266, Uxbridge UB9 5NX) or by email (info@albapublishing.com). Usually responds within four weeks, with submission feedback only if

94

requested. Authors contribute to editorial/publication/marketing costs.
For more information, see also: poetry publishers p15

ALCHEMY PRESS
SHORT STORY COLLECTIONS AND ANTHOLOGIES / NON-FICTION
alchemypress@gmail.com
www.alchemypress.co.uk
Editors: Peter Coleborn, Jan Edwards
Established 1998. Publications available direct from publisher website; by direct mail and email orders; at national literary events; and from Amazon and other bookshop websites.
Alchemy Press has won Best Collection in 2015 and Best Small Press in 2014 at the British Fantasy Society Awards.
GENRES: Horror; weird fiction; dark fantasy; supernatural; science fantasy.
SUBMISSIONS: Anthology submissions open to all during submission windows; other submissions by invitation only. Submit online at www.alchemypress.wordpress.com/submissions. Guidelines at www.alchemypress.wordpress.com/submissions/formatting and specific details are posted for individual anthologies when submissions are open. Usually responds within one to three months. Rejections may occasionally include unsolicited feedback; for a fee a further feedback is available. Authors are currently paid an advance/fee plus royalties and receive free copies of the book, although payment structure is subject to change.

ALLARDYCE, BARNETT, PUBLISHERS
MIXED-FORM COLLECTIONS AND ANTHOLOGIES
14 Mount Street, Lewes, East Sussex BN7 1HL
www.abar.net
Editor: Anthony Barnett
Mainly publishes poetry (see p16). Publications available direct from publisher website; by direct mail and email orders; from independent bookshops; from Amazon; and from SPD in the US.
GENRES: Literary; music.
SUBMISSIONS: By invitation only.
See also: poetry publishers p16 and *Snow Lit Rev* (mixed-form magazine) p256

ALMOND PRESS ☆
E-BOOKS / SHORT STORY COLLECTIONS AND ANTHOLOGIES
office@almondpress.co.uk
www.dystopianstories.com
Editor: Marek Lewandowski
Established 2012. Primarily publishes fiction. Publications available from Amazon and other bookshop websites.
GENRES: Fantasy/sci-fi; horror; dystopian. No non-fiction.
SUBMISSIONS: Submissions take place during competition time, with competitions being the submissions windows (see p94). Usually responds within one to three months. No feedback offered. Authors receive an advance/fee plus royalties and free copies of the book.

AND OTHER STORIES
E-BOOKS / NOVELS / SHORT STORY COLLECTIONS AND ANTHOLOGIES / NON-FICTION
Central Library, Surrey Street, Sheffield S1 1XZ

nichola@andotherstories.org
www.andotherstories.org
Editors: Tara Tobler, Stefan Tobler
Established 2010. Mainly publishes
fiction. Publications available in
chain bookshops nationwide; from
independent bookshops; at local
literary events; and from Amazon
and other bookshop websites.
Plans are in place for purchase
direct from the publisher. Also
offers a subscription: £22, £40 or
£55 per year for two, four or six
books per year.
And Other Stories was shortlisted
for the 2013 IPG Newcomer
Award. Its authors have also been
shortlisted for and won awards.
GENRES: Literary fiction and literary
non-fiction (subjects have included
death, migration and family).
SUBMISSIONS: Open to all, but
submitters are required to show
proof of purchase from the press.
Submit by post to Central Library,
Surrey Street, Sheffield S1 1XZ.
Guidelines at www.andotherstories.
org/submissions. Usually responds
within one to three months. A
standard rejection may occasionally
include unsolicited feedback.
Author payment is an advance/fee
plus royalties.
WE SAY: We looked at a PDF
proof of *Love* by Hanne Ørstavik,
translated by Martin Aitken. In the
past few years And Other Stories
has stepped away from its earlier
branding of a black-rimmed white
circle on an illustrated background,
instead using more photographic
imagery, with the And Other
Stories logo discretely in a corner.
The overall effect is sleeker but
still very striking, as *Love*'s dark
evening landscape with a pop of
bright yellow window, echoed by
the colouring of the title, attests.

The inner page design is as
professional as always, as we've
come to expect for And Other
Stories. Their publications more
than rival the standards of the
larger presses.
See also: poetry publishers p17

ANGRY ROBOT
E-BOOKS / NOVELS
20 Fletcher Gate, Nottingham
NG1 2FZ
incoming@angryrobotbooks.com
www.angryrobotbooks.com
Established 2008. Fiction publisher.
Publications available direct from
publisher website; in chain and
independent bookshops; and
from Amazon and other bookshop
websites.
Angry Robot publication *Apex*, by
Ramez Naam, won the 2016 Philip
K Dick Award.
GENRES: Sci-fi; fantasy.
SUBMISSIONS: Usually agent-only,
but there is a short window for
open submissions every 18-24
months. Submit by email to www.
angryrobotbooks.com/submissions.
Usually responds within one to
three months. Rejections may
occasionally include unsolicited
feedback. Authors receive an
advance and royalties.
WE SAY: Based on the e-book
excerpt we saw (396-page long
The Stars are Legion by Hugo
Award-winning and widely
translated author Kameron Hurley)
Angry Robot's books are on trend
with fellow contemporary SF
titles – and leading the pack in
terms of quality of writing. Angry
Robot have chosen a cover and
format that allows fans of the
genre to easily identify the title as
something they might enjoy. The
book itself has an immediate hook,

ARACHNE PRESS

NOVELS / SHORT STORY
COLLECTIONS AND
ANTHOLOGIES / NON-FICTION/
AUDIO BOOKS / E-BOOKS
100 Grierson Road, London
SE23 1NX
020 8699 0206
arachnepress.com
Editor: Cherry Potts

Established 2012. Mainly
publishes short fiction and
poetry (see p17). Expanding a YA
fiction list. Publications available
direct from publisher website; by
post and email order; at chain
bookshops and independent
bookshops nationwide; at
local literary events; and from
Amazon and other bookshop
websites, including distributor
inpressbooks.co.uk.
Arachne Press title *Devilskein
& Dearlove* by Alex Smith was
nominated for the Carnegie
Medal 2015, and title *Weird Lies*,
edited by Cherry Potts and Katy
Darby, won Best Anthology in
the 2014 Saboteur Awards.
GENRES: literary fiction; poetry;
Children's fiction; fantasy/sci-fi;
photography.
SUBMISSIONS: Particularly
welcome from all women,
disabled and D/deaf writers.
During submissions windows,
submit through Submittable
at arachnepress.submittable.
com/submit. Guidelines at
arachnepress.com/submissions.
Usually responds within one to
three months. Authors receive
royalties and free copies of the
book.

THEY SAY

Arachne Press is a micro-
publisher with ambitions. We
use our live events to promote
our books and find new writers
– your best route to publication
with us is to submit to a call
out for an anthology. If we
love your work and you are
prepared to back your writing,
by doing readings or bragging
on social media, then we might
invite you to put forward a
collection or novel. We give
feedback more sparingly than
we used to, but if we say it
shows promise we mean it!

**For more information, including
what We Say, see poetry
publishers p17**

being dedicated to 'all the brutal women' and has the sort of abrupt opening that snares the reader.

ARLEN HOUSE
NOVELS / SHORT STORY COLLECTIONS AND ANTHOLOGIES / NON-FICTION
42 Grange Abbey Road, Baldoyle, Dublin 13, Ireland
arlenhouse@gmail.com
Editor: Alan Hayes
Established 1975, Ireland's oldest feminist publisher. Award-winning publisher, publishing poetry (see p19), prose and mixed poetry/prose anthologies. Publications available from chain and independent bookshops nationwide, at national and local literary events, and from Amazon and other online bookshops. International distribution by Syracuse University Press.
GENRES: Literary.
SUBMISSIONS: Submissions by invitation only. Author deals vary from book to book depending on funding and sales forecasts, but may pay an advance, royalties, and/or copies of the publication. Solicited work may receive a response in one to three months.
For more information, including what We Say, see also: poetry publishers p19

AS YET UNTITLED
ARTISTS' BOOKS
5 Veales Rd, Kingsbridge, Devon TQ7 1EX
ayupublishing@gmail.com
www.asyetuntitled.org
Editor: Rosie Sherwood
Established 2012. Mixed form: artists' books. As Yet Untitled specialises in limited edition, hand made book art and live events.

Publications available direct from publisher website; from selected/ local chain bookshops; from independent bookshops; at local literary events; and at Artists' Book Fairs (National) and the Small Publishers Fair.
GENRES: Fantasy/sci-fi; graphic/ comics; literary fiction; poetry; visual arts. Strictly no non-fiction.
SUBMISSIONS: As Yet Untitled does not take submissions. Artists and writers are invited to collaborate with the press.
See also: poetry publishers p19

ASLS
PRINT
ASLS, 7 University Gardens, Glasgow G12 8QH
0141 330 5309
office@asls.org.uk
www.asls.org.uk
Established 1970. Publications available direct from publisher website; by post and email order; from chain bookshops nationwide; from independent bookshops; at national and local literary events; and from Amazon and other bookshop websites.
ASLS titles have won Saltire Society Research Book of the Year awards, and an ASLS title was shortlisted for the Saltire Society Scottish Book of the Year award in 2011.
GENRES: Short fiction and poetry (in New Writing Scotland); reprints of classic Scottish texts; collections of scholarly papers; study guides.
SUBMISSIONS: Submit by proposal form at asls.arts.gla.ac.uk/contact. html#A1. Usually responds within four to six months. No feedback offered with rejections. Successful contributors to New Writing Scotland are paid a fee and receive print copies of the book.

WE SAY: We looked at *A Portable Shelter* by Kirsty Logan: a beautiful, limited edition hardback, clothbound with silver embossed text on the cover, and thick inner paper for the 13 short stories in the collection. A high-art production, worthy of the Folio Society.
See also: poetry publishers p19 and New Writing Scotland (mixed-form magazine) p245

ASTON BAY PRESS
NOVELS
c/o Daniel Goldsmith Associates, Dallam Court, Dallam Lane WA2 7LT
www.astonbay.co.uk
Publishes crime and historical fiction; detective stories with female leads. Welcomes submissions from agents and authors.

ATLANTIC PRESS
GRAPHIC LITERATURE
info@atlanticpressbooks.com
www.atlanticpressbooks.com
Publishes limited edition first books by authorial illustrators. Looks for intriguing stories illustrated for an adult audience, or for an audience of all ages. Works in association with the MA in Authorial Illustration at Falmouth University.

AUGUR PRESS
NOVELS / NON-FICTION
info@augurpress.com
www.augurpress.com
Non-fiction and fiction. Books with an emphasis on enabling the reader 'to reflect, and to look beyond ... that which is immediately apparent'.
See also: poetry publishers p20

AURORA METRO ☆
E-BOOKS / NOVELS / NON-FICTION
67 Grove Avenue, Twickenham
TW1 4HX
020 3261 0000
submissions@aurorametro.com
www.aurorametro.com
Editor: Cheryl Robson
Established 1989. Also publishes scripts. Publications available direct from publisher website; by direct mail and email orders; from chain bookshops nationwide; from independent bookshops; at national and local literary events, and from Amazon and other bookshop websites.
Aurora Metro title *The Leipzig Affair* by Fiona Rintoul was shortlisted for the Scottish First Book of the Year Award 2015 by the Saltire Society.
In 2019 Aurora Metro was one of the three independent publishers nominated for an IPG Diversity Award, and founder Cheryl Robson was nominated for a Lifetime Achievement Award by the National Diversity Awards (at time of publication, winner announcements pending).
GENRES: Fiction by women; historical fiction; arts and culture non-fiction.
SUBMISSIONS: Open to all. Submit by post (67 Grove Avenue, Twickenham TW1 4HX) or email (submissions@aurorametro.com). Guidelines at www.aurorametro.com/newsite/contact-us/submit-your-work/#gsc.tab=0. Usually responds within one to three months. Rejections may occasionally include unsolicited feedback. Authors are paid an advance/fee plus royalties and receive free copies of the book.
WE SAY: Aurora Metro's impressive catalogue of books cover all ground, with publications catered to different age groups, genres

and forms. We looked at *The Colour of Things Unseen* by Annee Lawrence, a deeply passionate love story that explores divisions in culture, religion, and our individual experiences of the world. The book is bound by a soothing and alluring pastel-coloured cover, embodying the love of art explored throughout.

AVERY HILL PUBLISHING
GRAPHIC NOVELS
Unit 8, 5 Durham Yard, London E2 6QF
07725 595307
ricky@averyhillublishing.com
averyhillpublishing.com
Editors: Ricky Miller, David White
Established 2012. Primarily publishes graphic fiction. Publications available direct from publisher website; by post and email order; at major chain and independent bookshops; at literary events; and from Amazon and other bookshop websites.
Avery Hill Publishing author Tillie Walden won the awards for Best Newcomer and Best Artist at the 2016 Ignatz Awards.
GENRES: Science fiction; LGBTQ; comedy; literary; romance.
SUBMISSIONS: Submissions by invitation only. Usually responds to solicited submissions within four weeks. Rejections may occasionally include unsolicited feedback. Authors are paid royalties.
WE SAY: We looked at a digital version of *I Love This Part* by Tillie Walden. This graphic novel documenting the day-to-day conversations of two teenage girls slowly falling in love has an almost zine-like style – coloured entirely with black and white, with purple watercolours. The writing style is

subtle and delicate, the images conveying mood as much as the words do. There is a small author's bio at the end of the novel, as well as a dedication on the last page.

AWEN PUBLICATIONS
NOVELS / SHORT STORY COLLECTIONS / NON-FICTION / MIXED-FORM ANTHOLOGIES
12 Belle Vue Close, Stroud GL5 1ND
anthony@quintus1.plus.com
www.awenpublications.co.uk
Editor: Anthony Nanson
Established 2003. Publishes both prose and poetry (see p20). Publications available direct from the publisher website; by post and email order; from chain and independent bookshops; at local literary events; and from Amazon and other bookshop websites.
In 2013 Awen Publications won a Storytelling World Award (honours).
GENRES: Literary fiction; essays.
SUBMISSIONS: Submissions by invitation only. Authors are paid royalties and receive free copies of their book and a generous author discount.
WE SAY: Priding themselves as publishers of 'quality fiction, poetry and non-fiction that engage with the world', Awen Publications have a broad catalogue of texts on a variety of topics. However, they particularly show interest in imaginative and eco-conscious work. Their published pamphlet *An Ecobardic Manifesto* by performance storytellers Fire Springs, reflects Awen's interests through urgent and inquisitive prose. Clearly, this is a press with big ideas.
See also: poetry publishers p20

B SMALL PUBLISHING
CHILDREN'S NON-FICTION
sh@bsmall.co.uk
www.bsmall.co.uk
Editor: Sam Hutchinson
Established 1990. Publishes
non-fiction and activity books.
Publications available direct from
the publisher website; from chain
and independent bookshops; and
from Amazon and other bookshop
websites.
b small publishing won Small Press
of the Year, Southeast Region in
the 2019 British Book Awards.
GENRES: Children's non-fiction;
children's language learning.
SUBMISSIONS: b small publishing
generates the majority of their
list in-house. Please review the
press' catalogue closely before
submitting anything, but note
that it is rare for them to acquire
external titles.
WE SAY: b small publishing's
vibrant and colourful website
is immediately appealing and
welcomes users with cartoon
character graphics. As well as their
wide range of children's texts,
from dress-up guides to language-
learning books, b small also have
an informative blog and fun activity
hub. Adding to the welcoming feel
of the website, b small promote
inclusivity in their readership, as a
100% LGBT and women-owned
press and member of Inclusive
Minds.

BACKLASH PRESS
FICTION
www.backlashpress.com
Publisher: Gretchen Heffernan
Dedicated to releasing work that
'narrates a contemplated resistance
to obedience and trend'. Looks for
experimental, yet enduring fiction.

See also: poetry publishers p20 and
Backlash Journal (poetry magazine)
p270

BANIPAL PUBLISHING
NOVELS / SHORT STORY
COLLECTIONS AND ANTHOLOGIES
1 Gough Square, London EC4A 3DE
07979 540594
margaret@banipal.co.uk
www.banipal.co.uk
Editors: Margaret Obank and Samuel
Shimon
Established 1997. Publishes
translated poetry (see p21) and
prose alongside *Banipal Magazine*
(see p217). Publications available
direct from the publisher website;
at chain and independent
bookshops; and from Amazon and
other bookshop websites.
Banipal Publishing won the
2016 Sheikh Hamad Award for
Translation and International
Understanding, Doha, Qatar.
GENRES: Literary.
SUBMISSIONS: Open to
submissions, but because Banipal's
publications are all translations
(mainly from Arabic) the editors
primarily select the works to
translate and commission the
translations. Submit by email to
editor@banipal.co.uk. Guidelines
at www.banipal.co.uk/submissions.
Responds in over six months. No
feedback is offered with rejections.
Authors are paid a flat fee and
royalties, and receive copies of
their book.
See also: poetry publishers p21
and *Banipal Magazine* (mixed-form
magazine) p217

BANSHEE PRESS
NOVELS / SHORT STORY
COLLECTIONS
bansheelit@gmail.com

www.bansheelit.com
Editors: Laura Cassidy, Claire
Hennessy, Eimear Ryan
Established 2019. Mixed form,
publishing prose and poetry (see
p21). Publications available direct
from publisher website; by post
and email order; from major chain
and independent bookshops; at
national and local literary events;
and from Amazon and other
bookshop websites.
GENRES: Literary.
SUBMISSIONS: Does not accept
unsolicited submissions – authors
are found through literary magazine
Banshee (see p217). Authors are
paid an advance plus royalties.
See also: poetry publishers p21 and
***Banshee* (mixed-form magazine)**
p217

BARBICAN PRESS
FICTION / SHORT STORY
COLLECTIONS AND ANTHOLOGIES
/ NON-FICTION / E-BOOKS
www.barbicanpress.com
Editor: Martin Goodman
Looks for 'distinct voices' and
books that dare to be different,
across a range of disciplines.
Current catalogue includes works
from translated fiction to true-life
short stories.

BHP COMICS
GRAPHIC NOVELS / COMIC ART
BOOKS
Summertown Pavilion, 18-24 Middle
Way, Oxford OX2 7LG
0141 332 6034
web@bhpcomics.com
www.bhpcomics.com
Editor: Sha Nazir
Established 2015. Publishes
graphic novels and comic art
books. Publications available direct
from the publisher website; by

direct mail and email order; from
chain and independent bookshops;
at local and national literary events;
and from Amazon and other
bookshop websites.
BHP Comics publication *Rok of
the Reds* was shortlisted for the
2019 SBT Children's Book Awards;
Killtopia won Best Graphic Novel,
Best Writer and Best Artist at
the 2019 SICBA Awards, and
Best Creative Industries Award
at the 2018 Creative Edinburgh
Awards. BHP Comics was Highly
Commended for the British Book
Awards: Small Publisher of the Year
2019 and shortlisted for the Saltire
Awards: Publisher of the Year 2018
and 2017. BHP Comics publication
Freedom Bound was Highly
Commended for Saltire History
Book of the Year 2018.
GENRES: YA fantasy/adventure; sci-
fi; speculative fiction; non-fiction
history/politics; humour; art.
SUBMISSIONS: Open to all. Submit
by email to subs@bhpcomics.
com. No postal submissions are
accepted. Guidelines at bhpcomics.
squarespace.com/submissions?p.
Usually responds in one to three
months. No feedback offered with
rejections. Authors are paid an
advance fee plus royalties, and
receive free copies of their book.

BIRLINN PRESS
E-BOOKS / NOVELS / NON-FICTION
info@birlinn.co.uk
www.birlinn.co.uk
Managing director: Hugh Andrews
One of the larger independent
presses, with a wide range of
publications. Mixed form, fiction
and non-fiction. Imprints include
John Donald, Arena Sport and BC
Books.
See also: poetry publishers p21

BITTER LEMON PRESS
E-BOOKS / NOVELS
47 Wilmington Square, London
WC1 X0ET
fvh@bitterlemonpress.com
www.bitterlemonpress.com
Editor: François von Hurter
Established 2003. Fiction
publisher. Available from chain
and independent bookshops; and
from Amazon and other bookshop
websites.
GENRES: Crime.
SUBMISSIONS: Submissions from
agents only. Usually responds
within three months. Rejections
may occasionally include
unsolicited feedback. Authors are
paid an advance fee plus royalties.
WE SAY: We looked at two
digital books of Bitter Lemon
Press. The first, *Three Drops of
Blood and a Cloud of Cocaine* by
Quentin Mouron, is a from-French
translated 206-page crime novel.
The second, *A Quiet Place* by
Seichō Matsumoto, is a 235-page
criminal story, translated from
Japanese. The layout of both
books is nice, with justified text
and nevertheless not-too-full
pages, and attractive, high-quality
colourful covers.

BLACK & WHITE PUBLISHING
E-BOOKS / NOVELS / NON-FICTION
Nautical House, 104 Commercial
Street, Edinburgh EH6 6NF
0131 625 4500
mail@blackandwhitepublishing.com
www.blackandwhitepublishing.com
Editor: Emma Hargrave
Established 1992. Mainly publishes
fiction and non-fiction. Publications
available from chain bookshops
nationwide; from independent
bookshops; at local literary events;
and from Amazon and all other UK
bookshop websites.
GENRES: Crime/thriller/mystery;
historical fiction; literary fiction;
romance; YA; biography and true
stories; lifestyle; humour; sports
and leisure.
SUBMISSIONS: Open to all.
Submit via the website. Guidelines
at www.blackandwhitepublishing.
com/index.php/infopages/
submissions. Usually responds
within one to three months. If
no response after three months,
assume rejection. Individual
contracts for each writer.

BLACK DOG
NON-FICTION
info@blackdogonline.com
www.blackdogonline.com
Publishing art, fashion and
photography; and music, stage
and screen, illustrated books, Black
Dog aims for a 'fresh, eclectic take
on contemporary culture'.

BLACK PEAR PRESS
NOVELS / SHORT STORY
COLLECTIONS AND ANTHOLOGIES
/ E-BOOKS
office@blackpear.net
www.blackpear.net
Editors: Rod Griffiths, Polly Robinson,
Tony Judge
Established 2013. Mixed form.
Publications available direct from
publisher website, by post and
email order, at local literary events,
on Amazon and on other bookshop
websites.
GENRES: Crime/thriller/mystery;
literary fiction; poetry; YA. No
non-fiction.
SUBMISSIONS: Welcome during
submissions windows, otherwise
submissions are by invitation
only. Guidelines at blackpear.net/
submissions. Usually responds

within one to three months. Rejections may occasionally include unsolicited feedback. Authors receive royalties and a discount on the price of the book.
WE SAY: We looked at a PDF of *Seeds of Destruction* by Frances Bennett: a perfect-bound, 216-page publication, also available in digital format. A black cover with a coloured pencil sketch of a dandelion clock against stormy cliffs, and a rounded font. The layout is tidy and professional. The writing is tight and well-presented.
See also: poetry publishers p22

BLACK SHUCK BOOKS
E-BOOKS / NOVELS / SHORT STORY COLLECTIONS AND ANTHOLOGIES
steve@blackshuckbooks.co.uk
www.blackshuckbooks.co.uk
Editor: Steve J Shaw
Established 2015. Publications available direct from publisher website; by direct mail and email orders; at national and local literary events; and from Amazon.
GENRES: Horror.
SUBMISSIONS: By invitation only. Usually responds within one to three months, with feedback only if requested. Authors are paid an advance/fee plus royalties and receive free copies of the book.
WE SAY: We looked at a digital version of *Green and Pleasant Land*, a collection of 11 original horror stories by various authors. The print version comes with a green-black spooky coloured cover, with the authors' names printed in a large font. Although this contains all the need-to-know facts, a more creative cover would also have worked well here. The stories are

presented in different fonts, all starting with a black-white sketched illustration depicting the location of the story.

BLACKHEATH BOOKS
NOVELS
grunt.blackheath@virgin.net
www.blackheathbooks.org.uk
'A home for literary outsiders.' A very small press which hand-prints books using vintage equipment. Publications are limited print runs, with signed and numbered editions. Looking for 'future cult classic novels'.
See also: poetry publishers p22

BLUE NIB, THE ☆
SHORT STORY COLLECTIONS AND ANTHOLOGIES
Ecklands, Carnhill, Loughshinny, Skerries, Co Dublin
+353 858 513 376
info@thebluenib.com
www.thebluenib.com
Editors: Shirley Bell (poetry & EOC), Mimi Gladman (fiction) and Dave Kavanagh (online editor)
Established 2016. Publishes poetry (see p23), short fiction, essays and reviews, including mixed-form anthologies. Available direct from the publisher website, from independent bookshops, and from Amazon. *The Blue Nib* magazine (see p218) was longlisted for the 2018 Saboteur Awards Best Literary Magazine.
SUBMISSIONS: Submissions are open to all, during submissions windows. Guidelines at www.thebluenib.com/submission-guidelines. Usually responds in one to three months. Rejections may occasionally include unsolicited feedback. Unpaid, as The Blue Nib currently reinvests all funds

into publishing work by emerging authors.

See also: poetry publishers p23 and for more information, including what We Say, *The Blue Nib* (mixed-form magazine) p218

BLUEMOOSE BOOKS

E-BOOKS / NOVELS / NON-FICTION
25 Sackville Street, Hebden Bridge, Yorkshire HX7 7DJ
01422 842731
kevin@bluemoosebooks.com
www.bluemoosebooks.com
Editors: Lin Webb, Leonora Rustamova, Hetha Duffy
Established 2006. Mainly publishes fiction. Publications available direct from publisher website; by post and email order; at chain bookshops nationwide; at independent bookshops; at national and local literary events; and from Amazon and other bookshop websites.
Authors at Bluemoose books have won The Walter Scott Prize for Historical Fiction in 2018; The Portico Literature Prize 2015. The Gordon Burn Prize 2013 (Faber & New Writing North) and Northern Writers' Award 2014 (New Writing North) and been shortlisted for The Jerwood Fiction Uncovered Award 2015.
GENRES: Literary fiction.
SUBMISSIONS: Open to all. Submit by email to kevin@bluemoosebooks.com. Guidelines at bluemoosebooks.com/about. Usually responds within four to six months. Rejections may occasionally include unsolicited feedback. Authors receive royalties only, or advance/fee plus royalties, and free copies of the book.
WE SAY: The perfect-bound title we saw, *The Gallows Pole* by Benjamin Myers, had an eye-catching cover and an equally vibrant spine – the matte cover featuring the shadowing image of a man with pink coins covering his eyes, and the spine a dizzying pattern of bright pink and black lines. The other covers on their website are similarly imaginative and striking. With 374 off-white pages, Myers' novel about the Cragg Vale Coiners was forensically assembled from historical accounts and legal documents.

BOILER HOUSE PRESS

SHORT STORY COLLECTIONS AND ANTHOLOGIES / NOVELS / NON-FICTION
www.boilerhouse.press
publishing@uea.ac.uk
Based at the University of East Anglia, Boiler House Press is a new publisher of fiction, non-fiction, poetry and everything in-between. The website states that they are 'passionate about writing that breaks the mould; that surprises; that plays with-and-between the creative and the critical'. If submitting, do so via their website and allow at least a month for a response.
See also: poetry publishers p24

BOOK GUILD, THE

NOVELS / E-BOOKS / NON-FICTION
www.bookguild.co.uk
info@bookguild.co.uk
Publishes in poetry (see p24) and prose, including fiction, non-fiction, children's, biography and travel. Looking for commercial work. May offer successful submissions either a traditional publishing model or a 'partnership' model (requiring a financial contribution from the author). Full information at www.

bookguild.co.uk/publish-with-us.
See also: poetry publishers p24

BRIDGE HOUSE PUBLISHING
SHORT STORY COLLECTIONS AND
ANTHOLOGIES
www.bridgehousepublishing.co.uk
editor@bridgehousepublishing.co.uk
Founded in 2009, Bridge House
primarily publishes short story
anthologies and collections. The
press has an annual open call for
themed anthology submissions.
Writers wishing to publish a
single-author collection should first
be published in a Bridge House
anthology.

BROWN WATSON
CHILDREN'S BOOKS
www.brownwatson.co.uk
books@brownwatson.co.uk
Leicestershire-based press
specialising in publishing mass-
market children's books, fiction
and non-fiction: case-bound
books, board books, sticker books,
educational activity books and
pop-up books.

CANBURY PRESS
NON-FICTION
Kingston-upon-Thames, Surrey
canburypress@gmail.com
www.canburypress.com
Editor: Martin Hickman
Established 2013. Publications
available direct from the publisher
website; by direct post and email
order; from chain and independent
bookshops; at local and national
literary events; and on Amazon and
other bookshops websites.
Canbury Press was shortlisted for
Small Press of the Year (London) in
The British Book Awards 2019.
GENRES: Politics; health;
technology; memoir.

SUBMISSIONS: Proposals for
original, high-quality, popular
non-fiction are welcome to be
sent to canburypress@gmail.com.
Absolutely no fiction please (fiction
applications will not be read or
acknowledged). Usually responds
within four weeks with a brief
email. Author deals vary.

CANDLESTICK PRESS
SHORT STORY COLLECTIONS
Diversity House, 72 Nottingham Road,
Arnold, Nottingham NG5 6LF
01159 674455
info@candlestickpress.co.uk
www.candlestickpress.co.uk
Editors: Di Slaney, Katharine Towers
Established 2008. Mainly publishes
poetry (see p25). Publications
available direct from publisher
website; by direct mail and email
orders; from chain bookshops
nationwide; from independent
bookshops; at national and local
literary events; and from Amazon
and other bookshop websites.
GENRES: None specified.
SUBMISSIONS: By invitation
only. Feedback not offered with
rejections. Authors are paid a flat
fee and receive free copies of the
book.
**For more information see also:
poetry publishers p25**

CANONGATE
FICTION / NON-FICTION
support@canongate.co.uk
www.canongate.co.uk
Founded in 1973, this is one of the
largest independent presses: twice
winner of Publisher of the Year, and
behind the publication of Booker
Prize winner *Life of Pi* by Yann
Martel. Committed to unorthodox
and innovative publishing. No
unsolicited submissions please;

authors are advised to first get
representation.

CARCANET PRESS
ANTHOLOGIES
4th Floor Alliance House,
30 Cross Street, Manchester M2 7AQ
0161 834 8730
info@carcanet.co.uk
www.carcanet.co.uk
Editors: Michael Schmidt, Andrew
Latimer
Established 1969. Mainly publishes
poetry (see p25), but also some
fiction, non-fiction and mixed
prose/poetry anthologies.
Publications available direct from
the publisher website; at chain
and independent bookshops; at
national and local literary events;
and from Amazon and other
bookshop websites.
In 2019, Carcanet Press won
Northern Small Press of the Year
at the 2019 British Book Awards.
In 2018 it was made a finalist in
the Manchester Culture Awards
in the Outstanding Contribution
category and shortlisted for
Northern Publisher of the Year
in the Northern Soul Awards. It
was also shortlisted for the IPG
Alison Morrison Diversity Award
for a fourth year. In 2017 Carcanet
Press was shortlisted for the IPG
Diversity Award and the Northern
Soul Northern Publisher of the Year
Award.
Carcanet celebrated its 50th
anniversary from Autumn 2019 –
Summer 2020.
SUBMISSIONS: Open to all.
Guidelines at www.carcanet.co.uk/
cgi-bin/scribe?showinfo=ip002.
Rejections may occasionally
include unsolicited feedback.
**For more information, including
what We Say, see also: poetry
publishers p25 and *PN Review*
(poetry magazine) p279**

CARYSFORT PRESS
NON-FICTION
info@carysfortpress.com
www.carysfortpress.com
Leading Irish publisher of
contemporary writing for and
about the theatre, and about other
performing arts. Publications are
academic, but accessible to a
general readership.

CASSAVA REPUBLIC
NOVELS / NON-FICTION / SHORT
STORY COLLECTIONS
www.cassavarepublic.biz
info@cassavarepublic.biz
A Nigeria (Abuja)/London-based
press open to work from writers
of African origin, and 'especially
interested in submissions by
women, writers from North and
East Africa, the Caribbean, African-
American and black Europeans,
and those that explore uncharted
areas in African letters: diverse
sexualities, speculative fiction,
fantasy and crime'.
GENRES: Literary fiction, teen and
children's books, crime, romance
and narrative non-fiction.

CATNIP PUBLISHING
NOVELS / PICTURE BOOKS
www.catnipbooks.com
Editor: Liz Bankes
Established 2005. Fiction only.
Publications available from chain
bookshops nationwide; from
independent bookshops; at
national and local literary events;
from Amazon and other bookshop
websites; and direct from Bounce
Sales and Marketing. Schools
and libraries can order through
wholesalers.

Catnip title *Girl with a White Dog* was shortlisted for the Waterstones Children's Book Prize 2015.
GENRES: Children's fiction; YA; picture books.
SUBMISSIONS: Agent submissions only. Unsolicited submissions are not guaranteed a response. Usually responds within one to three months. Rejections may occasionally include unsolicited feedback, but not guaranteed. Authors are paid an advance/fee plus royalties.

CB EDITIONS
E-BOOKS / NOVELS / SHORT STORY COLLECTIONS / NON-FICTION
146 Percy Road, London W12 9QL
020 8743 2467
info@cbeditions.com
www.cbeditions.com
Editor: Charles Boyle
Established 2007. Publishes poetry (see p26), short fiction and other prose. Publications available direct from publisher website; at chain and independent bookshops nationwide; at national and local literary events; and from Amazon and other bookshop websites.
A multi-award-winning publisher: titles have won the Aldeburgh First Collection Prize (2009, 2011, 2013); the Scott Moncrieff Translation Prize (2014); the McKitterick Prize (2008) and the McKitterick Prize (2008)), as well as being shortlisted for the Goldsmiths Prize (2014) and the *Guardian* First Book Award (2014).
GENRES: Literary fiction.
SUBMISSIONS: Currently publishing only a small number of titles; please email info@cbeditions.com before submitting. No feedback offered with rejection. Authors are paid an advance/fee plus royalties,

and receive free copies of the book.
For more information, see also: poetry publishers p26

CHARCO PRESS
E-BOOKS / NOVELS / SHORT STORY COLLECTIONS
44-46 Morningside Road, Office 59, Edinburgh EH10 4BF
07426 459102
info@charcopress.com
www.charcopress.com
Editor: Carolina Orloff
Established 2016. Primarily publishes fiction. Publications available direct from the publisher website; by direct mail and email order; from chain and independent bookshops; public libraries; at national and local literary events; and from Amazon and other bookshop websites.
Charco Press has been awarded the titles of Emerging Publisher of the Year 2018 (Saltire Society), Creative Start-Up of the Year 2018 (Creative Edinburgh) and Scottish Small Press of the Year 2019.
GENRE: Literary.
SUBMISSIONS: Submitters must have a publication history. Submit by email (carolina@charcopress.com) or post (44-46 Morningside Road, Office 59, Edinburgh EH10 4BF). Usually takes over six months to reply. No feedback offered with rejections. Authors are paid an advance fee and royalties, and receive copies of their book.
WE SAY: Charco Press is a publisher that prides itself on bridging the gap between languages, bringing powerful Latin American writing into English. Their sleek website presents the translators as well as the authors who have created their work, and their array of

publications have consistently stylish covers. We also looked at PDF proofs of *Feebleminded* by Ariana Harwicz, translated by Annie McDermott and Carolina Orloff. Themes of familial human experiences reinforce the concerns for identity and belonging that this publisher emanates.

CHICKEN HOUSE ☆
NOVELS / E-BOOKS
01373 454488
hello@chickenhousebooks.com
www.chickenhousebooks.com
Editors: Rachel Leyshon and Kesia Lupo

Established 2000. Publishes fiction. Publications available from chain and independent bookshops; at national literary events; and on Amazon and other bookshop websites.

Chicken House publication *The Girl of Ink & Stars* by Kiran Millwood Hargrave won Waterstones' Children's Book of The Year.

GENRES: Children's middle grade; teen; young adult.

SUBMISSIONS: Submissions from agents only, except via the *Times*/Chicken House Children's Fiction Competition (see p306). All details are at www.chickenhousebooks.com/submissions. Usually responds within one to three months. Authors are paid an advance fee plus royalties.

WE SAY: We looked at three of Chicken House's paperback middle grade publications. *The Way Past Winter* by Kiran Millwood Hargrave has a beautiful sleeve design with copper foiling, French flaps and patterned end papers, as well as corner illustrations throughout. *Who Let The Gods Out* by Maz Evans is bright and attractive

with silver foil detailing, and an incredibly fun flip book illustration running along by the page numbers. *The Last Chance Hotel* by Nicki Thornton has a velvet matte cover with foil detailing and gorgeous page illustrations introducing each part of the novel.

CHOC LIT
E-BOOKS / NOVELS / SHORT STORY COLLECTIONS AND ANTHOLOGIES
Penrose House, Crawley Drive, Camberley, Surrey GU15 2AB
01276 274920
info@choc-lit.com
www.choc-lit.com

Established 2009. Fiction. Publications available from chain bookshops nationwide; from independent bookshops; and from Amazon and other bookshop websites.

Winner of 18 awards including, the 2017 Epic Romantic Novel of the Year Award from the Romantic Novelists' Association.

GENRES: Romance; women's fiction; fantasy; saga; historical fiction.

SUBMISSIONS: Open to all. Submit through www.submission.choc-lit.com. Usually responds within one to three months. Authors are paid royalties only.

WE SAY: Choc Lit continues to produce perfect-bound, glossy books that easily hold their own against Big Five commercial printing. We looked at *Oh Crumbs* by Kathryn Freeman, a commercial classic romance, complete with a dramatic start as our heroine finds her life turned upside down, and a new-job meet-cute with a man who, of course, harbours a secret. The cover is all pastel colours, swirling illustrations and curly fonts,

CINNAMON PRESS ☆

NOVELS / SHORT STORY
COLLECTIONS AND ANTHOLOGIES
Meirion House, Glan yr afon, Blaenau
Ffestiniog, Gwynedd LL41 3SU
01766 832112
jan@cinnamonpress.com
www.cinnamonpress.com
Editors: Jan Fortune and Adam Craig

Established 2005. Mixed form: alongside novels, short stories and creative non-fiction, it also publishes poetry (see p26). Publications available direct from publisher website; from chain and independent bookshops nationwide; at local literary events; from Amazon; and from Inpress Books. Titles from Cinnamon have won Scottish Arts Best First Book of the Year; Wales Book of the Year; and Wales Book of the Year Readers' Vote; and shortlisted for Wales Book of the Year and the Forward Prize for Best First Collection.

GENRES: Historical fiction; literary fiction; experimental; cross-genre; literary crime/thriller; literary exploratory fiction/sci-fi; landscape; creative biography; creative writing related.

SUBMISSIONS: Submit during submissions periods (see www. cinnamonpress.com/index.php/ about-cinnamon-press/submissions). Usually responds within one to three months. Submissions that came close to publication may receive some feedback with rejection. Authors are paid royalties only.

WE SAY: We looked at PDF copy of short story collection *Punch* by Kate North. The cover uses yellows and blues against a black background, bringing to mind the colours of a

bruise. Unusually, but pleasingly, the stories are preceded by the acknowledgements.

See also: poetry publishers p26 and *Envoi Poetry Journal* p272

They say

Cinnamon Press is 15 in 2020 and committed to keeping alive the passion that got us this far. We're a small, independent publisher based in North Wales and the Midlands. We select books that we feel passionate about and aim to be innovative, publishing fiction, poetry and selective non-fiction that is not defined by genre, but by unique voices with something to say. Our authors come from all over the world and we aim to remain outward looking. In addition to books we run mentoring, courses, competitions and literary events. Join our mailing list at www.cinnamonpress.com.

promising a proper break from the real world. We'd take this book on holiday.
See also: Ruby Fiction (prose publisher) p177

CILLIAN PRESS
E-BOOKS / NOVELS
83 Ducie Street, Manchester M1 2JQ
0161 864 2301
info@cillianpress.co.uk
www.cillianpress.co.uk
Established 2012. Fiction publisher. Publications available direct from publisher website; by post and email order; from chain bookshops nationwide; from independent bookshops; and from Amazon and other bookshop websites.
GENRES: Literary fiction; contemporary; YA; adult.

CIRCAIDY GREGORY PRESS
E-BOOKS / NOVELS
Creative Media Centre, 45 Robertson Street, Hastings, Sussex TN34 1HL
sales@circaidygregory.co.uk
www.circaidygregory.co.uk
A mixed form 'independent publisher for independent readers', Circaidy Gregory publishes non-fiction, short stories, childrens' fiction, plays and novels as well as poetry (see p27).
See also: poetry publishers p27

CLARET PRESS
FICTION AND CREATIVE NON-FICTION
51 Iveley Road, London SW4 0EN
020 7622 0436
contact@claretpress.com
www.claretpress.com
Editor: Katie Isbester
Established 2015. Primarily publishes fiction. Publications available from chain and independent bookshops; and from Amazon and other bookshop websites.
GENRES: Political thrillers, mysteries and adventures; historical untold moments and stories from pivotal points in modern history; issue-led romances and narratives; biographies and turbulent memoirs set in fraught locations; and escapist comedy fun with a political edge.
SUBMISSIONS: Submit only during submissions windows, by post (51 Iveley Road, London SW4 0EN) or email (contact@claretpress.com). Guidelines at www.claretpress.com/about. Usually responds within four weeks. No feedback offered with rejections. Authors are paid royalties and receive free copies of their book.
WE SAY: We looked at a digital version of *Brushstrokes in Time* by Sylvia Vetta, a 187-page diary-style memoir tale about a woman growing up during the Cultural Revolution in Beijing, China, who tells her story to her daughter. The cover, although simple, is stylish and suits the story. The inside shows full pages with calligraphic Chinese characters at the start of every chapter, which suits the story as the main character stresses the importance of the Chinese literary system to her daughter.

COLUMBA PRESS
E-BOOKS / NOVELS / MIXED-FORM COLLECTIONS AND ANTHOLOGIES / NON-FICTION
23 Merrion Square North, Dublin 2, Ireland
garry@columba.ie
www.columba.ie
Editor: Garry O'Sullivan
Established 1985. Also publishes poetry in mixed-form collections and anthologies (see p27).

Publications available direct from publisher website; by direct mail and email orders; from chain bookshops nationwide; from independent bookshops; at local literary events; and from Amazon and other bookshop websites.
GENRES: Catholicism; spirituality; history; reflection; prayer.
SUBMISSIONS: Open to all. Submit by email to garry@columba. ie. Usually responds within four weeks. Rejections may occasionally include unsolicited feedback. Authors are paid an advance/ fee plus royalties and receive free copies of the book.
See also: poetry publishers p27

COMMA PRESS ☆

SHORT STORY COLLECTIONS AND ANTHOLOGIES / E-BOOKS
Studio 510a, Fifth Floor, Hope Mill, 113 Pollard Street, Manchester M4 7JA
info@commapress.co.uk
www.commapress.co.uk
Editors: Ra Page, Sarah Cleave, Becca Parkinson, Zoe Turner
Established 2007. Fiction only. Publications available direct from publisher website; from chain bookshops nationwide; from independent bookshops; at national and local literary events; and from Amazon and other bookshop websites.
Comma Press title *Tea at the Midland*, a short story collection by David Constantine, won the 2013 Frank O'Connor International Short Story Prize, and the short story of the same name won the 2010 BBC National Short Story Prize. *The Iraqi Christ* by Hassan Blasim, translated by Jonathan Wright, won the 2014 Independent Foreign Fiction Prize. Comma

Press also actively works with writers, running short story courses and hosting the annual National Creative Writing Industry Day in Manchester.
GENRES: Literary fiction; sci-fi; horror; historical. No non-fiction.
SUBMISSIONS: Open to all. Submit by email to info@ commapress.co.uk. Guidelines at commapress.co.uk/resources/ submissions/. Usually responds in over six months. Rejections may occasionally include unsolicited feedback. Authors are paid a flat fee or royalties, depending on the type of book/funding.
WE SAY: In print, we saw *The Book of Khartoum*, edited by Raph Cormack and Max Shmookler, and *Iraq +100*, edited by Hassan Blasim, anthologies that both won the English Pen Award. These collections mix a sans-serif font in the titles with serif in the body text, but otherwise follow a standard design, with matte covers featuring graphic art. We also looked at a digital version of *Protest*, a 459-page anthology of 20 historic stories about resistance. Every story offers an inside perspective on a historic event, which is elaborated on in an afterword, written by a historian. Enthralling and informative.

COPY PRESS

SHORT STORY COLLECTIONS / NON-FICTION
51 South Street, Ventnor, Isle of Wight PO38 1NG
020 3 397 6575
info@copypress.co.uk
www.copypress.co.uk
Editors: Yve Lomax, Vit Hopley, Anne Tallentire, Kristen Kreider, Cecile Malaspina

Established 2012. Publishes contemporary writing including poetry (see p28). Publications available by direct mail and email order; from chain and independent bookshops nationwide; and from Amazon and other bookshop websites.
GENRES: Art; philosophy; politics.
SUBMISSIONS: Open to all. Submit by email to info@copypress.co.uk. Guidelines at www.copypress.co.uk/index/proposals. The press never charges a reading fee. Usually responds in one to three months. Rejections may occasionally include unsolicited feedback. Authors are paid royalties.
WE SAY: We looked at the online marketing page for *Blissful Islands* by Vit Hopley, described interestingly, as a work of prose, rather than as a novel or story collection. The cover image appears slightly abstract, pieces of mica on a dark background with the reflection of a light which, on reading the available extract, could be intended as rain on a window, or a wet road, or any number of things – we feel that the point of Copy Press' chosen publications is that such things are open to interpretation and possibility.
See also: poetry publishers p28

CORONA BOOKS UK
SHORT STORY ANTHOLOGIES / NON-FICTION
enquiries@coronabooks.com
www.coronabooks.com
Established 2015, and open to non-fiction or humour book submissions, with a fairly informal approach to submissions. Fiction is accepted only in the form of short stories during calls for anthology submissions – the press has published at least three horror story anthologies. See www.coronabooks.com/submissions for full guidelines.

CRESSRELLES PUBLISHING COMPANY LIMITED
FICTION AND NON-FICTION
10 Station Road Industrial Estate, Colwall, Worcestershire WR13 6RN
01684 540154
www.cressrelles.co.uk
simon@cressrelles.co.uk
Editor: Simon Smith
Established 1972. Fiction plays and non-fiction theatre books. Publications available by direct mail and email order; from chain bookshops nationwide; from independent bookshops; Amazon and other online bookshops.
GENRES: Theatre.
SUBMISSIONS: Submissions are open to all. Submit post (10 Station Road Industrial Estate, Colwall, Worcestershire WR13 6RN) or by email (simon@cressrelles.co.uk). Usually responds to submissions within four to six months. Rejections may occasionally include unsolicited feedback. Successful authors receive royalties and free copies of the publication.

CRINKLE CRANKLE PRESS
NON-FICTION
crinklecranklepress@gmail.com
Editor: Eleanor Margolies
Publications available by direct mail and email orders.
Crinkle Crankle Press won the Nick Reeves Award for Arts and the Environment.
GENRES: Non-fiction.
SUBMISSIONS: Currently closed.
WE SAY: We looked at a PDF of

various works, which ranged across articles, interviews and essays that all combine environmentalism and theatre, looking to address issues of e.g. climate change through performance, and examining various approaches, recounting how some projects have come together. The layout was straightforward and rather corporate, but the writing was interesting and accessible.
We enjoyed the interview with Jonathon Porritt, which examined how to strike a balance between sending a message and keeping an audience's attention.

CROWN HOUSE PUBLISHING

E-BOOKS / NON-FICTION
Crown Buildings, Bancyfelin, Carmarthenshire SA33 5ND
01267 211345
books@crownhouse.co.uk
www.crownhouse.co.uk
Established 1998. Non-fiction publisher. Publications available direct from publisher website; by post and email order; from chain bookshops nationwide; from independent bookshops; at local literary events; and from Amazon and other websites. Winner of the 2013 and 2014 Independent Publishing Guild Education Publisher of the Year Award; two publications from Crown House also won the 2017 ERA Educational Book of the Year Award.
GENRES: Education; health and well-being; neuro-linguistic programming (NLP); counselling, psychotherapy and hypnotherapy; and children's books.
SUBMISSIONS: Open to all. Submit by email to submissions@ crownhouse.co.uk. Guidelines are available at www.crownhouse. co.uk/about. Usually responds in up to six months. Rejections may occasionally include unsolicited feedback. Authors are paid royalties and receive free copies of the book.
WE SAY: The digital version of *Rules for Mavericks* by Phil Beadle we saw was entirely black and white, but the simplicity of its design ended there. On less than A5-sized pages, playful font choices draw attention to words and phrases, such as a madman posting a letter to the newspaper. Certain paragraphs break down completely and trickle down the page, or feature on bold pages of text twice the normal size, sometimes in all caps and sometimes on a black background. The rest of the book may have calmed down – we only saw the introduction.

CURRACH PRESS

NOVELS / MIXED-FORM COLLECTIONS AND ANTHOLOGIES / NON-FICTION
23 Merrion Square North, Dublin 2, Ireland
garry@columba.ie
www.currach.ie
Editor: Garry O'Sullivan
Established 2003. Mixed form: also publishes poetry (see p28). Publications available direct from publisher website; by direct mail and email orders; from chain bookshops nationwide; from independent bookshops; at local literary events; and from Amazon and other bookshop websites.
GENRES: Photography; health; Irish related; history; literary.
SUBMISSIONS: Open to all. Submit by email to garry@columba.

ie. Usually responds within four weeks. Rejections may occasionally include unsolicited feedback. Authors are paid an advance/ fee plus royalties and receive free copies of the book.
See also: poetry publishers p28

DAHLIA PUBLISHING
NOVELS / SHORT STORY COLLECTIONS AND ANTHOLOGIES
shaikhf@hotmail.com
www.dahliapublishing.co.uk
Editor: Farhana Shaikh
Established 2010. Also publishes poetry anthologies (see p28). Publications available direct from publisher website; by direct mail and email orders; from chain bookshops nationwide; and from independent bookshops.
GENRES: Literary.
SUBMISSIONS: Open to all. Submit by email (submissions@ dahliapublishing.co.uk) or by post (6 Samphire Close, Hamilton, Leicester LE5 1RW). Also accepts a Twitter pitch to @farhanashaikh. Guidelines at www.dahliapublishing. co.uk/submission-guidelines. Usually responds within four to six months. Rejections may occasionally include unsolicited feedback. Authors are paid royalties only and receive free copies of the book.
WE SAY: We took a browse through Dahlia Publishing's online bookshop; this publisher has an eye for cover design and blurb. With a palette of bold, dusky colours used across the various anthologies and novels published by the press, we feel we could spot a Dahlia book anywhere, and the commentary makes us want to read them. Images are refined, but robust and modern. The publisher

produces a couple of writing prize anthologies, and there's particular support for work by Asian writers.
See also: poetry publishers p28

DANCING BEAR BOOKS
NOVELS / SHORT STORY ANTHOLOGIES
hello@dancingbearbooks.co.uk
www.dancingbearbooks.com
Based across London and Newcastle, this new press (established in 2019) looks for work from début authors and emerging writers, and marginalised voices. All work must be fairytale, fantasy, myth or legend themed. Particularly interested in YA and New Adult, but will consider Adult work. Full submission guidelines are on the website, along with a list of books the editors love. The press is partnered with charity Coram Beanstalk, which provides reading support volunteers for children aged 3-13.

DARF PUBLISHERS
NOVELS / SHORT STORY COLLECTIONS AND ANTHOLOGIES / NON-FICTION
Brackenhill, Cotswold Road, Oxford OX2 9JG
enquiry@darfpublishers.co.uk
www.darfpublishers.co.uk
Editors: Ghassan Fergiani and Ghazi Gheblawi
Established 1981. Mainly publishes fiction. Publications available from chain bookshops nationwide, and on Amazon and other bookshop websites, including Google and Apple.
GENRES: Literary; translated fiction; history; classics; travelogue.
SUBMISSIONS: Open to all. Submit by email to submissions@ darfpublishers.co.uk. Guidelines

at www.darfpublishers.co.uk/
contact. Usually responds in one
to three months. Rejections may
occasionally include unsolicited
feedback. Authors are paid an
advance fee plus royalties.
WE SAY: We considered a PDF
proof of *Farewell, Damascus* by
Ghada Samman, a novel set in
1960s Damascus that examines the
corruption and oppression faced
during political transition. Lead
by a strong female protagonist,
Farewell, Damascus presents the
empowering story of a woman
taking control of her own life. Like
Darf Publishers' other titles, this
novel is fronted by an appealing,
colourful cover image, sitting
nicely within the publisher's stylish
website.

DAUNT BOOKS PUBLISHING
E-BOOKS / NOVELS / SHORT STORY
COLLECTIONS / NON-FICTION
publishing@dauntbooks.co.uk
www.dauntbookspublishing.co.uk
The publisher behind the popular
London bookshops, publishing
vibrant books and international
authors. Unsolicited manuscripts
welcomed, as the press looks for
début works by fresh voices.

DEAD INK
E-BOOKS / NOVELS / SHORT STORY
COLLECTIONS / NON-FICTION
nathan@deadinkbooks.com
www.deadinkbooks.com
Editor: Nathan Connolly
Established 2011. Publications
available direct from publisher
website; from chain bookshops
nationwide; from independent
bookshops; at national and local
literary events; and from Amazon
and other bookshop websites.
Dead Ink title *The Night Visitors*

by Jenn Ashworth and Richard V
Hirst won Best Novella in the 2017
Saboteur Awards.
GENRES: Literary fiction; crossover
fiction; non-fiction; horror;
speculative realism.
SUBMISSIONS: Open to all.
Submit by email to submissions@
deadinkbooks.com. Usually
responds within four to six months.
Rejections may occasionally include
unsolicited feedback. Authors are
paid an advance/fee plus royalties
and receive crowdfunding and free
copies of the book.
WE SAY: We looked at the digital
versions of two books: 257-page
Another Justified Sinner by Sophie
Hopesmith and 298-page *Guest* by
S J Bradley. Both books have the
same layout: simple but smart-
looking contents, with spacious
pages and long-read friendly
fonts. Both books fall under
Dead Ink's project 'Publishing the
Underground', which develops
careers of new and emerging
authors through crowdfunding and
with support from Arts Council
England.

DEDALUS LTD
E-BOOKS / NOVELS / SHORT STORY
ANTHOLOGIES / NON-FICTION
24-26 St Judith's Lane, Sawtry,
Cambridgeshire PE28 5XE
01487 832382
info@dedalusbooks.com
www.dedalusbooks.com
Editors: Eric Lane, Timothy Lane,
Marie Lane
Established 1983. Mainly publishes
fiction. Publications available from
chain bookshops nationwide;
from independent bookshops; at
national literary events; and from
Amazon and other bookshop
websites. In 2018, Dedalus began

a special promotion of women's literature for ten years to celebrate the centenary of women getting the vote in the UK and full voting rights in 1928.

Titles from Dedalus Books have won the Read Russia Prize 2015 and 2018, the Oxford-Weidenfeld Translation Prize 2008 and 2012 and been shortlisted on six other occasions, the Portuguese Translation Prize 2013, and the Polish Translation Prize 2014. Dedalus was the winner of the inaugural Small Press of the Year for the Eastern region.

GENRES: Literary fiction, upmarket crime/thriller/mystery, historical fiction. Has a penchant for the bizarre and grotesque. Accepts some literary non-fiction.

SUBMISSIONS: Open to all. Submit by post, sending a covering letter about the author with three sample chapters to Dedalus Limited, 24-26, St Judith's Lane, Sawtry, Cambridgeshire PE28 5XE. Usually responds within one to three months. No feedback usually offered with rejections, unless the writer has come very close to acceptance. Authors are paid an advance/fee plus royalties.

WE SAY: We reviewed *The Madwoman of Serrano* by Dina Salústio, whose work won an English Pen Award. The glossy paperback has a striking red cover, with prominent credit for the translator, Jethro Soutar, which we liked. At the end, there was a short section about Dedalus's mission statement and their forthcoming titles; cross-promotion of their authors is very important to them.

DIRT PIE PRESS
SHORT STORY ANTHOLOGIES

editors@riptidejournal.co.uk
www.riptidejournal.co.uk
Editors: Dr Virginia Baily, Dr Sally Flint
Established 2006. Literary fiction and poetry (see p30).

Publications available direct from publisher website; by post and email order; from independent bookshops; and at local literary events. All stockists are listed on the website.

GENRES: Children's fiction; drama and criticism; erotica; fantasy/sci-fi; graphic/comics; horror; romance.

SUBMISSIONS: Open to all, guidelines on the website. Submit by email to editors@riptidejournal. co.uk. Usually responds within four to six months. No feedback offered with rejections. Authors receive a flat fee.

For more information see *Riptide Journal* (mixed-form magazine) p252. See also: poetry publishers p30

DODO INK
E-BOOKS / NOVELS
thom@dodoink.com
www.dodoink.com
Editors: Thom Cuell, Sam Mills, Alex Spears
Established 2015. Publications available from chain bookshops nationwide; from independent bookshops; at local literary events; and from Amazon and other bookshop websites.

Dodo Ink was longlisted for the 2016 Republic of Consciousness Prize.

GENRES: Literary; experimental.

SUBMISSIONS: Open to all. Submit by email to thom@dodoink.com. Usually responds within one to three months. Rejections may occasionally include unsolicited feedback. Authors are paid an advance/fee plus royalties and receive free copies of the book.

DOG HORN PUBLISHING ☆
E-BOOKS / NOVELS / SHORT STORY COLLECTIONS AND ANTHOLOGIES / NON-FICTION
45 Monk Ings, Birstall, Batley WF17 9HU
01924 466853
editor@doghornpublishing.com
www.doghornpublishing.com
Editor: Adam Lowe
Established 2005. Also publishes poetry, see p30. Publications available direct from publisher website; by post and email order; from chain bookshops nationwide; from independent bookshops; at national and local literary events; and from Amazon and other bookshop websites, including lulu.com. Titles from Dog Horn have won the *Guardian* First Book Award (reader nomination); the Noble (not Nobel) Book Prize; and have had multiple honourable mentions in the Year's Best Horror.
GENRES: Drama and criticism; fantasy/sci-fi; horror; literary fiction; YA; food and drink; health and lifestyle; humour; music, stage and screen; society, education and politics; spirituality and beliefs; sports and leisure; travel.
SUBMISSIONS: Submissions by invitation only. On invitation, submit by email to editor@doghornpublishing.com. Guidelines at www.doghornpublishing.com/wordpress/about. Usually responds in over six months. Rejections may occasionally include unsolicited feedback. Authors are paid royalties only and receive free copies of the book.
For more information, see also: poetry publishers p30

DOIRE PRESS
E-BOOKS / SHORT STORY COLLECTIONS AND ANTHOLOGIES
Aille, Inverin, County Galway, Ireland
+353 091 593290
www.doirepress.com
Editor: John Walsh
Established 2007. Publishes poetry and short stories equally (see p30). Publications available direct from publisher website; from independent bookshops; at national literary events; from Amazon; and from kennys.ie. Doire Press title *Waiting for the Bullet* by Madeleine D'Arcy won the 2015 Edge Hill Readers' Prize and Breda Wall Ryan's *In a Hare's Eye* won the 2016 Shine/Strong Prize.
SUBMISSIONS: Only open to writers living in Ireland, and not actively seeking submissions (though open to being approached by writers familiar with Doire's books who are sure their work will be a good fit). Submit by post (Aille, Inverin, County Galway, Ireland) or by email (doirepress@gmail.com). Guidelines at www.doirepress.com/submissions. Usually responds within one to three months. No feedback offered with rejections. Book deals vary: authors may be paid royalties only; may be paid an advance/fee plus royalties; and/or may receive free copies of book – the deal depends on grant funding received.
For more information, including what We Say, see also: poetry publishers p30

DOME PRESS, THE
NOVELS
www.thedomepress.com
info@thedomepress.com
Founded in 2016 by literary agent

David Headley, The Dome Press publishes commercial fiction, with a strong skew towards crime and thriller. The website states that its 'ethos is to champion great storytelling and give authors a voice'. It accepts submissions direct from authors and from agents, when the submissions window is open – check the website before sending anything.

DOSTOYEVSKY WANNABE

NOVELS / SHORT STORY COLLECTIONS AND ANTHOLOGIES
dostoyevskywannabe@gmail.com
www.dostoyevskywannabe.com
Editors: Victoria Brown, Richard Brammer
Established 2014. Also publishes poetry and mixed-form anthologies (see p31). Publications available from Amazon.
GENRES: Experimental; literary; do-it-yourself; queer; underground fiction.
SUBMISSIONS: Open to all. Submit by email to dostoyevskywannabe@gmail.com. Guidelines at www.dostoyevsky.com/submit. Usually responds within four weeks. Authors are given two choices regarding royalties which are outlined in the submission guidelines.
WE SAY: We looked at three digital publications from DW, which included a novel (*Gaudy Bauble* by Isabel Waidner), a short story collection (*For We Are Young and Free* by Maddison Stoff) and an anthology of mixed poetry/prose (*Cassette 89*). The covers of each are stylish – they reminded us of the old Penguin book covers, but more contemporary, with 80s edge in the colouring of the images. The contents are professionally laid out, clean and spacious – particularly important in *Gaudy Bauble*, which has long, crowded paragraphs. The writing is unapologetically experimental, sometimes surreal. We particularly loved Kristen Felicetti's Reviews series in *Cassette 89*.
See also: poetry publishers p31 and *The All-New Swimmers Club* (mixed-form e-zine) p214

DUCKWORTH BOOKS

NON-FICTION / NOVELS
info@preludebooks.co.uk
www.duckworthbooks.co.uk
Established 1898 by the family of Virginia Woolf, became an imprint at Prelude Books in 2018. Publishes memoir, psychology, popular science, history and historical fiction. Accepts submissions, but may require some publishing history or writing experience. See www.duckworthbooks.co.uk/about/contact for guidelines.
See also: Farrago Books (prose publisher) p125

EARLYWORKS PRESS ☆

SHORT STORY COLLECTIONS AND ANTHOLOGIES / MIXED-FORM ANTHOLOGIES
Creative Media Centre, 45 Robertson St, Hastings TN34 1HL
kay@earlyworkspress.co.uk
www.earlyworkspress.co.uk
Editor: Kay Green
Established 2005. Mixed form. Earlyworks publishes short story, flash fiction and local interest (Hastings, Sussex), as well as mixed-form anthologies and poetry (see p31). Most books are anthologies of work by authors from the publisher's competition shortlists. Publications available

direct from publisher website; at independent bookshops; at local literary events; and online bookstores.

Discounted books are available to club members and competition shortlisted authors.

GENRES: Literary and all other genres (up to 8,000 words); flash fiction (up to 100 words).

SUBMISSIONS: As Earlyworks Press is a club for authors and illustrators – running writing competitions, producing winners' anthologies and some other books – please submit via competition initially (www.earlyworkspress.co.uk – see p307). The press often invites shortlisted authors to join in other publishing projects.

WE SAY: Earlyworks Press' website lists their full catalogue of fiction collections, all of which are compilations of shortlisted authors from their writing competitions. Their latest collection, *The Sorcery of Smog*, presents an ominous cover graphic and 24 stories that span widely in theme, from everyday occurrences to a 'physiological journey to the end of the world'.

See also: poetry publishers p31

EGAEUS PRESS

NOVELS / SHORT STORY COLLECTIONS / ANTHOLOGIES
Flat 2, The Butt of Sherry, 8 The Commons, Shaftesbury SP7 8JU
egaeuspress@gmail.com
www.egaeuspress.com
Editor: Mark Beech

Established 2011. Primarily publishes fiction, but also mixed-form books, anthologies and collections, including mixed poetry/prose anthologies and collections, and mixed fiction/ non-fiction anthologies. Publications available direct from the publisher website and from various bookshop websites.

GENRES: Supernatural; Gothic; strange; dark fantasy; experimental.

SUBMISSIONS: Open to all. Submit by email to egaeuspress@gmail. com. Usually responds in one to three months. Rejections may occasionally include unsolicited feedback. Authors and contributors are paid a flat fee.

WE SAY: Both of the publications we looked at from Egaeus Press, *Ragman & Other Family Curses* by Rebecca Lloyd and *The Book of Flowering*, an anthology edited by Mark Beech, are truly exquisite in quality. A real bijou object, *Ragman & Other Family Curses* is a small hardback from Egaeus's Keynote Editions with gold foiling adorning the cover and spine. *The Book of Flowering*, a matte hardback slightly larger than A5, has divinely illustrated endpapers and an ornate, Gothic title font.

ELLIOTT & THOMPSON

NON-FICTION / NOVELS
info@eandtbooks.com
www.eandtbooks.com
Specialises in 'popular and engaging' fiction and non-fiction. Several non-fiction titles from this press have won awards. Not currently open to fiction submissions, but see website for guidance on non-fiction proposals.

ELSEWHEN PRESS

NOVELS / SHORT STORY COLLECTIONS AND ANTHOLOGIES/ E-BOOKS
PO Box 757, Dartford, Kent DA2 7TQ
info@elsewhen.co.uk

www.elsewhen.press
Editor: Al Murray
Established 2011. Publications available direct from the publisher website; at national literary events; and can be ordered through any bookshop.
GENRES: Speculative fiction, i.e. sci-fi, fantasy, horror, paranormal.
SUBMISSIONS: Open to all, during submissions windows only. See elsewhen.press/index.php/submit for guidelines and submissions windows. Usually responds in one to three months. Submitters will receive an email with feedback. Authors receive an advance plus royalties, and free copies of the book.
WE SAY: Priding themselves on publishing new talent in speculative fiction, Elsewhen Press' website allows visitors to easily navigate their various titles. We viewed *The Deep and Shining Dark* by Juliet Kemp, the first novel in her Marek Series. With a vibrant, orange cover graphic, this is an eye-catching title that suggests mystery. Indeed, this book delves into the strange and uncertain.

EMMA PRESS, THE
E-BOOKS / SHORT STORY COLLECTIONS / NON-FICTION
16-26 Hylton Street, Jewellery Quarter, Birmingham B18 6HQ
hello@theemmapress.com
www.theemmapress.com
Editor: Emma Wright
Established 2012. Mainly publishes poetry (see p33). Publications available direct from publisher website; from chain bookshops nationwide; from independent bookshops; at national and local literary events; and from Amazon and other bookshop websites.

In 2016, The Emma Press won the Michael Marks award for Poetry Pamphlet Publishers.
GENRES: Literary.
SUBMISSIONS: Open to all, during submission windows. Submit online at www.theemmapress.com/about/submissions. Usually responds within four to six months. Rejections may occasionally include unsolicited feedback. Submitters are required to buy a book from the press. Authors are paid royalties only and receive free copies of the book.
For more information, including what They Say and what We Say, see also: poetry publishers p33

ÉPOQUE PRESS
NOVELS / SHORT STORY COLLECTIONS
info@epoquepress.com
www.epoquepress.com
Editor: Sean Campbell
Established 2017. Publishes fiction. Publications available from chain and independent bookshops, and from Amazon and other bookshop websites.
GENRES: Literary fiction.
SUBMISSIONS: Open to all. Submit by email to submissions@epoquepress.com. Guidelines at www.epoquepress.com/submissions. Usually responds in one to three months. Rejections may occasionally include unsolicited feedback. Authors are paid royalties only, and receive free copies of the book.
WE SAY: Époque Press' takes a minimalist approach to design. We looked at a PDF of *The Groundsmen* by Lynn Buckle. With its dark and intriguing cover page, this title suggests a disturbing tone which carries through into the

novel itself. Clearly, Époque Press aims to entice readers to learn more about their values by picking up the books themselves.
See also: *époque press e-zine* (mixed-form magazine) p225

EVERYTHING WITH WORDS

NOVELS
07768 356753
info@everythingwithwords.com
www.everythingwithwords.com
Editor: Mikka Haugaard

Established 2017. Publishes fiction. Publications available direct from the publisher website; by direct mail and email order; from chain and independent bookshops; at national literary events; and from Amazon and other bookshop websites.
Everything With Words publication *Notes on my Family* by Emily Critchley was nominated for the CILIP Carnegie Award 2019.
GENRES: Literary.
SUBMISSIONS: Open to all. Submit by email to info@everythingwithwords.com. Guidelines at www.everythingwithwords/submissions. Responds within one to three months. Rejections may include unsolicited feedback. Authors are paid an advance fee plus royalties, and receive free copies of their book.
WE SAY: Looking at Everything with Words' website, we found a small but growing collection of nicely produced children's and YA books,

EQUINOX PUBLISHING

NON-FICTION
info@equinoxpub.com
www.equinoxpub.com
Academic publisher of around 30 books per year, including

each with their own unique style and theme. Cover designs use eye-catching illustrations in dynamic colours. The site also spotlights one of the press' authors each month.

THEY SAY

Everything with Words publishes literary fiction. We began by publishing only for children and YA but from 2020 we will be publishing books for adults too. We are interested in fine writing of all kinds. No commercial fantasy, please or novels that belong too obviously to a genre.

122

journals, textbooks, anthologies, monographs and reference books

in the areas of archaeology, linguistics, cultural history, the

EYRIE PRESS ☆

NOVELS / NON-FICTION / E-BOOKS
March Town Hall, Market Place, March, Cambridgeshire PE5 8LR
info@eyriepress.co.uk
www.eyriepress.co.uk
Editor: Jane Spencer

Established 2014 (previously known as Bird's Nest Books, which is now an imprint). Publications available direct from the publisher website; from independent bookshops; at local literary events; and from Amazon and other bookshop websites.
GENRES: Contemporary; historical; speculative. Children's fiction through imprint Bird's Nest Books.
SUBMISSIONS: Submit only during submissions windows, by email to submissions@eyriepress. co.uk. Guidelines at www. eyriepress.co.uk/submissions. Usually responds within one to three months. Rejections may occasionally include unsolicited feedback. Authors are paid royalties and receive free copies of their book.
WE SAY: Despite being one of the smaller indies, the copy of Roy Peachey's *Between Darkness and Light* we looked at was of high quality, with a beautifully illustrated binding cover design. We particularly liked the style of the illustration. The book is a perfect-bound paperback and printed on bright white paper.

THEY SAY

Eyrie Press is a social enterprise which aims to publish more books by writers from East Anglia and/or which take a non-tokenistic approach to featuring communities under-represented in fiction, but we will also look at submissions that don't meet either criteria. Our focus is on well-crafted novels and novellas in the genres of contemporary, historical and speculative fiction. The press was formerly known as Bird's Nest Books, and we have retained that as our imprint which publishes children's books.

academic study of religion, cookery and popular music.

EYE & LIGHTNING BOOKS

E-BOOKS / NOVELS / NON-FICTION
dan@eye-books.com
www.eye-books.com
Editors: Daniel Hiscocks, Scott Pack
Established 1996. Publications available direct from publisher website; from chain bookshops nationwide; from independent bookshops; at national and local literary events; and from Amazon and other bookshop websites. Eye Books title *Self & I* was shortlisted for the New Angle Prize in 2019.
GENRES: Books which don't fit into straight genres.
SUBMISSIONS: Open to all. Submit by email to dan@eye-books.com. Guidelines at www.eye-books.com/submissions. Usually responds within one to three months. No feedback offered with rejections. Authors receive a profit share.
WE SAY: We looked at Eye Books' online catalogue. It's a very professional affair: their non-fiction, adventure-based book-of-the-month has blurb that includes praise from Bear Grylls, and their other titles are equally well turned out and presented. Peppered throughout, looking distinguished with black-band branding and a colourful stripe for the logo, with photographic images, are the 'Eye Classics'. This is a press that takes risks on content that doesn't necessarily chime with the Big Five publishers, so there's no feeling that calling these texts 'classic' is a reach.

FAHRENHEIT PRESS

E-BOOKS / NOVELS / SHORT STORY COLLECTIONS AND ANTHOLOGIES
07547 998834
chris@fahrenheit-press.com
www.fahrenheit-press.com
Editor: Chris McVeigh
Established 2015. Mainly publishes fiction. Varying subscriptions available via patreon.com. Publications available direct from publisher website; by post and email order; from selected chain and independent bookshops; at literary events; and from Amazon. Fahrenheit Press publication *A Place to Bury Strangers* by Grant Nicol was shortlisted for the Ngaio Marsh Award for Crime.
GENRES: Crime and thrillers.
SUBMISSIONS: Open to all. Submit by email to chris@fahrenheit-press.com. Guidelines at www.fahrenheit-presss.com/submissions.html. Usually responds within one to three months. Rejections may occasionally include unsolicited feedback. Authors are paid royalties.

FAIR ACRE PRESS

E-BOOKS / NOVELS / NON-FICTION
Primrose Cottage, Sweeney Mountain, Oswestry SY10 9EZ
01691 239466
fairacrepress@gmail.com
www.fairacrepress.co.uk
Editor: Nadia Kingsley
Established 2011. Also publishes poetry (see p34). Publications available direct from publisher website; from chain bookshops nationwide; from independent bookshops; at local literary events; and from Amazon.
Beyond Spring: Wanderings through Nature by Matthew Oates was shortlisted for both

124

BBC Countryfile Magazine's Best Country Book of the Year and the Richard Jeffries Book award; and was cited in the *Guardian* on their Best Nature Books of 2017 list. *Sitting Ducks* by Lisa Blower

FAIRLIGHT BOOKS

E-BOOKS / NOVELS / NOVELLAS
Summertown Pavilion, 18-24 Middle Way, Oxford OX2 7LG
01865 957790
submissions@fairlightbooks.com
www.fairlightbooks.com

Established 2017. Publishes fiction, including short stories on their website (see prose magazines, p291). Publications available direct from the publisher website; at chain and independent bookshops; and from Amazon and other bookshop websites.
Fairlight publication *Bottled Goods* by Sophie van Llewyn was longlisted for the 2019 Republic of Consciousness Prize, longlisted for the 2018 People's Book Prize, and longlisted for the 2019 Women's Prize for Fiction.
GENRES: Literary fiction; literary novellas (Fairlight Moderns); literary cross-genre fiction.
SUBMISSIONS: Open to all. Submit by email to submissions@ fairlightbooks.com. Guidelines at www.fairlightbooks.co.uk/ submissions. Usually responds in one to three months. Rejections may occasionally include unsolicited feedback.
WE SAY: We considered a PDF of *Travelling in the Dark* by Emma Timpany, a comforting exploration of our past and relationships. This novella

THEY SAY

Fairlight Books was founded in 2017 to publish, promote and support writers of literary fiction. One of its key aims is to make literary fiction more accessible to today's readers. It is particularly known for its Fairlight Moderns series, beautiful pocket-sized novellas and novels from around the world. The company also publishes literary short stories on its website, along with blogs and interviews about the love of quality fiction, beautiful books, and supporting UK's bookstores.

explores the charming landscape of New Zealand which recurs throughout. Its simple, orange-framed cover reflects the style given to all Fairlight Modern Publications, each with their own colour and central graphic, forming a uniform yet uniquely styled array of books.
See also: prose magazines p291

was shortlisted for Arnold Bennett literary award.

GENRES: Nature writing; wildlife photography; literary novel; plays; cartoons.

SUBMISSIONS: By invitation only. Guidelines at www.fairacrepress. co.uk/about/. Authors are paid royalties only and receive free copies of the book.

For more information see also: poetry publishers p34

FARRAGO BOOKS

NOVELS / E-BOOKS
13 Carrington Road, Richmond TW10 5AA
info@preludebooks.co.uk
farragobooks.com
Editors: Pete Duncan and Abbie Headon

Established 2016 as an imprint of Prelude Books. Publishes fiction. Publications available from major chain and independent bookshops; at local literary events; and from Amazon and other bookshop websites.

GENRES: Humour; cosy mystery; romantic comedy; science fiction and fantasy.

SUBMISSIONS: Open to all. Submit by post (Prelude Books, 13 Carrington Road, Richmond TW10 5AA) or email (info@preludebooks. co.uk). Usually responds within one to three months. May occasionally give unsolicited feedback, or feedback if requested. Authors are paid an advance plus royalties.

See also: Duckworth Books (prose publisher) p118

FENTUM PRESS

NON-FICTION / NOVELS
enquiries@fentumbooks.com
www.fentumbooks.com
Based in both London and

Italy, this press is 'committed to producing high quality fiction and non-fiction titles aimed at a wide audience' and says it supports all titles with sales and marketing campaigns.

FICTION DESK, THE

E-BOOKS / SHORT STORY ANTHOLOGIES
info@thefictiondesk.com
www.thefictiondesk.com
Fiction-specific: short stories anthologies pulled together from open submissions. The resulting book themes depend entirely on what the press has been sent.

FINCHAM PRESS

NON-FICTION / E-BOOKS / ANTHOLOGIES
Department of English and Creative Writing, University of Roehampton, London SW15 5PH
finchampress@roehampton.ac.uk
www.fincham.press
Established 2013. Publishes prose and poetry (see p35) – primarily used to focus on publishing anthologies of work by Roehampton students, but now expanding its output. Publications available direct from the publisher website; from Amazon; and from Roehampton University e-store.

SUBMISSIONS: Submitters may only submit during submission windows, by email to finchampress@roehampton.ac.uk. Currently focused on work from the university, but with plans to extend this output in the future, so keep checking the guidelines at www.fincham.press/submissions. Responds within one to three months. Authors and contributors are paid royalties only, and receive free copies of their book.

WE SAY: The copy of Melissa M Terras' *The Professor in Children's Literature* that we looked at is printed on thick gloss paper, and the digitised archive images throughout are of a high print quality. *The Unseen*, edited by Leone Ross, is also a perfect-bound paperback printed on thick cream paper. The cover has a professional finish with a simple but eye-catching design.
See also: poetry publishers p35

FINE FEATHER PRESS LTD
NON-FICTION
The Coach House, Elstead Road, Farnham GU10 1JE
apentney@gmail.com
www.finefeatherpress.com
Editors: Andrea Pinnington and Caz Buckingham
Established 2011. Publishes non-fiction for children. Publications available from chain and independent bookshops; and from Amazon and other bookshop websites.
Fine Feather Press was shortlisted for Small Publisher of the Year in the 2019 Bookseller Awards, Regional Finalist.
SUBMISSIONS: Not open to submissions.

FIREFLY PRESS
CHILDREN'S AND YA
www.fireflypress.co.uk
hello@fireflypress.co.uk
Firefly Press is based in Cardiff and Aberystwyth. Set up in 2013, it's one of the only dedicated children's publishers in Wales, publishing in all fiction genres for 5-19 years old, with the exception of picture books for pre-school children. It was the winner of the Branford Boase Award 2016 and shortlisted for IPG Best Newcomer Independent Publisher Awards 2017. Publication *The Clockwork Crow* by Catherine Fisher was shortlisted for the Blue Peter Award 2019. Submissions are only open at specific times of the year – see their website for more information.

FITZCARRALDO EDITIONS ☆
8-12 Creekside, London SE8 3DX
info@fitzcarraldoeditions.com
www.fitzcarraldoeditions.com
Editor: Jacques Testard
Established 2014. Mixed-form publisher: primarily publishes literary fiction and non-fiction/ essays. Publications available direct from publisher website; by post and email order; from chain bookshops and independent bookshops nationwide; at national and local literary events; and from Amazon. Offers a books subscription: £100 for twelve books, £70 for eight books, £35 for four.
Fitzcarraldo title *Flights* by Olga Tokarczuk, translated by Jennifer Croft, won the 2018 Man Booker International Prize.
SUBMISSIONS: Open to all. Usually responds within one to three months. Rejections may occasionally include unsolicited feedback. Authors are paid an advance/fee plus royalties.
WE SAY: Fitzcarraldo publications are instantly recognisable and top quality. We looked at *Pond* by Claire Louise-Bennett: an 184-page book of essays; paperback, with French flaps. The cover is plain: Fitzcarraldo's signature royal blue, with white text. (The fiction titles invert the colours.) The inner formatting, on high-grade white

FISH PUBLISHING ☆

SHORT STORY COLLECTIONS AND
ANTHOLOGIES
info@fishpublishing.com
www.fishpublishing.com
Editors: Clem Cairns, Jula Walton,
Mary-Jane Holmes, Adam Wyeth,
Tina Pisco, Simon Humphries,
Paul MacMahon

Established 1995. Mixed output –
including mixed poetry and prose
anthologies. Publications available
direct from the publisher website;
by direct mail and email order; at
chain and independent bookshops;
and from Amazon and other
bookshop websites.
GENRES: Short story; flash fiction;
short memoir.
SUBMISSIONS: Open to all. Submit
by post (Fish Publishing, Durrus,
Bantry, Co. Cork, Ireland), email
(info@fishpublishing.com) or via the
website at reader.fishpublishing.
com/accounts/login/?next=/.
Guidelines at www.fishpublishing.
com/writing-contests. Submissions
run as a competition, and so
charges an entry fee. Usually
responds immediately when entries
are made online. Fish publishes
the winning submissions from its
writing competitions and provides
a feedback/critique for submissions
for a fee. Contributors are paid a
flat fee and receive free copies of
the book.
WE SAY: Fish Publishing's 2019
anthology is perfect-bound with
a matte cover finish and a simple
design, and is a must-read for
anyone considering entering any of
the Fish Prizes. We like the way the
anthology design accommodates

THEY SAY

Fish is an independent press
created in 1995 by Clem Cairns
and Jula Walton to promote
new writers. We publish the
best submissions from the
short story, short memoir,
poetry and flash fiction
competitions in the annual
Fish Anthology. There are
cash prizes totalling £7,000,
and residences at Anam Cara,
Ireland and Casa Ana, Spain.
We have published more than
500 writers from all around
the world. Roddy Doyle and
Colum McCann are honorary
patrons. Our team of editors
led by Mary-Jane Holmes
and Adam Wyeth teach the
writing courses online and
provide editorial and critique
services.
www.fishpublishing.com

poems with longer line lengths
by publishing them horizontally
on the page.
See also: poetry publishers p35

paper, is clean and uncluttered, and the press uses its own serif typeface called Fitzcarraldo.

FLEDGLING PRESS

E-BOOKS / NOVELS / NON-FICTION
1 Milton Road West, Edinburgh
EH15 1LA
0131 6572 8188
clare@fledglingpress.co.uk
www.fledglingpress.co.uk
Editor: Clare Cain

Mainly publishes fiction. Publications available direct from publisher website; from chain bookshops nationwide; from independent bookshops; and from Amazon and other bookshop websites.

Fledging Press title *The Incomers* by Moira McPartlin was shortlisted for the 2012 Saltire First Book Prize. In 2017 *The Caseroom* by Kate Hunter was shortlisted for the same prize.

GENRES: Crime/thriller/mystery; historical fiction; YA; biography and true stories with a twist. Strictly no poetry, sci-fi, short stories or writing for children under 12.

SUBMISSIONS: Open to all. Submit by email to submissions@fledglingpress.co.uk. Guidelines at www.fledglingpress.co.uk/submissions. Aims to read submissions within six weeks. Rejections may occasionally include unsolicited feedback; confirmed feedback only if requested. Authors are paid an advance/fee plus royalties.

WE SAY: Of Fledgling Press' variety of books, we considered a PDF of the novel *Ghost* by Helen Grant. Set in a remote estate in Scotland, Grant writes a haunting tale of isolation and the remnants of the past. The ominous cover shows simply a key, encouraging readers to enter this spooky space; as the book chillingly writes, the house is haunted, 'but not by the ghost you think'.

FLIPPED EYE PUBLISHING

FICTION
books@flippedeye.net
www.flippedeye.net
Established 2001. Predominantly publishes poetry, but also some fiction.

For more information, see also: poetry publishers p37

FLY ON THE WALL PRESS ☆

SHORT STORY COLLECTIONS / ANTHOLOGIES
isabellekenyon@hotmail.co.uk
www.flyonthewallpoetry.co.uk
Editor: Isabelle Kenyon

Established 2018. Mainly publishes poetry (p37), but also some prose and mixed-form anthologies. Available direct from the publisher website, from selected chain and independent bookshops, at national literary events, and from Amazon and other online bookshops.

Fly on the Wall poetry anthology *Please Hear What I'm Not Saying* was shortlisted for the 2018 Saboteur Awards Best Anthology, and Fly on the Wall was longlisted for the 2019 Saboteur Awards Innovative Publisher category.

GENRES: Political; literary

SUBMISSIONS: Submissions are open to all, during submissions windows. Submitters must buy a publication from the press. Submit by email to isabellekenyon@hotmail.co.uk. Guidelines at www.flyonthewallpoetry.co.uk. Usually responds within four weeks, but for an optional fee, writers can receive an expedited response. Rejections may occasionally include unsolicited feedback. Authors are paid royalties and receive free copies of their book. **For more information, including what We Say, see poetry publishers p37 and *Fly on the Wall Webzine* (mixed-form magazine) p227**

FOR BOOKS' SAKE
SHORT STORY ANTHOLOGIES
www.forbookssake.net
Mixed-form publisher. Publishes fiction and non-fiction prose, but also some poetry (see p38). Publications available direct from publisher website; from selected/ local chain bookshops; from independent bookshops; and at national and local literary events. For Book's Sake title *Furies: A poetry anthology of women warriors* was runner-up for the Best Anthology prize at the 2015 Saboteur Awards.
GENRES: Literary fiction; YA; biography and true stories; music, stage and screen; society, education and politics.
SUBMISSIONS: Open to self-identifying women, and especially encouraged from women of colour, disabled women, queer women, trans women and women from low-income backgrounds. Submit, during submissions windows only, via Submittable (forbookssake. submittable.com/submit – guidelines at same address). Usually responds within four weeks. **For more information, see also poetry publishers p38 and *For Books' Sake* (mixed-form e-zine) p227**

FOX SPIRIT BOOKS
E-BOOKS / NOVELS / SHORT STORY COLLECTIONS AND ANTHOLOGIES / NON-FICTION / MIXED-FORM ANTHOLOGIES
adele@foxspirit.co.uk
www.foxspirit.co.uk
Editor: Adele Wearing
Established 2012. Mainly publishes fiction, but does publish non-fiction, as well as some poetry collections, and prose/poetry anthologies (see p38). Also publishes historical martial arts manuals. Publications available from Amazon (and worldwide Amazon sites); and at select events. Fox Spirit Books won the 2015 British Fantasy Society award for Best Small Press.
GENRES: Fantasy; sci-fi; horror; crime; mash-ups.
SUBMISSIONS: Submit only during submissions windows. See submissions guidelines at www. foxspirit.co.uk/sample-page/ submissions/ for full instructions and details of author renumeration. Feedback not usually offered with rejections. Will try to provide feedback on request, but this is not always possible.
See also: poetry publishers p38

GALLEY BEGGAR PRESS ☆
E-BOOKS / NOVELS / SHORT STORY COLLECTIONS / NON-FICTION
info@galleybeggar.co.uk
www.galleybeggar.co.uk
Editors: Eloise Millar, Sam Jordison
Established 2012. Mainly publishes fiction, including Galley Beggar singles – long short stories available as downloads. Publications available direct from publisher website; by post and email order; from chain bookshops nationwide; from independent

bookshops; at national and local literary events; and from bookshop websites.

Won the Baileys Prize for Fiction 2014 with Eimear McBride's *A Girl is a Half-Formed Thing*, The Desmond Elliott Prize for début fiction in 2018 for Preti Taneja's *We That Are Young* and the Republic Of Consciousness Prize in 2019 for Alex Pheby's *Lucia*. Shortlisted for the Booker Prize 2019 with *Ducks, Newburyport* by Lucy Ellman.

GENRES: Literary fiction; narrative non-fiction.

SUBMISSIONS: Open to all, within submissions windows. Submit by email to submissions@galleybeggar.co.uk. Guidelines at www.galleybeggar.co.uk/2-submissions. Usually responds within four to six months. Rejections may occasionally include unsolicited feedback. Authors are paid an advance/fee plus royalties.

WE SAY: We considered a PDF copy of *Lucia* by Alex Pheby. Behind the simple, bright yellow cover is a novel imagining the silenced life of Lucia Joyce, daughter of James Joyce. In response to the near erasure of her existence, Pheby respectfully and darkly explores what might have occurred in Lucia's troubled life, with sheer intellectual integrity. Rather than attempting to speak for a silenced life, this novel cleverly explores the danger being spoken for by others.

GATEHOUSE PRESS

SHORT STORY COLLECTIONS / NOVELLAS

32 Grove Walk, Norwich, NR1 2QG
admin@gatehousepress.com
www.gatehousepress.com

Editors: Meirion Jordan, Andrew McDonnell, Julia Webb, Anna de Vaul, Sam Ruddock

Established 2006. Publishes short novellas in their New Fictions series. Publications available direct from publisher website; from selected/local chain bookshops; from independent bookshops; at national and local literary events; and from bookshop websites.

GENRES: Literary fiction.

SUBMISSIONS: Submit during submissions windows. Usually responds within one to three months. No feedback offered with rejections. Writer payment/remuneration varies according to publication.

For more information, see *Lighthouse* (mixed-form magazine) p237. See also: poetry publishers p39

GHASTLING PRESS, THE

SHORT STORY ANTHOLOGIES, ARTWORK AND ILLUSTRATION

editor@theghastling.com
www.theghastling.com

Editor: Rebecca Parfitt

Established 2014. Primarily publishes fiction. Publications available from the publisher website and from Amazon.

GENRES: Graphic/comics; horror; literary fiction.

SUBMISSIONS: During submissions windows, submit by email to editor@theghastling.com. Usually responds within one to three months.

For more information, including what We Say and what They Say, see *The Ghastling* (prose magazine) p293

GRAFFEG

PICTURE BOOKS / NON-FICTION

www.graffeg.com

croeso@graffeg.com
Publishes illustrated books about food, arts, culture, heritage and architecture, gardens, landscapes, photography, sport and lifestyle, as well as illustrated children's fiction books up to young adult readers. Submissions by new authors and illustrators are reviewed only during the submission windows.

GRANTA BOOKS
NOVELS / SHORT STORY COLLECTIONS AND ANTHOLOGIES / NON-FICTION
12 Addison Avenue, London W11 4QR
020 7605 1360
info@granta.com
www.granta.com
Editors: Sigrid Rausing, Laura Barber, Bella Lacey,
Anne Meadows, Ka Bradley, Rachael Allen, Sinéad O'Callaghan
Established 1989. Publications available from chain bookshops nationwide; from independent bookshops; at national and local literary events; and from Amazon and other bookshop websites. Shortlisted for the 2014 Independent Publisher of the Year Award.
GENRES: Literary fiction; history; popular science and nature; technology; medicine; society, education and politics; travel; poetry.
SUBMISSIONS: Agented submissions only. Usually responds within four weeks. Rejections may occasionally include unsolicited feedback. Writers are paid an advance/fee plus royalties.
WE SAY: A stalwart of the indie publishing world, Granta's publications are first rate in terms of quality and production values, and often make a splash in literary circles. The paperback copy of *Convenience Store Woman* by Sayaka Murata, translated by Ginny Tapley Takemori, is well designed, with an embossed, spot UV cover and enticing review quotes on the front and back.
See also: *Granta Magazine* **(mixed-form magazine) p230**

GREEN BEAN BOOKS
CHILDREN'S / PICTURE BOOKS
www.greenbeanbooks.com
michael@greenbeanbooks.com
Publishes original and inspiring Jewish books targeted at children aged zero to six. Green Bean Books is interested in publishing stories about Jewish holidays or those with important Jewish moral lessons. They accept unsolicited manuscripts.

GRIMBOLD BOOKS ☆
NOVELS / SHORT STORY COLLECTIONS AND ANTHOLOGIES / E-BOOKS
admin@grimboldbooks.com
www.grimboldbooks.com
Editors: Sammy H K Smith, Zoë Harris, Joanne Hall, Kate Coe
Established 2013. Publishes fiction. Publications available from chain and independent bookshops nationwide; and from Amazon and other bookshop websites. Grimbold Books won the British Fantasy Award for Best Independent Press in 2017.
GENRES: Science fiction; fantasy; dark fantasy; speculative fiction.
SUBMISSIONS: Submit during submissions windows only by email to admin@grimboldbooks.com. Guidelines at www.kristell-ink.com/submissions-closed. The press never charges a reading fee. Usually responds in one to three

132

months. Feedback is provided with rejections only if requested. Authors are paid royalties, and receive free copies of the book.
WE SAY: We looked at *Blood and Thorn* by M E Rodman, *Seven Deadly Swords* by Peter Sutton, and *Malarat* by Jessica Rydill. All three books explore fascinating landscapes and kingdoms, with strong protagonists fighting to reach their destiny. Grimbold Press embraces all things fantasy and sci-fi, particularly enjoying books that embark on unique tales of the strange and unexpected.
See also: prose publishers Kristell Ink p145 and Tenebris p190

GRIST
MIXED-FORM ANTHOLOGIES
mhm.hud.ac.uk/grist/
Grist is the publishing branch of the University of Huddersfield, and produces acclaimed anthology *Grist*, which includes poetry and short prose. Submissions are through competitions. Also publishes some single-author books.
See also: poetry publishers p41

GUILDHALL PRESS
NOVELS / NON-FICTION / E-BOOKS
info@ghpress.com
www.ghpress.com
One of Northern Ireland's leading independent publishers. Established 1979. Produces award-winning books of fiction, local history, literary, academic, social issue, Irish language and photographic publications, specialising in illustrated publications and websites.

GUILLEMOT PRESS
SHORT STORY COLLECTIONS
Cornwall
editor@guillemotpress.co.uk
www.guillemotpress.co.uk
Editors: Luke Thompson and Sarah Cave
Established 2016. Primarily publishes poetry (see p41), but also some short story collections. Publications available direct from the publisher website, and from independent bookshops. Guillemot Press won the 2018 Michael Marks Award for Publishers.
SUBMISSIONS: Open to all. Submit by email to editor@guillemotpress.co.uk. Usually responds in one to three months. Rejections may occasionally include unsolicited feedback.
See also: poetry publishers p41

GUPPY BOOKS
CHILDREN'S FICTION
Brackenhill, Cotswold Road, Oxford OX2 9JG
www.guppybooks.co.uk
bella@guppybooks.co.uk
Editor: Bella Pearson
Established 2018. Publishes children's fiction up to age 18, including books in verse (see p41). No non-fiction or picture books. Publications available from chain and independent bookshops nationwide; at national and local literary events; and from Amazon and other bookshop websites.
GENRES: Children's; middle-grade; young adult.
SUBMISSIONS: Submissions accepted from agents and from previously published writers. Open to unsolicited submissions during submissions window only. Guidelines at www.guppybooks.co.uk/contact-us. Usually responds in one to three months. Rejections may occasionally include unsolicited feedback. Authors are

paid an advance fee and royalties. **WE SAY:** We considered PDFs of *The Extremely Inconvenient Adventures of Bronte Mettlestone* by Jaclyn Moriarty and *Gloves Off* by Louisa Reed, two very different yet equally fascinating books. Moriarty's novel is rife with adventure and mystery, whilst Reed's novel is written in poetry – an increasingly popular style for children's books (see poetry publishers p41), and explores the life of a girl fighting back against the injustices she has faced. They are both exciting and deeply moving.
See also: poetry publishers p41

GYLPHI LIMITED
E-BOOKS / NON-FICTION (ACADEMIC)
PO Box 993, Canterbury CT1 9EP
info@gylphi.co.uk
www.gylphi.co.uk
Established 2007. Academic non-fiction. Publications available direct from publisher website; from chain bookshops nationwide; from independent bookshops; and from Amazon.
GENRES: Academic books on twentieth- and twenty-first-century arts and humanities subjects for university-level study and research.
SUBMISSIONS: Usually from writers holding a university doctorate. Submit by post (Submissions, Gylphi Limited, PO Box 993 CT1 9EP) or by email (info@gylphi. co.uk). Usually responds within one to three months, with feedback. Authors receive free copies of the book.

HAFAN BOOKS (REFUGEES WRITING IN WALES)
SHORT STORY ANTHOLOGIES
c/o Tom Cheesman, Dept of Languages, Swansea University SA2 8PP
t.cheesman@swansea.ac.uk
lulu.com/hafan
sbassg.wordpress.com
Editors: Tom Cheesman, Jeni Williams
Established 2003. Mixed form: publishes poetry (see p41) and prose, and various refugee-related books and booklets. Publications available direct from publisher website; by post and email order; at local literary events; and from Amazon.
SUBMISSIONS: Open to all, by invitation only. Author contributions needed. Submit by email to t.cheesman@swansea. ac.uk. Usually responds within four weeks. Rejections may occasionally include unsolicited feedback. Authors receive free copies of the book; no fee or royalties.
See also: poetry publishers p41

HASHTAG PRESS ☆
NOVELS / SHORT STORY ANTHOLOGIES / NON-FICTION / E-BOOKS
10 Bankfields, Headcorn, Kent TN27 9RA
info@hashtagpress.co.uk
www.hashtagpress.co.uk
Editors: Helen Lewis and Abiola Bello
Established 2016. Publications available direct from the publisher website; by post and email order; from chain and independent bookshops; and on Amazon and other bookshop websites.
GENRES: Thriller; fantasy; self-help; memoir.
SUBMISSIONS: Open to all. Submit via email to submissions@ hashtagpress.co.uk. Guidelines at www.hashtagpress.co.uk/ submissionguidelines. Usually

responds within four weeks. Rejections may sometimes include feedback or referral to an editor. Authors are paid royalties and receive free copies of their books, but must contribute to publishing/ marketing costs. Hashtag Press also has a self-publishing service called INK!

WE SAY: Branding themselves as a 'boutique' publisher, Hashtag Press publish a vast range of children's books, from picture books to gripping YA. We looked at *The Ghosteleers* by Philip Beicken, which follows the adventures of Norman and his cat in the afterlife. With a fun, vibrant cover and playful fonts within, this is children's literature at its best.

HEAD OF ZEUS

E-BOOKS / NOVELS / SHORT STORY COLLECTIONS AND ANTHOLOGIES / NON-FICTION
020 7253 5557
hello@headofzeus.com
www.headofzeus.com
Editors: Anthony Cheetham, Nicolas Cheetham, Laura Palmer, Rosie de Courcy, Neil Belton, Richard Milbank, Madeleine O'Shea

Established 2012. Mixed form. Publications available from chain bookshops nationwide; from independent bookshops; at national and local literary events; and from Amazon and other bookshop websites.

Winner of Digital Business of the Year at *The Bookseller* Awards 2015.

GENRES: Crime/thriller/mystery; fantasy/sci-fi; historical fiction; literary fiction; romance; children's; lifestyle; biography and true stories; history; popular science and nature; society, education and politics.

SUBMISSIONS: Submit through the online form at www.headofzeus. com.

WE SAY: One of the largest and most established indie presses still open to unsolicited submissions. Titles are available in print and digital formats. The paperback we checked out, *The Washington Stratagem* by Adam LeBor, is an adult thriller with a striking cover but slightly flimsy page quality. A slick website, elegant catalogue and active social media presence complete the polished HoZ package.

HEADPRESS

NON-FICTION E-BOOKS
Apt 29603, Chynoweth House, Trevissome Park, Truro TR4 8UN
headoffice@headpress.com
headpress.com
Editor: David Kerekes

Established 1991. Publishes non-fiction. Publications available direct from publisher website; from chain and independent bookshops nationwide; and from Amazon and other bookshop websites. Headpress was nominated for the 2018 Bram Stoker Awards, for the best non-fiction horror related title.

GENRES: Cult film; music; popular culture.

SUBMISSIONS: Open to all. Submit by email to headoffice@headpress. com. Guidelines at headpress.com/ about-us. Usually responds in one to three months. Rejections may occasionally include unsolicited feedback. Authors are paid an advanced fee plus royalties, and receive free copies of the book.

WE SAY: One look at Headpress' website immediately demonstrates their love of both 'pop' and 'unpop' culture. We viewed essay collection *The Beatles, or the 'White Album'* edited by Mark Goodall, exploring The Beatles' most controversial album. Presented in a two-column format, this book takes on the style of a newspaper article. After also considering travel memoir *I Am the Dark Tourist* by H E Sawyer, it is clear that Headpress explore a diverse range of topics.

HENNINGHAM FAMILY PRESS
NOVELS / NON-FICTION
david@henninghamfamilypress.co.uk
www.henninghamfamilypress.co.uk
Editors: David and Ping Henningham
Established 2006. Primarily publishes fiction, but also non-fiction and poetry (see p43). Publications available direct from the publisher website; from chain and independent bookshops; at national literary events; and from hive.co.uk and other bookshop websites.
Henningham Family Press was shortlisted for The Republic of Consciousness Prize 2019, and was a Regional Finalist for Small Press of the Year in the The British Book Awards 2019.
GENRES: Literary.
SUBMISSIONS: Currently only open to women and BAME authors. Submit via email to david@henninghamfamilypress.co.uk. Guidelines at www.henninghamfamilypress.co.uk/submissions. Usually responds within four weeks. Offers feedback where possible. Authors are paid an advance fee plus royalties, and receive free copies of their book.
WE SAY: Looking at Henningham Family press' website, this publisher pursues a variety of creative projects. Their chosen publications particularly show interest in the themes of money, history and religion. The family origins of the press are clear, giving their aesthetic a homely feel with broad creative horizons.
See also: poetry publishers p43

HERA
NOVELS / E-BOOKS / AUDIOBOOKS
submissions@herabooks.com
www.herabooks.com
Editor: Keshini Naidoo
Established 2018. Publishes fiction. Publication available direct from the publisher website; from selected major chain bookshops; and from Amazon.
Hera was nominated for the Romantic Novelists Association Awards.
GENRES: Romance; crime.
SUBMISSIONS: Open to all. Submit by email to submissions@herabooks.com. Guidelines at www.herabooks.com/submissions. Usually responds in one to three months. Rejections may occasionally include unsolicited feedback. Authors are paid royalties.
WE SAY: This new, female-led press aims to publish the best commercial fiction, spanning from psychological thrillers to intoxicating romance. Hera Books' website showcases all of their authors and books, with an impressive number in just one year of publishing. The designs rival the slickest of the Big Five publishers' genre fiction – this is a press that knows commercial marketing.

HI VIS PRESS
NOVELS / ANTHOLOGIES
contact@hi-vispress.com
www.hi-vispress.com

Editors: Sophie Pitchford, Jim Gibson, Ben Williams

Established 2016. Also publishes poetry (see p44). Publications available direct from publisher website; from selected/local chain bookshops; from independent bookshops; and at national literary events.

GENRES: Social realism; literary fiction; working class writing; experimental form poetry and prose.

SUBMISSIONS: During submission windows only. Submit by email to contact@hi-vispress.com. Usually responds within one to three months, with feedback only if requested. Authors are paid royalties only and receive free copies of the book.

See also: poetry publishers p44 and *Low Light Magazine* (mixed-form magazine) p239

HISTORY PRESS, THE
NON-FICTION / E-BOOKS
97 St George's Place, Cheltenham GL50 3QB
01242 895310
lperehinec@thehistorypress.co.uk
www.thehistorypress.co.uk
Editor: Laura Perehinec

The History Press is an amalgamation of a number of longstanding imprints, the oldest of which – Phillimore – was founded in 1897. The press in its current guise was created in 2007. Publications available from chain and independent bookshops; at local and national literary events; and from Amazon and other bookshop websites.

The History Press publication *PrettyCityLondon* was shortlisted for the 2018 British Book Design & Production Awards in the Lifestyle Illustrated category.

GENRES: Narrative non-fiction; biography and memoir; general non-fiction; illustrated non-fiction.

SUBMISSIONS: Open to all. Submit via email to web@thehistorypress.co.uk. Guidelines at www.thehistorypress.co.uk/writing-for-us. Endeavours to respond in one to three months, but given the large volume of submissions, cannot always reply regarding unsuccessful proposals. Authors are paid an advance fee and royalties.

WE SAY: At a hefty 424 pages long, *A History of the World with the Women Put Back In* by Kerstin Lücker and Ute Daenshel (translated from the original German by Ruth Ahmedzai Kemp and Jessica West) rightly won an English Pen award. The beautiful cover design featuring women from around the world framed against a sea-like background entices the reader to open the book. It seems appropriate for both children and adults, highlighting some key names in the opening pages with illustrations before diving into in-depth history with key facts highlighted in blue.

HOGS BACK BOOKS
CHILDREN'S BOOKS
enquires@hogsbackbook.com
www.hogsbackbooks.com

Bright and beautiful children's picture books and non-fiction books up to age ten. Welcomes submissions both directly from authors and through agents. Though registered in Wiltshire, the commissioning editor is based in France, so for the sake of postage costs, we recommend subbing by

HOLLAND PARK PRESS ☆

NOVELS / NOVELLAS / SHORT
STORY COLLECTIONS / E-BOOKS
46 Baskerville, Malmesbury SN16 9BS
publishing@hollandparkpress.co.uk
www.hollandparkpress.co.uk

Established 2009. Mixed form:
also publishes poetry (see p44).
Publications available direct from
publisher website; by direct mail
and email orders; from chain
bookshops nationwide; from
independent bookshops; at national
and local literary events; and from
Amazon.
Holland Park Press was the joint
winner of the Oxford-Weidenfeld
Translation Prize in 2016 and was
shortlisted for the Etisalat Prize
for Literature in 2013. Holland
Park Press publication *Live Show,
Drink Included* by Vicky Grut was
shortlisted for the 2019 Edgehill
Short Story Prize.
GENRES: Literary.
SUBMISSIONS: Open to all.
Submit by email to publishing@
hollandparkpress.co.uk. Guidelines
at www.hollandparkpress.co.uk/
submissions.php. Usually responds
within one to three months. No
feedback offered with rejections.
Authors are paid royalties only and
receive free copies of the book.
WE SAY: We saw Karen Jenning's
autobiographical novel *Travels With
My Father*. The cover is primarily
dark teal with a matte coat, and
features an abstract image of a man
writing at a desk. The inner design
is clean and professional. The novel
is a memoir-travelogue, written in
the first person as the narrator faces
the aftermath of her father's death.

Holland Park Press

THEY SAY

Holland Park Press, founded
in 2009, is a privately-owned
independent company
publishing literary fiction:
novels, novellas, short stories;
and poetry. The company
is run by brother and sister
team Arnold and Bernadette
Jansen op de Haar, who
publish an author not just
a book. Holland Park Press
specialises in finding new
literary talent by accepting
unsolicited manuscripts from
authors all year round and by
running competitions. It has
been successful in giving older
authors a chance to make
their début and in raising the
profile of Dutch authors in
translation.

See also: poetry publishers p44

email. Guidelines at
www.hogsbackbooks.com/HBB/
images/Submissions.pdf

HOLLAND HOUSE BOOKS
NOVELS / NOVELLAS
Holland House, 47 Greenham Road,
Newbury, Berkshire RG14 7HY
01635 36527
contact@hhousebooks.com
www.hhousebooks.com
Editors: Robert Peett, Natasha
Robson
Established 2012. Fiction.
GENRES: Literary fiction. Some
literary non-fiction.
SUBMISSIONS: Open to all. Submit
via www.hhousebooks.com/
submissions (guidelines at the
same address). Usually responds
within four weeks.

HONEST PUBLISHING
E-BOOKS / NOVELS / SHORT STORY
COLLECTIONS / GRAPHIC NOVELS /
MIXED-FORM ANTHOLOGIES
Unit 1B, Clapham North Arts Centre,
26-32 Voltaire Road, London SW4 6DH
info@honestpublishing.com
www.honestpublishing.com
Editors: Chris Greenhough, Daniel
Marsh
Established 2010. Mixed output
– also publishes poetry (see p44).
Publications available direct from
publisher website; from major
chain and independent bookshops;
and from Amazon and other
bookshop websites.
Ward Wood author Joe Stein was
on the longlist of ten for the Crime
Writers' Association Dagger in the
Library award 2016.
GENRES: Literary; satire.
SUBMISSIONS: Open to all, but
only during submission windows.
Submit by post (Unit 1B, Clapham
North Arts Centre, 26-32 Voltaire

Road, London SW4 6DH) or by
email (info@honestpublishing.
com). Guidelines at www.
honestpublishing.com/submissions.
Usually responds within one to
three months. No feedback offered
with rejection. Authors are paid
royalties and receive free copies of
the book.
See also: poetry publishers p44

HONNO WELSH WOMEN'S PRESS
E-BOOKS / NOVELS / SHORT STORY
ANTHOLOGIES / NON-FICTION
14 Creative Units, Aberystwyth Arts
Centre, Aberystwyth, Ceredigion
SY23 3GL
01970 623150
post@honno.co.uk
www.honno.co.uk
Editor: Caroline Oakley
Established 1986. Mainly fiction,
including classics. Publications
available direct from publisher
website; from chain bookshops
nationwide; from independent
bookshops; at national and local
literary events; and from Amazon
and other bookshop websites.
Winner of the Bread and Roses
Award for Radical Publishing 2015
with *Here We Stand: women
changing the world.*
GENRES: Crime/thriller/mystery;
historical fiction; literary fiction;
biography and true stories.
SUBMISSIONS: Submissions only
open to women who are Welsh or
living in Wales or have a significant
Welsh connection. Submit by post
to Commissioning Editor,
14 Creative Units, Aberystwyth Arts
Centre, Aberystwyth, Ceredigion
SY23 3GL. Guidelines at www.
honno.co.uk/infowriters.php.
Usually responds within four
to six months. Rejections may

occasionally include unsolicited feedback. Writers receive a flat fee or an advance/fee plus royalties, as well as free copies of their book.

WE SAY: We looked at *All Shall be Well*, a perfect-bound 356-page anthology that is professionally designed with a smart matte cover. Printed on quality paper, each item in the anthology is heralded by an image and, interestingly, it includes fiction and non-fiction pieces.

This publication is full of wit and demonstrates the talent of Welsh women writers.

HOPEROAD PUBLISHING / SMALL AXES

NOVELS / E-BOOKS
PO Box 55544, Exhibition Road, London SW7 2DB
020 7370 3567
rosemarie@hoperoadpublishing.com
pete@hoperoadpublishing.com
www.hoperoadpublishing.com
Editors: Rosemarie Hudson (HopeRoad) and Pete Ayrton (Small Axes)

HopeRoad was established in 2010 and publishes fiction and YA fiction. Imprint Small Axes publishes post-colonial novels and e-books. Publications available direct from the publisher website; from independent bookshops; and libraries.

HopeRoad has been nominated for the Carnegie Medal, longlisted for International IMPAC Dublin Literary Award and shortlisted for the Little Rebels Award.

GENRES: Fiction; YA fiction; post-colonial novels.

SUBMISSIONS: Open to all during submissions windows, otherwise by invitation only. Submit by post (PO Box 55544, Exhibition Road, London SW7 2DB) or email (info@hoperoadpublishing. com). Responds within one to two months. Rejections may occasionally include unsolicited feedback. Authors are paid an advance fee plus royalties.

WE SAY: From HopeRoad and their imprint Small Axes, we looked at *The Wild Book* by Juan Villoro, a tantalising adventure for YA readers, journeying through a magical library. It's a welcoming read, formatted with intricate pen-and-ink illustrations decorating the beginning of each chapter. The more serious *The Nowhere Man* by Kamala Markandaya, written for adults, explores racism in 1970s London and includes an introductory essay that was first featured in *The Paris Review*. These two vastly contrasting books are unified in their cultural grounding as HopeRoad aims to champion the authors with African, Asian, Caribbean, and other neglected voices.

HORRIFIC TALES PUBLISHING

E-BOOKS / NOVELS / AUDIOBOOKS
admin@horrifictales.co.uk
www.horrifictales.co.uk
Editors: Steve Lockley, Lisa Lane, Dion Winton-Polack, Amanda Rutter, Kerri Patterson, Graeme Reynolds

Established 2011. Fiction. Publications available from chain bookshops nationwide; and from Amazon and other bookshop websites.

Horrific Tales titles *High Moor*, *High Moor 2: Moonstruck*, *Whispers* and *Angel Manor* were all semi-finalists in the Bram Stoker awards (2011, 2012, 2013, 2014). *Bottled Abyss* was a finalist in the Bram Stoker Awards (2012). *The Grieving Stones* was a finalist in the

British Fantasy Awards (2017).
GENRES: Horror.
SUBMISSIONS: Open to all, during submissions windows. Submit by email to submissions@horrifictales. co.uk. Guidelines at www. horrifictales.co.uk/submissions. Usually responds within one to three months. Rejections may occasionally include unsolicited feedback. Authors are paid an advance/fee plus royalties and receive free copies of the book.
WE SAY: We saw PDF copies of *Lucky's Girl* by William Holloway and *Bottled Abyss* by Benjamin Kane Ethridge – both available as print and e-books. Horrific Tales' titles sport classic horror covers – *Lucky's Girl* is a doozy: a cross between the old Pan Horror anthologies and *Goosebumps*. The inner pages are well formatted, with the occasional illustrative decoration between chapters.

HURST STREET PRESS
SHORT STORY COLLECTIONS AND ANTHOLOGIES / NON-FICTION
OVADA, 14a Osney Lane, Oxford OX1 1NJ
general@hurststreetpress.co.uk
www.hurststreetpress.co.uk
Editors: Beth Sparks, Shoshana Kessler
Established 2015. Mixed form. Hurst Street Press publishes short story collections and anthologies and non-fiction books, as well as mixed-form anthologies and poetry (see p45). Publications available direct from publisher website; from selected/local chain bookshops and from independent bookshops.
GENRES: Experimental.
SUBMISSIONS: Open to all. Submit by post (Studio 1, OVADA, 14a Osney Lane, Oxford, OX1 1NJ) or by email (general@hurststreetpress. co.uk). Usually responds within one to three months. Rejections may occasionally include unsolicited feedback. Authors are paid royalties only.
See also: poetry publishers p45 and *IRIS* (mixed-form magazine) p233

IGNITE BOOKS
NOVELS / NON-FICTION
hello@ignitebooks.co.uk
www.ignitebooks.co.uk
Described by one reviewer as 'an act of defiance', Ignite works to prove that 'unmarketable' books can be marketed, taking on entertaining tales and great stories that aren't easily categorised. Bold, genre-defying writing in all forms.

INDIGO PRESS, THE
NOVELS / SHORT STORY COLLECTIONS / NON-FICTION / E-BOOKS
The Indigo Press, 50 Albemarle Street, Mayfair, London W1S 4BD
020 7297 4311
publish@theindigopress.com
www.theindigopress.com
Editor: Susie Nicklin
Established 2017. Mainly publishes fiction. Publications available direct from the publisher website; by post and email order; from chain and independent bookshops; at national and local literary events; and on Amazon and other bookshops websites.
GENRES: Literary fiction; non-fiction; crime fiction; essays; current affairs.
SUBMISSIONS: Open to all. Submit by email to publish@ theindigopress.com. Guidelines at www.theindigopress.com/contact. Usually responds within four weeks. Rejections may occasionally

141

include unsolicited feedback. Authors are paid an advance fee plus royalties.

WE SAY: We looked at *Wonder Valley* by Ivy Pochoda, a perfect-bound paperback with French flaps. The cover design is enticing, depicting silhouetted palm trees against the sunset with a pop of neon for the title and author, fitting for the novel itself which is a portrait of contemporary L.A. narrated by a cast of six eclectic characters.

INFINITY PLUS

NOVELS / SHORT STORY
COLLECTIONS / NON-FICTION
kbrooke@infinityplus.co.uk
www.infinityplus.co.uk
Editor: Keith Brooke
Established 2010. Publications available in print and as e-books from Amazon and other bookshop websites, and can be ordered by bookshops.
GENRES: Fantasy/sci-fi; horror; biography and true stories.
SUBMISSIONS: Submissions by invitation or query only. Usually responds within four weeks. Rejections may occasionally include unsolicited feedback. Authors are paid royalties and receive free copies of the book.

INFLUX PRESS

NOVELS / SHORT STORY
COLLECTIONS AND ANTHOLOGIES
/ CREATIVE NON-FICTION /
E-BOOKS
The Greenhouse, 49 Green Lanes, London NA6 9BU
www.influxpress.com
Editors: Kit Caless, Gary Budden
Established 2012. Mixed form: fiction, creative non-fiction. Publications available direct from

publisher website; from chain bookshops nationwide; from independent bookshops; at local literary events; and from Amazon and other bookshop websites. Influx title *Above Sugar Hill* by Linda Mannheim was nominated for the Edge Hill Short Story Prize.
GENRES: Literary fiction; weird fiction; London writing; city literature; biography and true stories; history; society, education and politics; travel.
SUBMISSIONS: During submissions windows only, otherwise agented submissions or submissions by invitation only. Submit by email to submissions@influxpress.com. Guidelines at www.influxpress.com/submissions. Usually responds within four to six months. No feedback offered with rejections. Authors are paid royalties only or an advance/fee plus royalties, and receive free copies of the book.
WE SAY: We looked at *An Unreliable Guide to London*, which features 23 stories by London inhabitants (with names we know including Eley Williams, Aki Schilz, Salena Godden) relating tales of their lesser-known corners of London. The cover design parodies guidebooks: the landscape is there, but not as you know it. The cover warns 'limited scope – bad advice – no practical use' – but we found that this collection had particular use in reframing a city everyone thinks they know, and commenting on the changes taking place there.

INSPIRED QUILL

NOVELS / SHORT STORY
COLLECTIONS / NON-FICTION /
E-BOOKS
info@inspired-quill.com

www.inspired-quill.com
Established 2011. Publications
available direct from mail
and e-mail orders; from chain
bookshops nationwide; at national
and local literary events; and from
Amazon and other bookshop
websites. In 2016, Inspired Quill
was shortlisted by the Polari
Literary Salon for the Polari First
Book Prize.
GENRES: Literary fiction; fantasy/
sci-fi; steampunk; YA; LGBT.
SUBMISSIONS: Open to all, during
submission windows. Submit by
email to sjslack@inspired-quill.com.
Guidelines at www.inspired-quill.
com/submissions. Usually responds
in one to three months. Rejections
include personalised rejection
letter with editorial feedback on
the submission and cover letter
where appropriate. Depending on
workload, occasional on-page edits
are also provided (usually up to five
pages). Authors are paid royalties
only and receive free copies of
book.

IRON PRESS
COLLECTIONS AND ANTHOLOGIES
5 Marden Terrace, Cullercoats,
North Shields NE30 4PD
0191 253 1901
peter@ironpress.co.uk
www.ironpress.co.uk
Editor: Peter Mortimer
Established 1973. Primarily
publishes poetry (see p47), but
also releases some prose (fiction,
drama, etc). Publications available
direct from publisher website;
by post and email order; from
selected/local chain bookshops;
from independent bookshops; and
via Inpress Ltd.
Iron Press' 2014 Iron Age Literary
Festival won Best Event: Tyneside
in The Journal Culture Awards.
GENRES: Literary.
SUBMISSIONS: Contact the
press before submitting work:
see the website for guidelines.
Submit by post (5 Marden
Terrace, Cullercoats, North
Shields NE30 4PD) or by email
(ironpress@blueyonder.co.uk).
Usually responds within one to
three months. Rejections may
occasionally include unsolicited
feedback. Authors are paid a flat
fee.
WE SAY: The 68-page A5
perfect-bound book we
considered, *The Water Thief and
the Manatee* by Kitty Fitzgerald,
used slightly better materials
than the poetry collection we saw
(see poetry publishers p47). The
paperback cover is of a heavier
weight, and dark blue endpapers
were also included. Designated
'A Modern Fable', beautiful, full
colour artwork done by the cover
artist is interspersed throughout,
but the use of coloured font in
each chapter page's title seems a
little unnecessary. The font used
is larger than normal, though
appropriate for the fable styling.
See also: poetry publishers p47

ISTROS BOOKS
NOVELS / SHORT STORY
COLLECTIONS / NON-FICTION /
E-BOOKS
Conway Hall, 25 Red Lion Square,
London WC1R 4RL
info@istrosbooks.com
www.istrosbooks.com
Editor: Susan Curtis
Established 2010. Primarily
publishes fiction. Publications
available direct from publisher
website; from chain bookshops
nationwide; from independent

bookshops; and from Amazon and other bookshop websites.

GENRES: Literary fiction; history; society, education and politics.

SUBMISSIONS: Publication history required, as submissions are by invitation only. Submit by email to contact@istrosbooks.com. Usually responds within four weeks. Rejections may occasionally include unsolicited feedback. Authors are paid royalties and receive free copies of the book.

WE SAY: Specialising in translated work from Eastern Europe, Istros is on a mission to change the image of that region from 'grey tower blocks and cabbage' to the vibrant culture they are familiar with. A glance through their catalogue reveals designs that reflect this ethos: original illustrated covers with grey backgrounds and technicolour images. With their signature bright stripe of colour running down the edge of each cover, Istros books are instantly recognisable.

IVY PRESS

ILLUSTRATED NON-FICTION
www.ivypress.co.uk
Integrated, illustrated non-fiction books for the international market, released under three imprints. Subject areas include popular culture; art and design; crafts; general reference; health and parenting; mind, body, spirit; humour and novelty. Unsolicited proposals welcome (synopses, not manuscripts) by email (ivyauthors@quarto.com) or post.

JACARANDA BOOKS

E-BOOKS / NOVELS / SHORT STORY COLLECTIONS AND ANTHOLOGIES / NON-FICTION

27 Old Gloucester Street, London WC1N 3AX
office@jacarandabooksartmusic.co.uk
www.jacarandabooksartmusic.co.uk
Editor: Valerie Brandes

Established 2013. Also publishes illustrated books. Publications available direct from publisher website; from chain bookshops nationwide; from independent bookshops; at national and local literary events; and from Amazon and other bookshop websites. Jacaranda Books title *The Book of Harlan* by Bernice L McFadden won the 2017 NAACP Award for Literature.

GENRES: Literary fiction; crime fiction; romance fiction; biography and memoir; travel writing.

SUBMISSIONS: Agented submissions only, during submission windows. Submit by email to office@jacarandabooksartmusic.co.uk. Guidelines at www.jacarandabooksartmusic.co.uk/contact/. Usually responds within one to three months. Rejections may occasionally include unsolicited feedback. Authors are paid an advance/fee plus royalties and receive free copies of the book.

JOHN CATT EDUCATIONAL

NON-FICTION
www.johncattbookshop.com
enquiries@johncatt.com
Established in 1959, John Catt Educational publishes high quality guidebooks, magazines and educator-focused professional development books. They welcome submissions on all ideas relating to education.

144

KATABASIS

NON-FICTION / ANTHOLOGIES
020 7485 3830
10 St Martin's Close, London
NW1 0HR
katabasis@katabasis.co.uk
www.katabasis.co.uk
Editor: Dinah Livingstone
Established 1967. Primarily
publishes English and Latin
American poetry (see p47),
but also some non-fiction and
mixed poetry/prose anthologies.
Publications available direct from
the publisher website; by direct
mail and email order; from chain
and independent bookshops
nationwide, at national and local
literary events, and from Amazon.
SUBMISSIONS: Submissions by
invitation only. Solicited work may
receive a response within four
weeks. No feedback offered with
rejections.
**For more information, including
what We Say, see also: poetry
publishers p47**

KENILWORTH PRESS

NON-FICTION
www.quillerpublishing.com
admin@quillerbooks.com
Publishes a selection of
instructional equestrian books
covering all disciplines. The press
in an imprint of Quiller Publishing
(p173) and is the exclusive
publisher of the training manuals
for the British Horse Society and
exclusive distributor for The Pony
Club. They have an open call for
submissions, as well as suggestions
for future work.
**See also: Quiller Publishing (prose
publisher) p173**

KHIDR COLLECTIVE

SHORT STORY ANTHOLOGIES

69 Uxbridge Road, Shepherds Bush,
London W12 8NR
07852 337369
khidrcollective@googlemail.com
www.khidrcollective.co.uk
Editors: Zain Dada, Raeesah Akhtar,
Zainab Rahim and Nishat Alam
Established 2017. Publishes both
prose and poetry anthologies
(see p48). Publications available
direct from the publisher; by
direct mail and e-mail orders; from
independent bookshops; and at
local literary events.
GENRE: Literary.
SUBMISSIONS: Open to all. Submit
by email to khidrcollective@
googlemail.com. Guidelines
at www.khidrcollective.co.uk.
Usually responds in one to three
months. No feedback offered with
rejections. Contributors are paid a
flat fee.
**See also: poetry publishers p48
and for more information, including
what We Say, see Khidr Collective
Zine (mixed-form magazine) p235**

KNIGHT ERRANT PRESS

NOVELS / NON-FICTION / SHORT
STORY COLLECTIONS AND
ANTHOLOGIES / E-BOOKS
knighterrantpress@outlook.com
www.knighterrantpress.com
Editors: Nathaniel Kunitsky and
Rhiannon Tate
Established 2017. Publishes poetry
(see p48) and prose. Publications
available direct from the publisher
website; from independent
bookshops; and at local literary
events.
GENRES: Literary; speculative
fiction; LGBTQIA; words in
translation; romance.
SUBMISSIONS: Open to all during
submissions windows, otherwise
by invitation only. Submit by

145

email to knighterrantpress@
outlook.com. Guidelines at
www.knighterrantpress.com/
page. Responds within one to
three months. Rejections include
feedback only if requested.
Authors are paid an advance
fee plus royalties, and receive
free copies of their book. Some
crowdfunding required.
See also: poetry publishers p48

KNIGHTS OF
NOVELS / NON-FICTION
97 Granville Arcade, London SW9 8PS
07956 516938
afelone@knightsof.media
www.knightsof.media
Editors: Aimée Felone and David
Stevens
Established 2017. Primarily publishes
fiction, but also some non-fiction.
Publications available from chain and
independent bookshops; at national
literary events; and from Amazon
and other bookshop websites.
Co-founder and editor Aimée
Felone won the Kim Scott Walwyn
Prize 2019. The Prize recognises
the professional achievements and
promise of women in publishing.
GENRES: Children's fiction; non-
fiction.
SUBMISSIONS: Open to all. Pitch
via live chat on the publisher's
website. Guidelines at knightsof.
media/submissions. Usually
responds in up to three months.
Rejections may occasionally
include unsolicited feedback.
Authors are paid an advance fee
plus royalties.
WE SAY: We looked at a copy of
Jason Reynolds' middle grade
novel *Ghost*, a very high-quality
perfect-bound paperback. The
cover design is stylishly illustrated
in a style which will appeal to

young audiences with bright, bold
colours and spot UV detailing.
The text inside is easy to read and
appropriately sized for middle
grade readers.

KRISTELL INK
NOVELS
www.grimboldbooks.com
The science fiction and fantasy
imprint of Grimbold Books (see
p131). Check for open submissions
before sending your manuscript.
**For more information, see also:
Grimbold Books (prose publisher)
p131**

LAGAN PRESS
NOVELS / NON-FICTION
info@laganpress.co
www.laganpress.co
Mixed form: also publishes poetry
collections. Looks for work of
'literary, artistic, social and cultural
importance to the north of Ireland'.
Irish and Ulster-Scots language
work also welcomed.
See also: poetry publishers p49

LANTANA PUBLISHING
PICTURE BOOKS
65 Peak Hill, London SE26 4NS
submissions@lantanapublishing.com
www.lantanapublishing.com
Editor: Alice Curry
Established 2014. Publishes diverse
and inclusive picture books. Offers
a subscription package of £25 for
three books per year, or £50 for
six books per year. Publications
available direct from the
publisher website; from chain and
independent bookshops; at local
and national literary events; and
from Amazon and other bookshop
websites.
Publications from Lantana
Publishing won the Children's

Africana Book Award 2016 and 2019, and the 3-Star Teach Early Years Award. *You're Safe With Me* by Chitra Soundar and Poonam Mistry was shortlisted for the 2019 Kate Greenaway Medal.

GENRES: Contemporary stories for children; slice of life; adventure; realism; fantasy.

SUBMISSIONS: Open to all, particularly welcoming submissions from new and aspiring BAME authors and illustrators. Submit by email to submissions@lantanapublishing.com. Guidelines at www.lantanapublishing.com/pages/submissions. If you haven't received a response after 12 weeks, please assume the press wasn't able to take your story through to publication. Authors are paid an advance fee and royalties, and receive free copies of their book.

WE SAY: Lantana is a social enterprise children's publisher that donates one book for every book sold on their website, believing firmly that books should be inclusive to all children. We looked at PDFs of *You're Safe with Me* by Chitra Soundar and Poonam Mistry, and *Nimesh the Adventurer* by Ranjit Singh and Mehrdokht Amini. It is difficult to describe how truly stunning these books are – filled with beautiful patterns and full-page illustrations, adult readers will be tempted to display them on the wall. The writing is clear and fun, and they are enthralling and exciting for readers.

LAURENCE KING PUBLISHING
NON-FICTION
commissioning@laurenceking.com
www.laurenceking.com
Publisher of gift books, student support books and activity sheets, life style, graphic design, children's activity and education, and many more – Laurence King is open to proposals for new products. Full guidelines on their website at www.laurenceking.com/getting-published. Strictly no fiction.

LAWRENCE AND WISHART
NON-FICTION / MIXED-FORM ANTHOLOGIES
Central Books Building, Freshwater Road, Chadwell Heath RM8 1RX
020 8597 0090
office@lwbooks.co.uk
www.lwbooks.co.uk
Editor: Katharine Fletcher

Established 1936. As well as non-fiction and mixed poetry/prose anthologies (see also p50), they also publish six different journals, with between two and four issues each year for each title, including *Soundings* (see p257). Publications available direct from the publisher website; at chain and independent bookshops; and from Amazon and other bookshop websites.

GENRES: Political history; political analysis; philosophy; cultural theory and analysis; biography; poetry.

SUBMISSIONS: Open to all, submit by email (submissions@lwbooks.co.uk) or post (Lawrence and Wishart, Central Books Building, Freshwater Road, Chadwell Heath RM8 1RX). Guidelines at www.lwbooks.co.uk/about-us#authors. Usually responds in one to three months. Rejections may occasionally include unsolicited feedback. Contributors are paid royalties only and receive free copies of their book.

See also: poetry publishers p50 and *Soundings* (prose magazine) p257

147

LEGEND PRESS

NOVELS / NON-FICTION / E-BOOKS
Legend Press, 51 Gower Street,
London WC1E 6HJ
020 7936 9943
info@legend-paperbooks.co.uk
www.legendpress.co.uk
Editor: Lauren Parsons
Established 2005. Publications
available from chain and
independent bookshops; at
national and local literary events;
and from Amazon and other
bookshop websites.
Legend Press was shortlisted
for Bookseller Independent
Publisher of the Year 2011,
and Legend Press publisher
Tom Chalmers won the Global
Outstanding Young Person Award
in the Big Ben Awards 2018.
GENRES: Literary; crime;
commercial; historical.
SUBMISSIONS: Submit by email
to info@legend-paperbooks.
co.uk, during submissions
window only. Guidelines at
www.legendtimesgroup.co.uk/
legend-press/submissions. Usually
responds in one to three months.
Rejections may occasionally
include unsolicited feedback.
Authors are paid an advance fee
plus royalties.
WE SAY: Looking at Legend Press'
website, their range of titles
appear to cover different genres
and moods. We looked at a PDF
of *Into the River* by Mark Brandi, a
haunting tale of two young boys'
troubles and their growth into
adulthood. This book explores the
trauma and friendship of growing
up, appealing to a relatable
experience whilst also exploring
the sinister and unusual.

LES FUGITIVES

E-BOOKS / TRADE PAPERBACKS
91 Cholmley Gardens, Fortune Green
Road, London NW6 1UN
info@lesfugitives.com
www.lesfugitives.com
Publisher and Editor: Cécile Menon
Established 2014. A feminist
press dedicated to short works
of outstanding literary merit by
francophone female authors
previously unavailable in English.
Publications available from chain
bookshops and independent
bookshops nationwide, in the EU
and ANZ; from Amazon and other
online retailers.
Les Fugitives has won and been
nominated for over six different
awards. This includes being short-
and longlisted for the French-
American Foundation Translation
Prize and the Best Translated
Book Awards in the US, the Scott
Montcrieff Prize and the Translators
Association First Translation Prize
in the UK, as well as winning an
English PEN Award in 2017, and
the 2016 Scott Montcrieff Prize,
which was awarded for the press'
first title *Suite for Barbara Loden*,
by Nathalie Léger (co-translated
by Natasha Lehrer and Cécile
Menon). Several titles have been
listed in Best Books of the Year by
the *Times Literary Supplement*,
the *White Review*, the *Guardian*,
and the *Financial Times*. All titles
by Les Fugitives are published by
independent publishers in the US,
including The Feminist Press and
New Directions, among others.
GENRES: Fiction and non-fiction.
SUBMISSIONS: Accepted from
translators, agents and French
publishing houses. Publication
history required. Usually responds
within one to three months.

148

Authors are paid an advance on royalties.

WE SAY: We looked at extracts on LF's website, with an admonishment from the editor that she 'wouldn't know which title would be most representative of the press'. The images we looked at showed flapped paperback books, with textured, muted colours (usually blues), and contrasting title text, with the very discreet 'double dot' logo in the bottom right-hand corner. These are classy affairs, with the extra appeal that even in thumbnail size, the name of the translator is clear. The review blurb with each title is impressive to say the least.

LIBERTIES PRESS

E-BOOKS / NOVELS / NON-FICTION / SHORT STORY COLLECTIONS
+353 86 853 8793
sean@libertiespress.com
www.libertiespress.com
Editor: Seán O'Keeffe
Established 2003. Publishes both prose and poetry (see p51). Publications available direct from the publisher website; at chain and independent bookshops; and from Amazon and other bookshop websites. Liberties Press publication *Setting the Truth Free: The Inside Story of the Bloody Sunday Justice Campaign* won the 2012 Christopher Ewart-Biggs Memorial Prize.

GENRES: Literary fiction; crime fiction; history; biography/memoir.

SUBMISSIONS: Open to all, submit by email to sean@libertiespress.com. Guidelines at www.libertiespress.com/submissions. Liberties Press charges a fee to consider a manuscript for publication (currently €495 for

fiction, €295 for non-fiction/poetry, incl VAT). For this it prepares a report, covering the content/structure, literary quality, and marketability of the work, and can then arrange a meeting to discuss next steps. Aims to respond to enquiries within 24 hours, and, if the author decides to go ahead, aims to complete the report within six weeks. Contributors are paid a flat fee and royalties, and receive free copies of their book. Authors also contribute to marketing and publishing costs.

WE SAY: Neat and whimsical, the collection we reviewed – *The Goose Tree* by Moyra Donalson – is a slim, A5, perfect-bound volume printed on plain cream paper, with no-fuss fonts and a quirky, illustrated feather-themed cover. All the key components of a classy collection with no frills. Conversely, the hardback edition of *Clearing the Hurdles* by J B McGowan was weighty and authoritative, with soft matte pages interspersed with glossy colour photographs. A publisher with many strings to their bow.

See also: poetry publishers p51

LILLIPUT PRESS, THE

NOVELS / SHORT STORY COLLECTIONS / NON-FICTION
62-63 Sitric Road, Arbour Hill, Dublin 7, Ireland
+353 (01) 671 16 47
publicity@lilliputpress.ie
www.lilliputpress.ie
Editor: Antony Farrell
Established 1984. Publications available direct from the publisher website; by post and email order; from chain and independent bookshops; at national and local literary events; and from Amazon

and other bookshop websites. The Lilliput Press was shortlisted for The Bookseller Small Press of the Year Award 2019.

GENRES: Irish interest; Irish history; biography; memoir; literary fiction.

SUBMISSIONS: Open to all. Submit via post to Submissions Editor, The Lilliput Press, 62-63 Sitric Road, Arbour Hill, Dublin 7, Ireland. Guidelines at www.lilliputpress.ie/submissions. Usually responds in four to six months. Rejections may occasionally include unsolicited feedback. Authors are paid an advance fee plus royalties.

WE SAY: We looked at a few different PDF proofs of Lilliput's offerings. All are cleanly laid out, with the inner title page echoing the cover design. Lilliput doesn't adhere to a single template for their publications, so for example, *Love Notes From A German Building Site* by Adrian Duncan has wider leading and more white space on the page than *The Cruelty Men* by Emer Martin - a small thing to note but an important signifier of the care taken with the work. The covers make use of photographic images and careful title design, to reflect the mood of the text within.

LINEN PRESS ☆

E-BOOKS / NOVELS / SHORT STORY COLLECTIONS AND ANTHOLOGIES / NON-FICTION
8 Maltings Lodge, Corney Reach Way, London W4 2TT
020 8995 4488
lynnmichell0@googlemail.com
www.linen-press.com
Editor: Lynn Michell

Established 2007. Mainly publishes fiction. Publications available direct from publisher website; by post and email order; at local literary events; and from Amazon and other bookshop websites. Linen Press was a finalist in the 2015 Women in Publishing Pandora Award.

GENRES: Literary fiction; women's writing.

SUBMISSIONS: Open to all. Submit via www.linen-press.com/submit, completing the form which requests 1,000 words. If the sample is appealing, a further 50 pages may be requested. Full guidelines are at www.linen-press.com/submit. Usually responds within four weeks. Regretfully, feedback is no longer offered on submissions. Authors receive an advance fee and royalties.

WE SAY: The A5-sized, perfect-bound copy of *The Dancing Girl & the Turtle* by Karen Kao we saw had a lovely photo on the glossy cover of a woman mid-movement. Printed on white paper, the novel follows Song Anyi's story of survival in her fight for independence after being raped, through prostitution, opium dens, and her experiences with self-harm, as China prepares for war with Japan.

LITRO MAGAZINE LTD

SHORT STORY COLLECTIONS
020 3371 9971
info@litro.co.uk
www.litro.co.uk
Editors: Eric Akoto, Precious Williams

Established 2005. Fiction. Litro also runs a literary agency. Publications available direct from publisher website; from chain bookshops nationwide; from independent bookshops; at national and local literary events; and at galleries and public spaces across London.

GENRES: Crime/thriller/mystery;

drama and criticism; literary fiction; art, fashion and photography; food and drink; music, stage and screen; science, technology and medicine; society, education and politics; travel.

For a fuller description of this press, see *Litro Magazine* (mixed-form magazine and e-zine) p237

LITTLE ISLAND BOOKS
BOOKS FOR CHILDREN / E-BOOKS
7 Kenilworth Park, Dublin 6W, Republic of Ireland
siobhan.parkinson@littleisland.ie
www.littleisland.ie
Editors: Siobhán Parkinson and Matthew Parkinson-Bennett
Established 2010. Publishes both prose and poetry (see p51) for children. Publications available direct from the publisher website; by post and email order; from chain and independent bookshops; at national and local literary events; and from Amazon.
Little Island Books won the Bookseller Award for Irish Small Press of the Year in 2019, and the Special Award of the Reading Association of Ireland in 2011. Several of its authors have also won awards, including the Lollies award in 2017.
GENRES: Children's / UA fiction; children's literary fiction; teen and YA literary fiction; non-fiction / information books for children; Irish interest books for children; picture books.
SUBMISSIONS: Open to all, when publishing lists are not full. Submit via the website at www.littleisland.ie/submissions, where guidelines are also available. Usually responds in one to three months. The press gives feedback if editors feel a book has potential, even if it is

not for them, and will occasionally explain why they can't consider a book. Authors are paid an advance fee plus royalties, and receive free copies of their book.
WE SAY: Navigating Little Island's website was a pleasure; each dynamic, vibrant page celebrates the range of books they publish and the children and teens who enjoy them. Their vast collection of published works is spread across different age ranges amongst children, although they also pride their books on being read by adults too.
See also: poetry publishers p51

LITTLE TOLLER BOOKS
NON-FICTION
jon@littletoller.co.uk
www.littletoller.co.uk
Editor: Adrian Cooper
Established 2009. Publications available direct from publisher website; by post and email order; from chain bookshops nationwide; from independent bookshops; at national and local literary events; and from Amazon and other bookshop websites.
Books often longlisted for relevant prizes.
GENRES: Travel; natural landscape and place writing. No fiction.
SUBMISSIONS: Agent submissions only, by email to gracie@littletoller.co.uk. Usually responds within four to six months. Rejections may occasionally include unsolicited feedback. Authors are paid an advance/fee plus royalties.
WE SAY: *King of Dust: Adventures in Forgotten Sculpture* by Alex Woodcock is an immaculately presented hardcover edition with a striking illustrated jacket, quirky endpapers, and fascinating

maps and illustrations, with a biography and colour photograph of the author on French flaps. Very professional and extremely high quality.

See also: *The Clearing* (mixed-form magazine) p221

LONELY PRESS, THE

SHORT STORY COLLECTIONS / MIXED-FORM ANTHOLOGIES
62 Kings Road, Cardiff CF11 9DD
johnlavin@thelonelycrowd.org
www.thelonelycrowd.org
Editor: John Lavin

Established 2015. Publishes poetry and prose, including book-sized mixed-form journal *The Lonely Crowd* (p238). Publications available direct from the publisher website; from independent bookshops; and at local literary events.

GENRES: Literary.

SUBMISSIONS: Open to all, during submissions windows – but please note The Lonely Press is not currently open to submissions of full short story collections. Usually responds to submissions in four to six months. No feedback is offered with rejections. Authors receive free copies of their book. See *The Lonely Crowd* (p238) for how to submit work to anthologies.

See also: poetry publishers p52. For more information, including what We Say, see *The Lonely Crowd* (mixed-form magazine) p238

LOOSE CHIPPINGS

NON-FICTION
contact@loosechippings.org
www.loosechippings.org
Editor: Arthur Cunynghame

Largely publishes non-fiction, including travel and memoir – but open to fiction submissions.

LUATH PRESS

NOVELS / NON-FICTION
www.luath.co.uk
sales@luath.co.uk

Established in 1981, Edinburgh-based Luath Press publishes across a wide range of genres, including literary, children's, biography, travel, poetry (see p52) and more. Most of its books have a Scottish connection, but editors 'are always looking out for new and innovative books and authors, whatever the background'. Postal submissions only.

See also: poetry publishers p52

LUNA PRESS PUBLISHING ☆

NOVELS / SHORT STORY COLLECTIONS AND ANTHOLOGIES / NON-FICTION / GRAPHIC NOVELS / E-BOOKS
149/4 Morrison Street, Edinburgh EH3 8AG
lunapress@outlook.com
www.lunapresspublishing.com
Editor: Francesca T Barbini

Established 2015. Publishes fiction. Publications available direct from the publisher; by post or email order; from chain and independent bookshops; at literary events; and from Amazon and other bookshop websites. Luna Press Publishing won the 2018 British Fantasy Award for best non-fiction.

GENRES: Science fiction; SFF non-fiction; horror; fantasy.

SUBMISSIONS: Open to all, though fiction should be submitted only during open submissions windows. Non-fiction/academic submissions, for Academia Lunare, are welcome all year round. Submit by email to lunasubmissions@outlook.com. Guidelines at www.lunapresspublishing.com/submissions. Usually responds in one to three months. Rejections may occasionally include unsolicited feedback. Authors are paid royalties only, or an advance plus royalties, and receive free copies of the book.

WE SAY: We looked at a PDF of *The Prisoner* from Luna Press' A Darkness in Mind series, written by Robert S Malan and illustrated by John Cockshaw. This publication blends illustrated novella with the graphic novel, using dark tones and obscure graphics throughout to support the sinister theme of its writing. The hybridity of its form, with images and words interlaced throughout, shows the creativity of this press, with dark illustrations reflecting the thrilling design of Luna Press' website.

MAGIC OXYGEN ☆

NOVELS / SHORT STORY ANTHOLOGIES / NON-FICTION / MIXED-FORM ANTHOLOGIES / E-BOOKS
The Flat, 53 Broad Street, Lyme Regis DT7 3QF
01297 442824
editor@magicoxygen.co.uk
www.magicoxygen.co.uk
Editor: Simon West

Established 2012. Mainly publishes fiction, but also some poetry (see p52). Publications available direct from publisher website; from major chain and independent bookshops; at local literary events; and from Amazon and other bookshop websites.
GENRES: Self-help; romance; comedy; sci-fi.
SUBMISSIONS: Submissions are usually by invitation only. Work should be sent to editor@magicoxygen.co.uk. Usually responds within one to three

months. Rejections may include occasional unsolicited feedback. Authors receive royalties.
WE SAY: We made use of the 'Look in the Book' feature in Magic Oxygen's online shop. The books usually have covers featuring photographic images with heavy, stylised fonts. The inner pages revert to standard serif. They seem a little stretched, but we suspect this is an effect of the online preview. We were particularly struck by Trish Vickers' *Grannifer's Legacy*. Vickers has been blind for 11 years, and wrote the book by hand. On one disastrous day, the pen ran out – and the local police deciphered the indents to recover the work. This is the sort of personal warmth and community effort that seems to lie under much of Magic Oxygen's work.
See also: poetry publishers p52

MANDRAKE OF OXFORD

NON-FICTION / FICTION
mandrake@mandrake.uk.net
www.mandrake.uk.net
A publisher with wide-ranging interests including, but not limited to mysticism, true crime, philosophy, paganism, erotica, paranormal and strange phenomena, and looking for fiction based around the occult, myths, sci-fi and erotica. Open submissions, but please follow the clearly explained guidelines at www.mandrake.uk.net/contact/submissions.

MANTLE LANE PRESS

NOVELLAS / SHORT STORY COLLECTIONS AND ANTHOLOGIES / NON-FICTION
01530 830811
matthew@red-lighthouse.org.uk

www.mantlelanepress.co.uk
Editor: Matthew Pegg
Established 2015. Also publishes scripts. Publications available direct from publisher website; from chain bookshops nationwide; from independent bookshops; at local literary events; and from Amazon and other bookshop websites.
GENRES: Literary; slipstream.
SUBMISSIONS: Open to all, during submission windows. Certain publication opportunities may only be available to Midlands writers. Submit online at greensubmissions.com/537/mantle-lane-press/index.php. Guidelines for each publishing opportunity are posted on www.mantlearts.org.uk. Usually responds within one to three months. Rejections may occasionally include unsolicited feedback. Authors are paid a flat fee and receive free copies of the book.
WE SAY: We looked at a digital version of the 53-page story collection *A Far Cry* by Valentine Williams. It presents four short alluring stories about how change occurs in far-away communities. The book shows a beautifully illustrated cover, complementing one of the stories about a young girl finding a whale's valuable 'ambergris'. The book is pocket-sized, perfect to read on the move.

MARGŌ COLLECTIVE
E-BOOKS / NOVELS
www.margocollective.com
hello@margocollective.com
Established 2017. Indie publisher of writers and stories from the edges.
GENRES: Literary fiction, speculative fiction, experimental, non-conforming, cross-genre, YA.

SUBMISSIONS: Open to all. Submit by email to submissions@margocollective.com. Guidelines at www.margocollective.com/submissions. Usually responds within one to three months. Authors receive royalties only or a flat fee only (depending on the type of book/funding), plus free copies of the book.

MATTHEW JAMES PUBLISHING
NON-FICTION / NOVELS
Unit 46, Goyt Mill, Upper Hibbert Ln, Marple, Stockport SK6 7HX
www.matthewjamespublishing.com
Long-established press, publishing local interest non-fiction, spirituality and prayer, religious education and theology, and children's books (through imprint Tiny Tree Children's Books– see p192). Open to unsolicited submissions, with full and clear guidelines at www.matthewjamespublishing.com/submissions.
For more information see also: Tiny Tree Children's Books (prose publisher) p192

MAYFLY PRESS
NOVELS
submissions@mayfly.press
www.newwritingnorth.com/projects/mayfly-press/
'Good books from the North of England.' Mayfly and imprint Moth (crime writing) look for work from writers in the North of England, and authors include Benjamin Myers and Michael Donovan. Check the website for details of open submissions windows.

MERCIER PRESS
NON-FICTION / NOVELS
Unit 3B Oak House, Bessboro Road,

MOTHER'S MILK BOOKS ☆

E-BOOKS / NOVELS / SHORT STORY ANTHOLOGIES / NON-FICTION
teika@mothersmilkbooks.com
www.mothersmilkbooks.com
Editor: Dr Teika Bellamy

Established 2011. Mixed form: also publishes poetry (see p54). Publications available direct from publisher website; from independent bookshops; at national and local literary events; and from Amazon. Mother's Milk Books has won numerous awards. Founder Teika Bellamy received the Women in Publishing's New Venture Award for pioneering work on behalf of under-represented groups in society. Mother's Milk Books title *Baby X* won the Commercial Fiction category of the Eric Hoffer Award in 2017. The poetry duets pamphlet, *Inheritance*, by Ruth Stacey and Katy Wareham Morris, won Best Collaborative Work in the 2018 Saboteur Awards.

GENRES: Commercial fiction; literary fiction; fairy tales; fantasy; sci-fi.

SUBMISSIONS: During submissions windows only. Submit by email to submissions@mothersmilkbooks.com. Guidelines at www.mothersmilkbooks.com/index.php/submissions. Submitters are required to buy a book from the press. Usually responds within one to three months. Rejections may occasionally include unsolicited feedback. Authors are paid an advance/fee plus royalties and receive free copies of the book.

WE SAY: We looked at a PDF of *The Forgotten and Fantastical 5*, the fifth in a series of beautifully designed short story anthologies filled with 'modern fables and ancient tales'. It contains 14 stories by some familiar names (Angela Readman and Rosie Garland particularly caught our eye). Detailed illustrations by Emma Howitt grace the title page of each story. The anthology closes with a page each of fascinating insights from the writers on how their stories came about. Mother's Milk continues to be a stylish and admirable operation.

See also: poetry publishers p54

Blackrock, Cork, Ireland
info@mercierpress.ie
www.mercierpress.ie
Established 1944. Publications
available direct from publisher
website; from chain bookshops
nationwide; from independent
bookshops; at local literary events;
and from Amazon and other
bookshop websites.
GENRES: History; lifestyle; food
and drink; current affairs; sport;
adult and YA fiction.
SUBMISSIONS: Open to all. Submit
by email to commissioning@
mercierpress.ie. Guidelines at
www.mercierpress.ie/submit.
Usually responds within one to three
months. Rejections may occasionally
include unsolicited feedback.
Authors are paid royalties.

MIRA PUBLISHING
NON-FICTION / FICTION
info@mirapublishing.com
www.mirapublishing.com
Mira Publishing is part of Mira
Intelligent Read cic (Community
Interest Company) and publishes
fiction and non-fiction based on
contemporary topics. It aims to
enrich international literature
and looks to publish books from
different countries and in English
and other languages.

MONSTROUS REGIMENT PUBLISHING
NOVELS / SHORT STORY
ANTHOLOGIES / NON-FICTION
editor@monstrous-regiment.com
www.monstrous-regiment.com
Editors: Lauren Nickodemus,
Ellen Desmond
Established 2017. Also publishes
poetry in mixed-form anthologies
(see p54). Publications available
direct from publisher website; by

direct mail and email orders; and at
local literary events.
GENRES: Non-fiction commentary;
confessional essay; topical prose;
creative non-fiction; literary fiction.
SUBMISSIONS: Open to all, during
submission windows. Submit by
email (editor@monstrous-regiment.
com) or online (www.monstrous-
regiment.com/contact). Guidelines
at www.monstrous-regiment.com/
submissions/. Usually responds
within four weeks, with feedback
only if requested. Authors are paid
a flat fee.
See also: poetry publishers p54 and
***Monstrous Regiment* (mixed-form**
magazine) p242

MORBID BOOKS
FICTION/ NON-FICTION
www.morbidbooks.net
info@morbidbooks.net
Based in South London, Morbid
Books claims to be 'a Temple of
Surrealist Literature'. It publishes
books in limited editions of up to
500 and is open to proposals all
year round.
See also: poetry publishers p54 and
***A Void* (prose magazine) p214**

MUDFOG PRESS
SHORT STORY COLLECTIONS
c/o Beacon Guest, Chop Gate,
Stokesley TS9 7JS
contact@mudfog.co.uk
www.mudfog.co.uk
Editors: Pauline Plummer, Jo Heather,
David Lynch, Adrienne Silcock, Geoff
Strange
Established 1993. Mixed form:
also publishes poetry (see p55).
Publications available direct from
the publisher website.
GENRES: Short fiction /
environmental writing.
SUBMISSIONS: Favours writers

in the Tees Valley, stretching from Whitby to Sunderland, West to Darlington. However also occasionally publishes writers outside this area. Submit by post (Beacon Guest, Chop Gate, Stokesley TS9 7JS) or by email (contact@mudfog.co.uk). Guidelines at www.mudfog.co.uk/submissions. Usually responds within one to three months. Rejections may occasionally include unsolicited feedback. Authors are able to buy a number of their books at cost-price and sell them at sales price.

WE SAY: We looked at a PDF proof of *Line Drawings* by Craig Campbell. The back cover features plenty of blurb about this Teeside-set short story collection, promising a gritty series of authentic vignettes, and the cover art helps set the tone of what to expect with a sketch filter-effect image of a large crocodile tattoo on a man's back, and more arm tattoos on the back cover. The inner page layout is clear and well-spaced, with a short biography and photograph of the writer on the final page. The writing has a strong sense of voice, with no punches pulled.

See also: poetry publishers p55

MURDER SLIM PRESS

NOVELS / SHORT STORY COLLECTIONS AND ANTHOLOGIES / E-BOOKS
22 Bridge Meadow, Hemsby, Norfolk NR29 4NE
01904 733767
murderslimpress@aol.com
www.murderslim.com
Editor: Steve Hussy
Established 2004. Publishes fiction. Publications available direct from the publisher website; by direct mail and email order; and from Amazon and other bookshop websites.
Murder Slim Press publications have been listed and nominated for numerous awards, including *The Migrant* by u.v. ray being listed as a runner up in the 2014 Saboteur Awards.
GENRES: Urban grit; confessional; crime; realist.
SUBMISSIONS: Submissions by invitation only, to murderslimpress@aol.com. Information available at www.murderslim.com. Responds to submissions within one to three months. Rejections may include unsolicited feedback. Authors are paid royalties only.
WE SAY: We considered an online extract of anthology *Savage Kick #10*, including *The Janitor* by Jack D Larsen. This dark, sinister text twists with suspense and creates the tone reflected in Murder Slim's website. With ominous graphics tiled between the press' name, their website is somehow both simple yet strange, obscure, and fiercely unique.

MUSWELL PRESS

NOVELS / SHORT STORY COLLECTIONS / NON-FICTION / E-BOOKS
72 Cromwell Avenue, London N6 5HQ
sarah@sarahbeal.co.uk
www.muswell-press.co.uk
Editor: Sarah Beal
Publishes fiction and non-fiction. Publications available from chain and independent bookshops, and from Amazon and other bookshop websites.
GENRES: Contemporary fiction; historical fiction; biography/memoir; travel; narrative non-fiction.

SUBMISSIONS: Open to all (though submission windows may come into effect if the press is overwhelmed with submissions). Submit by email to info@muswell-press.co.uk. Usually responds in one to three months. Rejections may occasionally include unsolicited feedback.

MYRIAD EDITIONS
FICTION / GRAPHIC NOVELS / NON-FICTION
Myriad Editions, New Internationalist Publications, The Old Music Hall, 106–108 Cowley Rd, Oxford OX4 1JE
01865 403345
info@myriadeditions.com
www.myriadeditions.com
Editors: Candida Lacey, Corinne Pearlman

Established 1993. Predominantly publishes original fiction, political non-fiction and graphic novels. Publications available direct from publisher website; from chain bookshops nationwide; from independent bookshops; at national and local literary events; and from Amazon and other bookshop websites.
London Triptych by Jonathan Kemp and *The Last Pilot* by Benjamin Johncock won the Authors' Club Best First Novel Award respectively in 2010 and 2016. Margaret Busby won the Africa Writes Lifetime Achievement Award in 2019 for *New Daughters of Africa*. Elizabeth Haynes' début novel, *Into the Darkest Corner*, became a bestseller as did her début historical novel, *The Murder of Harriet Monckton*.
GENRES: Literary fiction and non-fiction, including memoir; crime fiction; historical fiction; short stories; feminist non-fiction; graphic novels, including graphic memoir and graphic medicine.
SUBMISSIONS: Periodically open to all. Submit by email to submissions@myriadeditions.com. Guidelines at www.myriadeditions.com/about/submissions. Usually responds within one to three months. Authors are paid an advance plus royalties, and receive free copies of the book.
WE SAY: We considered a few publications from the last few years, each of which maintained high-quality, contemporary cover designs, on a size slightly smaller than A5. The paperback covers varied, with 2015's 312-page *The Longest Fight* by Emily Bullock moving to a slightly glossy finish, but 2017's 474-page *The Favourite* by S V Berlin returned to the previous matte style. The pages also changed in this latter to a softer, more high-quality feel, with a different perfect-binding that made the book easier to peruse.

MYRMIDON BOOKS LTD
E-BOOKS / NOVELS / NON-FICTION
Rotterdam House, 116 Quayside, Newcastle upon Tyne NE1 3DY
0191 206 4005
ed@myrmidonbooks.com
www.myrmidonbooks.com
Editor: Ed Handyside

Established 2006. Mainly publishes fiction. Publications available by post and email order; from chain bookshops nationwide; from independent bookshops; at national and local literary events; and from Amazon and other bookshop websites. Awards include winning the 2013 Man Asian Literary Prize and Walter Scott Prize for Best Historical Fiction.
GENRES: Crime/thriller/mystery; fantasy/sci-fi; historical fiction;

158

literary fiction; romance; biography
and true stories; history; humour.
SUBMISSIONS: Open to all. Submit
by post (Myrmidon, Rotterdam
House, 116 Quayside, Newcastle
upon Tyne NE1 3DY) or by email
(ed@myrmidonbooks.com).
Guidelines on the website. Usually
responds in over six months. No
feedback offered with rejections.
Authors are paid royalties only, or
an advance/fee plus royalties.
WE SAY: Big Five publications from
a small press. Myrmidon books
come complete with the blurb,
the marketing, the formatting
and the materials to be at home
in any bookshop. We particularly
loved the cover of *Angel* by Jon
Grahame, with its bolted-iron title
and action-filled, yet ethereal,
images.

NEEM TREE PRESS
NOVELS / E-BOOKS / SHORT STORY
COLLECTIONS / GRAPHIC NOVELS /
ILLUSTRATED BOOKS
www.neemtreepress.com
A London-based publisher
that accepts manuscripts from
anywhere in the world and in any
language, for readers age 12 to
adult. They publish fiction and
non-fiction, within 'broad themes
and their intersections' including
historical, current social, art, music,
culture, science and more, and
in all formats including graphic
novels and illustrated books. Full
guidelines are available on their
website.

NEON BOOKS
E-BOOKS / NOVELS / SHORT STORY
COLLECTIONS AND ANTHOLOGIES
info@neonbooks.org.uk
www.neonbooks.org.uk
Editor: Krishan Coupland

Established 2006. Also publishes
poetry (see p56). Publications
available direct from publisher
website; by direct mail and
email orders; from independent
bookshops; at national literary
events; and from Amazon and
other bookshop websites. Neon
Books title *The Mesmerist's
Daughter* won the 2015 Best
Novellas Saboteur Award.
GENRES: Sci-fi; horror; slipstream;
magical realism; surrealism.
SUBMISSIONS: Open to all,
during submission windows.
Submit by email to info@
neonbooks.org.uk. Guidelines
at www.neonbooks.org.uk/
guidelines/. Usually responds
within one to three months.
Rejections may occasionally
include unsolicited feedback for
a fee. Submissions hold a tip-jar
option, but this does not affect
publisher's decision. Authors are
paid royalties only and receive
free copies of the book.
**See also: poetry publishers p56.
For more information, including
what We Say, see *Neon Literary
Magazine* (mixed-form magazine)
p243**

NEW ISLAND
NOVELS / NON-FICTION
info@newisland.ie
www.newisland.ie
New Island started out as Raven
Arts Press in the 1980s and
continues to commit to publishing
'exceptional literature and
groundbreaking non-fiction'. It
publishes various series, including
Fiction Firsts, which focuses on
début work.
See also: poetry publishers p56

NEW WELSH REVIEW ☆
E-BOOKS / NOVELS / NON-FICTION / NOVELLAS
PO Box 170, Aberystwyth SY23 1WZ
01970 628410
editor@newwelshreview.com
www.newwelshreview.com
Editor: Gwen Davies
Established 1988. Mixed form. Also publishes the winners of the annual New Welsh Writing Awards (see p310) and translated works. Publications available direct from the publisher website; by post and email order; from selected major chain bookshops and independent bookshops; at local literary events; and from www.gwales.com.
GENRES: Fiction; non-fiction; poetry; opinion; essays.
SUBMISSIONS: Open to all. Submit by post (Submissions, PO Box 170, Aberystwyth SY23 1WZ) or by email (editor@newwelshreview.com). Guidelines at www.newwelshreview.com/submissions.php. Usually responds within one to three months. No feedback offered with rejections. See also New Welsh Writing Awards p310.
For more information, including what We Say, see also: *New Welsh Review* (mixed-form literary magazine) p243

NEWCON PRESS
E-BOOKS / NOVELS / SHORT STORY COLLECTIONS AND ANTHOLOGIES / NON-FICTION
41 Wheatsheaf Road, Alconbury Weston, Cambridgeshire PE28 4LF
finiang@aol.com
www.newconpress.co.uk
Editor: Ian Whates
Established 2006. Also publishes poetry (see p57). Publications available direct from publisher website; from chain bookshops nationwide; from Amazon; and at genre themed literary events. Jaine Fenn's short story 'Liberty Bird' from NewCon Press anthology *Now We Are Ten* won the BSFA Award for best short fiction in 2017.
GENRES: Sci-fi; fantasy; horror; slipstream; general criticism and review.
SUBMISSIONS: Submissions by invitation only. Author payment varies depending on the published work.
See also: poetry publishers p57

NIGHTJAR PRESS
SHORT STORY CHAPBOOKS
63 Ballbrook Court, Wilmslow Road, Manchester M20 3GT
nightjarpress@gmail.com
nightjarpress.weebly.com
Editor: Nicholas Royle
Established 2009. Single-story chapbooks. Publications available direct from publisher website; by post and email order; from selected/local chain bookshops; from independent bookshops; and at local literary events,
GENRES: Fantasy; horror; literary fiction; uncanny/Gothic.
SUBMISSIONS: Open to all – but strongly encourages writers to research what the press does before submitting. Submit by post (63 Ballbrook Court, Wilmslow Road, Manchester M20 3GT) or by email (nightjarpress@gmail.com). Guidelines at nightjarpress.weebly.com/about.html. Usually responds within one to three months. Rejections may occasionally include unsolicited feedback. Authors are paid a flat fee.
WE SAY: Limited edition, single short story chapbooks of between 12–16 pages. The stories are published in pairs, and designed

to a consistent house style of textbook-ish covers with carefully selected complementary images linking the pairs together. Inside are simple, well-formatted inner pages. The stories published are distinctly odd and uncanny – take a good look before you submit. Each chapbook is signed by the author. We liked the succinct author bios on the back covers.

NO EXIT PRESS

NOVELS / NON-FICTION / E-BOOKS
Coleswood Road, Harpenden
AL5 1EQ
01582 766348
publicity@oldcastlebooks.com
www.noexit.co.uk
Editors: Ion Mills, Geoffrey Mulligan, Clare Quinlivan, Katherine Sunderland
Established 1987. Primarily publishes fiction. Publications available direct from the publisher website; by direct mail and email order; from chain and independent bookshops; at local and national literary events; and from Amazon and other bookshop websites. No Exit Press publication *Dodgers* by Bill Beverly, won the 2017 British Book Award for Best Crime and Thriller Novel.
GENRES: Crime; literary; historical; espionage.
SUBMISSIONS: Submissions via agents only (please see sister press Verve Books, p199, for unagented submissions). Full information at www.noexit.co.uk/submissions. Authors are paid an advance fee and royalties.
WE SAY: We looked at *Dodgers* by Bill Beverly, which presents the thrilling journey, both physical and mental, of a protagonist grappling with a high-stakes job. Exclusively publishing crime fiction, Dodgers

greatly exemplifies No Exit Press' highly extensive collection of dark and dangerous stories. This is clearly a press with great experience, and the perfect home for gripping crime fiction.

NOSY CROW

NOVELS / PICTURE BOOKS / NON-FICTION
hello@nosycrow.com
www.nosycrow.com
Established 2011. Publisher of parent-friendly children's books for ages 0-14 yrs, both commercial fiction and non-fiction (YA or New Adult), and creates interactive multimedia apps.
Multi-award-winning publishers, including the 2016 IPG Independent Publisher of the Year Award and Children's Publisher of the Year Award.
SUBMISSIONS: Open to all, preferably by email. Guidelines at nosycrow.com/contact/submission-guidelines. Tries to respond to all submissions within six months.

NOTTING HILL EDITIONS

NON-FICTION ESSAYS / ANTHOLOGIES
contact@nottinghilleditions.com
www.nottinghilleditions.com
Editor: Kim Kremer
Established 2011. Only publishes essays, but on any subject, and some anthologies. Publications available direct from publisher website; by post and email order; from chain bookshops nationwide; from independent bookshops; at national and local literary events; and from Amazon and other bookshop websites, including the *Guardian* bookshop.
Notting Hill Editions won the 2011 Red Dot Design Award.

161

GENRES: Essays on art, architecture and photography; biography and true stories; history; science, technology and medicine; society, education and politics. No fiction.
SUBMISSIONS: Open to all. Submit by email to contact@nottinghilleditions.com. Usually responds within one to three months. Rejections may occasionally include unsolicited feedback. Authors are paid a flat fee or royalties only, and receive free copies of the book.
WE SAY: Notting Hill Editions publishes both print and e-book. The print books are stunning: hardback cloth-bound books with bright bold covers and thick high-quality paper, which look fantastic on a shelf. These are books that readers collect for decoration as much as for content – which is not to belittle the intelligent, thoughtful writing within.

NOTTINGHAM REVIEW, THE
E-BOOKS / SHORT STORY ANTHOLOGIES
thenottinghamreview@gmail.com
www.thenottinghamreview.com
Editor: Spencer Chou
Established 2015.
GENRES: Literary fiction.
SUBMISSIONS: Open to all. Submit by email to thenottinghamreview@gmail.com. Usually responds within four weeks. Rejections may occasionally include unsolicited feedback.
For more information, see also: *The Nottingham Review* (mixed-form magazine) p246

O'BRIEN PRESS, THE
NON-FICTION / CHILDREN'S BOOKS/ E-BOOKS
12 Terenure Road East, Dublin 6, Ireland
+353 1 492 3333
books@obrien.ie
www.obrien.ie
Established 1974. Publications available direct from the publisher website; from chain and independent bookshops; and from Amazon. The O'Brien Press was a winner in the An Post Irish Book Awards 2018.
GENRES: Non-fiction; children's books.
SUBMISSIONS: Submit by post to The O'Brien Press, 12 Terenure Road East, Dublin 6, Ireland. See www.obrien.ie/submissions for guidelines.
WE SAY: Judging by *Blazing a Trail: Irish Women Who Changed the World* by Sarah Webb and Lauren O'Neill, we'd happily tout O'Brien as a big new up-and-comer in children's book publishing. This immaculately presented perfect-bound hardcover boasts embossed lettering on the cover, quirkily illustrated endpapers, and gorgeous artwork throughout. Bright, colourful and appealing – a brilliantly conceived and executed product.

OFFORD ROAD BOOKS
NOVELS / SHORT STORY COLLECTIONS AND ANTHOLOGIES / NON-FICTION
offordroadbooks@gmail.com
www.twitter.com/offordroadbooks
Editors: Martha Sprackland, Patrick Davidson Roberts
Established 2017. Also publishes poetry (see p57). Publications available by direct mail and email orders; from selected/local chain bookshops; from independent bookshops; at local literary events; and from Amazon.
GENRES: Literary fiction; essays.

SUBMISSIONS: Open to all. Submit by post (29a Womersley Road, Crouch End, London N8 9AP) or by email (offordroadbooks@gmail. com). Usually responds within four weeks. Rejections may occasionally include unsolicited feedback. Authors receive a small fee.
For more information, including what We Say, see also: poetry publishers p57

OLD STREET PUBLISHING
E-BOOKS / NOVELS / NON-FICTION
info@oldstreetpublishing.co.uk
oldstreetpublishing.co.uk
An award-winning publisher, which won the IMPAC with Rawi Hage's *De Niro's Game*, and the BBC National Short Story Award.

OLDCASTLE BOOKS
E-BOOKS / NOVELS / NON-FICTION
PO Box 394, Harpenden AL5 1XJ
01582766348
cqoldcastle@gmail.com
www.oldcastlebooks.co.uk
Editor: Clare Quinlivan
Established 1985. Publications available direct from publisher website; from chain bookshops nationwide; from independent bookshops; at national and local literary events; and from Amazon and other bookshop websites. Oldcastle Books title *Dodgers* by Bill Beverly has won four awards including the British Book Award for Best Crime & Thriller Novel 2017 and the LA Times Book Prize 2017.
GENRES: Crime; literary fiction; commercial fiction; historical fiction.
SUBMISSIONS: Open to all. Submit by post (Oldcastle Books, PO Box 394, Harpenden AL5 1XJ) or by email (cqoldcastle@ gmail.com). Guidelines at www. oldcastlebooks.co.uk/submissions. Usually responds within one to three months. Rejections may occasionally include unsolicited feedback. Authors are paid an advance/fee plus royalties.
WE SAY: Oldcastle Books directed us to their catalogue, where the wares of its imprints (No Exit Press, Pocket Essential, Kamera Books, Creative Essentials and Oldcastle) are on display. This publisher knows the market – the cover designs are professional and easily sit within genre conventions, so a casual browser instantly knows the type of book they are looking at. At a glance, we were able to peg No Exit Press as a crime/thriller imprint and Oldcastle as literary.

ONEWORLD
NON-FICTION
www.oneworld-publications.com
info@oneworld-publications.com
Founded in 1986, Oneworld focuses on publishing stimulating non-fiction. The press publishes more than 100 books per year and is responsible for publishing two Man Booker Prize winners, as well as Tayari Jones, whose *An American Marriage* won the 2019 Women's Prize for Fiction. They welcome book proposals all year round but ask that they be 'clear, concise and well researched'.

ONSLAUGHT PRESS, THE
PICTURE BOOKS / GRAPHIC NOVELS
www.onslaughtpress.com
onslaughtpress@gmail.com
Based in East Oxford, publishing about ten books per year. Specialises in poetry books and haiku (see p58) but also publishes

163

picture books, which range from illustrated prose stories to graphic novels. Publishes in a variety of languages including Irish, Scots, Scottish Gaelic, Cornish, French, Japanese and English.
See also: poetry publishers p58

ONSTREAM BOOK PUBLICATIONS
NON-FICTION
info@onstream.ie
www.onstream.ie
This Irish publisher focuses primarily on non-fiction, though has been known to publish some fiction. Also offers a service helping first time authors to submit to other publishers.

OPEN PEN
NOVELETTES
sean@openpen.co.uk
www.openpen.co.uk
Editor: Sean Preston
Established 2018. Publishes fiction novellas, with a subscription offer of £20 for four books. Publications available direct from the publisher website; by direct mail and email order; at chain and independent bookshops; and from Amazon and other bookshop websites.
GENRES: Literary fiction.
SUBMISSIONS: Open only to people who have been published in *Open Pen* magazine (see p295). Submit by email to submissions@fairlightbooks.com. Authors are paid royalties and receive free copies of their book.
See also: prose magazines p295

ORENDA BOOKS
NOVELS / E-BOOKS
info@orendabooks.co.uk
www.orendabooks.co.uk
Editor: Karen Sullivan

Established 2014. Publications available direct from the publisher website; from chain and independent bookshops; at national and local literary events; and from Amazon and other bookshop websites.
Orenda Books was shortlisted for the IPG Newcomer Award 2015 and 2016, and was a Bookseller Rising Star in 2016.
GENRES: Literary fiction; crime fiction; translated fiction.
SUBMISSIONS: Open to all, during submissions windows. Submit by email to westcamel@orendabooks.co.uk. Guidelines at www.orendabooks.co.uk/submissions. Usually responds in one to three months. Rejections may occasionally include unsolicited feedback. Authors are paid an advance fee plus royalties.
WE SAY: We looked at an e-book of *Snowblind* by Ann Cleeves – a thrilling Icelandic tale presented in a travel-themed format with maps, locations and dates provided throughout. The blurred and obscure text used in the cover design, with a faded sepia image, brings about a sinister feel before you've even entered the story. Orenda Books' website is loaded with a variety of other titles, all carrying their own unique design.

OTTER-BARRY BOOKS
PICTURE BOOKS
info@otterbarrybooks.com
www.otterbarrybooks.com
A children's book publisher producing high quality picture books and picture information books, two of Otter-Barry's publications were shortlisted for the CLiPPA Prize in 2019. Their work addresses big themes for

young minds. Best approached through an agent.
See also: poetry publishers p58

OUEN PRESS ☆
NOVELS / SHORT STORY COLLECTIONS AND ANTHOLOGIES / NON-FICTION / E-BOOKS
Suite One, Ingles Manor, Castle Hill Avenue, Folkestone, Kent CT20 2RD
info@ouenpress.com
www.ouenpress.com
Editor: Paula Comley
Mainly publishes fiction. Publications available by post and email order; in chain bookshops nationwide; at local literary events; and from various bookshop websites.
GENRES: Contemporary fiction; travel literature; biography.
SUBMISSIONS: Open to all. Submit by email to submissions@ouenpress.com. Guidelines at www.ouenpress.com. Usually responds within one to three months. No feedback offered with rejection. Authors are paid royalties and receive free copies of the book.

OUT-SPOKEN PRESS
E-BOOKS / NON-FICTION
Future Studio, 237 Hackney Road, London E2 8NA
press@outspokenldn.com
www.outspokenldn.com/press
Editor: Anthony Anaxagorou
Established 2015. Primarily publishes poetry (see p59), but also some non-fiction. Publications available direct from the publisher website; from chain and independent bookshops; at national and local literary events; and from Amazon.
SUBMISSIONS: Authors are paid royalties and receive free copies of

their book.
For more information, including what We Say, see also: poetry publishers p59

OWN IT!
NOVELS / IMMERSIVE DIGITAL BOOKS
stories@ownit.london
ownit.london
Self-described 'storytelling lifestyle brand, telling stories across books, music, fashion and film', with publishing just one of its branches. OWN IT! novel *No Place to Call Home* by JJ Bola was longlisted for the *Guardian* Not The Booker Prize 2017. Looks for artists to collaborate with.

PALEWELL PRESS LTD
E-BOOKS / NOVELS / SHORT STORY COLLECTIONS AND ANTHOLOGIES / NON-FICTION
enquiries@palewellpress.co.uk
www.palewellpress.co.uk
Editor: Camilla Reeve
Established 2016. Mixed form: also publishes poetry (see p60). Publications available direct from publisher website; at local literary events; and from Amazon and other bookshop websites.
GENRES: Memoir; human rights and social history; environment.
SUBMISSIONS: Open to all, but must relate to subject areas. Submit by email (enquiries@palewellpress.co.uk) or by post (384 Upper Richmond Road West, London SW14 7JU). Usually responds within four weeks. Rejections may occasionally include unsolicited feedback. Authors are paid royalties only and receive free copies of the book. For authors in mainland

PAPILLOTE PRESS
NOVELS / SHORT STORY
COLLECTIONS / NON-FICTION /
PICTURE BOOKS / E-BOOKS
23 Rozel Road, London SW4 0EY
info@papillotepress.co.uk
www.papillotepress.co.uk
Editor: Polly Pattullo

Established 2004. Books from
the Caribbean. Mainly publishes
fiction, but also some poetry
(p61). Publications available via
the publisher's website; from chain
and independent bookshops; and
from Amazon. Papillote Press has
published three YA novels that
were winners of the Burt Award for
YA Caribbean Literature: *Gone to
Drift* by Diana McCaulay; *The Art
of White Roses* by Viviana Prado-
Núñez and *Home Home* by Lisa
Allen-Agostini.
GENRES: Literary; non-fiction
history/social science; children's
picture books; YA.
SUBMISSIONS: Open to all.
Submit by post (23 Rozel Road,
London SW4 0EY) or email (info@
papillotepress.co.uk). Usually
responds within four weeks.
Rejections may occasionally include
unsolicited feedback. Authors are
usually paid an advance fee and
royalties. An alternative model,
which is sometimes available, is for
author to pay for publication costs
and to take all income from sales.
WE SAY: We looked at a PDF proof
of *In the Forests of Freedom*, by
Lennox Honychurch – a non-fiction
history book, cannily designed
with monochrome images dotted
throughout the informative
chapters in the manner of a

THEY SAY

Papillote Press was conceived
to publish books from the
Caribbean island of Dominica,
as a way of supporting local
writers and reflecting its
culture and literary heritage.
Since then it has expanded to
publish books from the wider
Caribbean. It was started
by Polly Pattullo, a former
journalist, who lives in both
Dominica and London, UK.
Someone once called Papillote
Press 'small and invaluable'
and it remains small and we
hope invaluable. The list is a
quality-rich mix.

textbook. We also looked at PDF
proofs of *Home Home* by Lisa
Allen-Agostini and *The Orchid
House* by Phyllis Shand Allfrey.
The cover design is bright and
engaging, frequently featuring
painted illustrations.
See also: poetry publishers p61

166

UK, publisher shares cost of launch.
WE SAY: We looked at *Three Days in Damascus* by Kim Schultz, a 278-page A5 paperback with a glossy cover. The size and paper thickness meant the book was flexible, and the sparse inner design featured wide margins and an increased line height. The memoir, following the author's time interviewing Iraqi refugees in the Middle East, also includes instant messaging conversations, dictionary entries, and emails featuring their own font and style.
See also: poetry publishers p60

PARALLEL UNIVERSE PUBLICATIONS
E-BOOKS / NOVELS / SHORT STORY COLLECTIONS AND ANTHOLOGIES
130 Union Road, Oswaldtwistle, Lancashire BB5 3DR
paralleluniversepublications@gmx.co.uk
www.parallelpublications.blogspot.co.uk
Editors: David A. Riley, Linden Riley
Established 2012. Also publishes poetry (see p61). Publications available direct from publisher website; by direct mail and email orders; from chain bookshops nationwide; from independent bookshops; and from Amazon and other bookshop websites.
GENRES: Horror; fantasy; sci-fi.
SUBMISSIONS: Open to all. Submit by post (Parallel Universe Publications, 130 Union Road, Oswaldtwistle, Lancashire BB5 3DR) or by email (paralleluniversepublications@gmx.co.uk). Guidelines at www.parallelpublications.blogspot.co.uk/p/submissions.html. Usually responds within one to three months. Rejections may occasionally include unsolicited feedback. Authors are paid royalties only.
WE SAY: We looked at a digital versions of the short story collections *Parlour Tricks* by Carl Baker and *Radix Omnius Malus* by Mike Chinn. The covers of each are dark and ominous (fittingly), and both had cleanly laid out inner pages, with 15 stories from Baker and 16 from Chinn – notably, stories in both collections have been previously published in anthologies and magazines. Both collections provide insight into the author and work: Chinn's collection includes a six-page introduction to his work by David A Sutton, while Baker's work, however, has a section entitled 'Inner Circle' in which each story is compared to a parlour trick, and some insight into its writing is provided – a nice touch.
See also: poetry publishers p61

PARTHIAN BOOKS
E-BOOKS / NOVELS / SHORT STORY COLLECTIONS AND ANTHOLOGIES / NON-FICTION
The Old Surgery, Napier Street, Cardigan SA43 1ED
info@parthianbooks.com
www.parthianbooks.com
Editors: Susie Wild, Richard Davies and Carly Holmes
Established 1993. Publications available direct from publisher website; from chain bookshops nationwide; from independent bookshops; at national and local literary events; and from Amazon and other bookshop websites. Parthian Books title *Ironopolis* by Glen James Brown was short-listed for the Orwell Prize in 2019. Parthian was Wales Publisher of the Year in 2019.

GENRES: Literary; Welsh; feminist/women's writing; historical.

SUBMISSIONS: Open to all. Submit by post. Guidelines at www.parthianbooks.com/pages/contact-us. Usually responds within one to three months. No feedback offered with rejections. Author payment is dependent on deal but mostly fee/royalties.

PATRICIAN PRESS
NOVELS / SHORT STORY COLLECTIONS / E-BOOKS
12 Lushington Road, Manningtree
CO11 1EF
07968 288651
patricia@patricianpress.com
editorial@patricianpress.com
www.patricianpress.com
Editors: Patricia Borlenghi, Mark Brayley, Anna Johnson

Established 2012. Mainly publishes fiction, but also some poetry books (see p62) and poetry-and-prose anthologies. Publications available direct from publisher website; from selected/local chain bookshops; from independent bookshops; at local literary events; and from Amazon and other bookshop websites, including The Great British Bookshop website.

GENRES: Historical fiction; literary fiction; experimental fiction; children and teenagers; food and drink; society, education and politics.

SUBMISSIONS: Open to new and unpublished writers without agents. Please submit only during submissions windows via the form at www.patricianpress.com/submissions (guidelines at the same address). Usually responds within one to three months. Rejections may occasionally include unsolicited feedback.

Authors are paid royalties only.
See also: poetry publishers p62

PEEPAL TREE PRESS
NOVELS / SHORT STORY COLLECTIONS AND ANTHOLOGIES
contact@peepaltreepress.com
www.peepaltreepress.com
Editors: Jeremy Poynting, Kwame Dawes, Jacob Ross, Kadija Sesay

Established 1986. Mixed form: also publishes poetry (see p62). Specialises in Caribbean and Black British writing. Publications available direct from publisher website; by post and email order; from chain bookshops and independent bookshops nationwide; at national and local literary events; and from Amazon and other bookshop websites. Peepal Tree title *Sounding Ground* by Vladimir Lucien was overall winner for The OCM Bocas Prize for Caribbean Literature 2015.

GENRES: Drama and criticism; literary fiction; historical fiction; biography and true stories; history; music, stage and screen.

SUBMISSIONS: Open to all, specialising in Caribbean and Black British writing. Submit through Submittable at peepaltreepress.submittable.com (guidelines at same address). Usually responds within four to six months. Rejections may occasionally include unsolicited feedback, and some manuscripts by UK-based authors are offered a (free) in-depth reader report through the press' Inscribe Writer Development Programme. Authors are paid royalties only.
For more information, including what We Say, see also: poetry publishers p62

168

PEIRENE PRESS ☆
NOVELS / NOVELLAS / SHORT
STORY COLLECTIONS
020 7686 1941
meike.ziervogel@peirenepress.com
www.peirenepress.com
Editor: Meike Ziervogel
Established 2010. Fiction publisher.
Book-club subscription £35/year
for three books. Available direct
from publisher website; by post
and email order; from chain and
independent bookshops; at local
literary events; and from Amazon
and other bookshop websites.
Peirene Press translator Jamie
Bulloch won the 2014 Schlegel-
Tieck Prize for his translation of *The
Mussel Feast* by Birgit Vanderbeke.
GENRES: Literary; fiction in
translation.
SUBMISSIONS: For translation
proposals: submission any time.
For works written in English:
commissioned work only.
Usually responds within one to
three months. Rejections may
occasionally include unsolicited
feedback. Authors receive an
advance fee plus royalties.
WE SAY: The perfect-bound books
produced by Peirene have matte
paperback covers with a cohesive
geometric design featuring
a photograph overlaid with a
rectangular colour block wrapping
around to the back. All publications
are less than 200 pages, and aim
to be able to be read in the time it
takes to watch a film. We saw *Her
Father's Daughter* by Marie Sizun,
which also featured hardcover-style
folds and a note about Peirene's
social activism: 50p of each sale
supports either Counterpoint Arts
or the Maya Centre.

PENINSULA PRESS
NON-FICTION / NOVELS / SHORT
STORY COLLECTIONS
400 Kingsland Road, Haggerston,
London E8 4AA
info@peninsulapress.co.uk
peninsulapress.co.uk
Editors: Jake Franklin, Samuel Fisher,
Will Rees
Established 2017. Primarily
publishes non-fiction. Publications
available direct from the publisher
website; at chain and independent
bookshops; and from Amazon and
other bookshop websites.
SUBMISSIONS: Submissions
welcome only during submissions
windows. Usually responds in one
to three months, with feedback
provided for all submissions
sent during specified submission
windows. Authors are paid an
advance fee plus royalties.

PENKHULL PRESS
E-BOOKS / NOVELS / SHORT STORY
COLLECTIONS
penkhullpress@gmail.com
www.thepenkhullpress.wordpress.com
Editor: Peter Coleborn
Established 2015. Publications
available direct from publisher
website; by direct mail and email
orders; at local literary events; and
from Amazon and other online
bookstores.
GENRES: Literary; crime; women's;
war stories; general.
SUBMISSIONS: By invitation only.
Query by email to penkhullpress@
gmail.com. Usually responds within
one to three months. Rejections
may occasionally include
unsolicited feedback for a fee.
Authors are paid royalties only and
receives free copies of the book.
WE SAY: We looked at digital
versions of *Fables and Fabrications*

by Jan Edwards, a 187-page collection of stories and haikus about mystery, mirth and the macabre; and *Picking up the Pieces* by Misha Herwin, a 284-page story about three women who lose everything in life they took for granted. Both books are professionally designed, with relatively big serif fonts.

PENNED IN THE MARGINS
E-BOOKS / NOVELS / NON-FICTION / NOVELLAS
Toynbee Studios, 28 Commercial Street, London E1 6AB
020 7375 0121
info@pennedinthemargins.co.uk
www.pennedinthemargins.co.uk
Editor: Tom Chivers
Established 2006. Mixed form: also publishes poetry (see p63). Publications available direct from publisher website; by post and email order; from selected/ local chain bookshops; from independent bookshops; at local literary events; and from Amazon. Penned in the Margins' first published novel was shortlisted for the Gordon Burn Prize in 2015.
GENRES: Drama and criticism; literary fiction and non-fiction.
SUBMISSIONS: Publication history required. Submit by email to submissions@pennedinthemargins. co.uk. Usually responds within one to three months. Rejections may occasionally include unsolicited feedback. Authors are paid royalties only.
For more information, see also: poetry publishers p63

PENNYSHORTS ☆
SHORT FICTION SINGLE E-BOOKS
editor@pennyshorts.com
www.pennyshorts.com
Editor: Catherine Horlick
Established 2015. Short fiction of all genres. Digital publications available by post and email order – accessible by purchase only.
GENRES: Crime/thriller/mystery; fantasy/sci-fi; horror; historical fiction; romance; biography and true stories.
SUBMISSIONS: Open to all. Submit by email to editor@pennyshorts. com. Usually responds within four weeks. Rejections may occasionally include unsolicited feedback.
WE SAY: Lovely e-book nuggets to dip in and out of – we were impressed by the marketing strategy behind Pennyshorts, ensuring authors are paid. The e-books/pdfs are very simple – the illustrations for the stories that appear on the website don't carry over to the e-pubs we looked at. Tightly written and edited fiction straight to your device. Highly recommended.

PERIDOT PRESS
FICTION / NON-FICTION
www.peridot.co.uk
enquiries@peridot.co.uk
Publishes writing across a variety of genres. They state that their tastes are 'eclectic, with our only qualification being that the books we publish should enlighten and inspire readers.' The press is interested in fiction and non-fiction, as well as ideas for a publishing project. They are happy to hear from previously published and new authors.

PETER OWEN PUBLISHERS
E-BOOKS / NOVELS
info@peterowen.com
www.peterowen.com

One of the longest-established small presses, founded by Peter Owen (1927-2016) six years after the Second World War and instrumental in bringing the best international literature to the British market. Still publishing fiction and non-fiction, authors include seven Nobel Prize winners. A very highly regarded press.

PHAETON PUBLISHING LTD
NOVELS / NON-FICTION / SHORT STORIES
phaeton@iol.ie
www.phaeton.ie
Established 2017, and specialises in 'engaging books (both print and e-formats) of international interest for thoughtful readers'. Their catalogue includes a range of serious and entertaining non-fiction. Check the website for open submissions windows.

PILOT PRESS
FICTION / NON-FICTION
www.pilotpress.tumblr.com
pilotpresslondon@gmail.com
Established in 2017, Pilot Press is a not-for-profit organisation publishing contemporary queer literature and art. Each print run is funded by donation, usually from those involved in its creation, or as a gesture of good will from its readers.

PILRIG PRESS
NOVELS / E-BOOKS / NON-FICTION
enquiries@pilrigpress.co.uk
www.pilrigpress.co.uk
Founded in late 2010, and looking for literary fiction and new crime fiction, as well as historical fiction and non-fiction with a focus on Scotland. Wants to encourage new Scottish talent, but not exclusively.

PINTER & MARTIN LTD
E-BOOKS / NON-FICTION
6 Effra Parade, London SW2 1PS
020 3633 6879
info@pinterandmartin.com
www.pinterandmartin.com
Established 1997. Publications available direct from publisher website; from chain bookshops nationwide; from independent bookshops; at local literary events; and from Amazon and other bookshop websites.
GENRES: Pregnancy, birth and parenting; health and nutrition; yoga; psychology.
SUBMISSIONS: Submissions only accepted within specified themes. Submit by email (submissions@pinterandmartin. com). Guidelines at www. pinterandmartin.com/submissions. html. Usually responds within four weeks. Rejections may occasionally include unsolicited feedback. Authors are paid an advance/ fee plus royalties and receive free copies of the book.
WE SAY: We looked at *The Positive Birth Book* by Milli Hill – a larger than A5 perfect-bound paperback with 320 pages of information, photographs, and illustrations aimed at preparing parents and helping them communicate their wishes to healthcare providers. Inside the bright, glossy cover, the book is broken down into sections by common questions or themes, with many examples and first-hand accounts to illustrate.

PLATYPUS PRESS
E-BOOKS / NOVELS / SHORT STORY COLLECTIONS AND ANTHOLOGIES / NON-FICTION
enquiries@platypuspress.co.uk
www.platypuspress.co.uk

Editors: Michelle Tudor, Peter Barnfather

Established 2015. Mainly publishes poetry (see p63). Publications available direct from publisher website; at local literary events; and from Amazon and other bookshop websites.

GENRES: Literary.

SUBMISSIONS: Open to all. Submit by email to submissions@platypuspress.co.uk. Guidelines at www.platypuspress.co.uk/submit. Usually responds within four weeks. No feedback offered with rejections. Authors are paid royalties only and receive free copies of the book.

See also: poetry publishers p63 and *Wildness* (mixed-form magazine) p265

PLUTO PRESS

NON-FICTION / E-BOOKS
www.plutobooks.com
Editors: David Castle, David Shulman, Anne Beech

Active for over 40 years, and independent since 1979. One of the world's leading radical publishers, specialising in progressive, critical perspectives in politics and the social sciences. Known for working very closely with authors and open to proposals.

SUBMISSIONS: See the extensive submission information available at www.plutobooks.com/page/authors.

POOLBEG PRESS

NOVELS / CHILDREN'S / NON-FICTION
info@poolbeg.com
www.poolbeg.com
One of Ireland's most established presses (since 1976), and

particularly known for nurturing new women's writing. Emphasis is on fiction, with some non-fiction, and children's fiction for ages six to 12.

See also: Ward River Press p200

PROFILE BOOKS

NOVELS / NON-FICTION / SHORT STORY COLLECTIONS / E-BOOKS
info@profilebooks.com
www.profilebooks.com
Founded in 1996, Profile Books is one of the largest independent publishers in the UK that still accepts unsolicited submissions – though double check that a submissions window is open before sending your work. Its imprints include Serpent's Tail, Tuskar Rock and the Economist Books, and it has won Independent Press of the Year three times. Profile Books and its imprints publish a huge range of work from names you'll definitely recognise (Mary Beard, Susan Hill and Sarah Perry, amongst others).

PROLEBOOKS ☆

MIXED-FORM ANTHOLOGIES
01204497726
admin@prolebooks.co.uk
www.prolebooks.co.uk
Editors: Brett Evans, Phil Robertson

Established 2010. Mainly publishes poetry (see p65). Publications available direct from publisher website and by direct mail and email orders.

GENRES: Literary; engaging; accessible; challenging; entertaining.

SUBMISSIONS: Work for anthology publication is usually selected from competition entries. Authors are paid royalties only.

See also: poetry publisher p65 and *Prole* (mixed-form magazine) p249

PROTOTYPE
NOVELS, SHORT STORY
COLLECTIONS
71 Oriel Road, London E9 5SG
admin@prototypepublishing.co.uk
www. prototypepublishing.co.uk
Editor: Jess Chandler
Established 2019 as the rebranded
Test Centre. Publishes fiction,
poetry, interdisciplinary projects
and anthologies. Publications
available direct from publisher
website; via distributor NBN
International; from a selection of
independent and chain bookshops
nationwide; and at local literary
events and book fairs.
GENRES: Novels, short stories and
experimental prose.
SUBMISSIONS: Open year-round.
Submit by post (71 Oriel Road,
London E9 5SG) or by email
(admin@prototypepublishing.
co.uk). Guidelines at www.
prototypepublishing.co.uk/
submissions. Responses within
three months. Authors are paid in
royalties.
WE SAY: *Fatherhood* by Caleb
Klaces features a stark cover with
black text on a white background,
and an ink line drawing of what
could be a baby, but is open to
interpretation. We were looking
at a PDF proof of the book, but
the bright pink inners were still
startling and refreshing. The book
itself combines prose and poetry
– described on the back cover as
'verse fiction'; Prototype is not afraid
to publish experimental works.
**See also: poetry publishers p65 and
mixed-form magazine p249**

PS PUBLISHING
E-BOOKS / NOVELS / SHORT STORY
COLLECTIONS AND ANTHOLOGIES
/ NON-FICTION
Grosvenor House, 1 New Road,
Hornsea, East Yorkshire
01964 537575
nickycrowther@pspublishing.co.uk
www.pspublishing.co.uk
Editor: Nicky Crowther
Established 1991. Mainly publishes
fiction, but also some poetry
(see p66). Publications available
direct from publisher website;
from Amazon and other bookshop
websites; and at the British Science
Fiction Convention and British
Fantasy Convention.
PS Publishing won The Karl
Wagner Award at the British
Fantasy Awards 2012.
GENRES: Crime/thriller/mystery;
fantasy/sci-fi; horror; literary fiction;
biography and true stories.
SUBMISSIONS: Submissions
welcome by invitation only or
from agents, during submissions
windows. Submit by email to
nickycrowther@pspublishing.
co.uk. Usually responds within one
to three months. Rejections may
occasionally include unsolicited
feedback. Authors may be paid
a flat fee; royalties only; or an
advance/fee plus royalties; and/
or receive free copies of the book
(depending on agreement).
See also: poetry publishers p66

PUBLISHING PROJECT, THE
www.ueapublishingproject.com
publishing@uea.ac.uk
Based at the University of East
Anglia, The Publishing Project
encourages writers to get in touch
to discuss the best means, method
or form of publication for your
work. Along with its imprints Boiler
House Press (p24) and Strangers
Press (p187) they publish a wide
variety of fiction, poetry, life-
writing, journalism, audio/visual

173

work, literary translations and
formally experimental approaches
to all modes and forms of writing.
See also: poetry publishers p66

PUSHING OUT THE BOAT
MIXED-FORM ANTHOLOGIES WITH
VISUAL ART
info@pushingouttheboat.co.uk
www.pushingouttheboat.co.uk
Established 2000. Creative writing
(poetry, see p66, and prose with
visual art). Available direct from
the publisher website, by direct
mail and email, from chain and
independent bookshops, local
literary events, and local galleries/
coffee houses etc.
SUBMISSIONS: Submissions
are open to all, during
submissions windows only. To
submit follow the instructions
at www.pushingouttheboat.
co.uk/instructions, with
additional guidelines at www.
pushingouttheboat.co.uk/hints-
and-tips. Usually responds in four
to six months, with the selection
decision made available to writers
in their web-record on the online
submission system. Contributors
receive free copies of the book.
**See also: poetry publishers p66
and for more information, including
what We Say, *Pushing Out The Boat*
(mixed-form magazine) p251**

PUSHKIN PRESS
NOVELS / NON-FICTION
books@pushkinpress.com
www.pushkinpress.com
Managing director: Adam
Freudenhaim
Established 1997. One of the
larger indie presses, with a wide
range across fiction and non-
fiction, including novels, essays,
memoirs and children's book.

Styles range from timeless classic
to urgent contemporary. Includes
imprint One.

QUARTET BOOKS
FICTION / NON-FICTION
www.quartetbooks.co.uk
info@quartetbooks.co.uk
London-based press primarily
publishing fiction and non-fiction.
They are interested in literature
which poses an alternative to
mainstream works, but do not
accept unsolicited submissions.

QUILLER PUBLISHING
NON-FICTION
www.quillerpublishing.com
admin@quillerbooks.com
Publishes a variety of instructional
non-fiction books. Their product
lines include: food and drink,
humour, natural history, wildlife art,
mountain climbing and country
sport. They have also diversified
to publish biographies. Authors
should contact the press if they
would like to discuss projects.
**See also: Kenilworth Press (prose
publisher) p144**

RACK PRESS
NON-FICTION
The Rack, Kinnerton, Presteigne,
Powys LD8 2PF
07817 424560
rackpress@nicholasmurray.co.uk
www.rackpress.blogspot.com
Editor: Nicholas Murray
Established 2005. Primarily
publishes poetry (see p67).
Publications available direct from
publisher website; by post and
email order; from chain bookshops
and independent bookshops
nationwide; at national and local
literary events; and from bookshop
websites.

Rack Press won the 2014 Michael Marks Award for Publisher of the Year.

GENRES: Poetry criticism.

SUBMISSIONS: Open to all. Submit by post (The Rack, Kinnerton, Presteigne, Powys, Wales LD8 2PF) or by email (rackpress@ nicholasmurray.co.uk). Guidelines at www.nicholasmurray.co.uk/ About_Rack_Press.html. Please check the publisher's website to confirm whether submissions are currently being accepted. Usually responds within four weeks. Rejections may occasionally include unsolicited feedback. Authors receive free copies of the book, plus other copies at discount price for sale at readings etc.

For more information, see also: poetry publishers p67

RED HARE PUBLISHING

ART / NON-FICTION
www.redharepublishing.co.uk
info@redharepublishing.co.uk

North Norfolk based publisher dedicated to making 'beautiful books for book lovers'. They are especially interested in books about art and Norfolk but are also working on an eclectic mix of future titles.

RED PRESS

NON-FICTION / PHOTOGRAPHY / NOVELS / SHORT STORY ANTHOLOGIES / MIXED-FORM ANTHOLOGIES / E-BOOKS / AUDIOBOOKS
info@redpress.co.uk
www.redpress.co.uk
Editor: Katherine Knotts, FRSA

Established 2017. Publishes big ideas in social justice, in whichever form is appropriate, including non-fiction, some fiction and photography, as well as poetry and mixed prose/poetry anthologies (see p68). Publications available direct from the publisher website; from chain and independent bookshops; and from Amazon and other bookshop websites. Red Press was recognised as one of the Top 100 Changemakers in the UK by the *Big Issue*.

GENRES: Social commentary; political commentary; narrative non-fiction, photography, mixed memoir.

SUBMISSIONS: Open to all. Submit by email to submissions@redpress. co.uk. Usually responds within four weeks. Rejections may occasionally include unsolicited feedback. Author deals vary, and may include a flat rate for the author, an advance plus royalties, free copies of the book, crowdfunding, or the author contributing to editorial/ publication/marketing costs.

WE SAY: One look at Red Press' website is enough to recognise the bold personality of this publisher, which describes itself as a social purpose organisation. We looked at an e-book of *The Anatomy of Silence* edited by Cyra Perry Dougherty, a collection of essays on the silence around sexual violence. From this painful topic comes a raging voice that echoes the publisher's ambition for raising discussion around social issues and using words to instigate change.

See also: poetry publishers p68

RED SQUIRREL PRESS

E-BOOKS / NOVELS / SHORT STORY COLLECTIONS / NON-FICTION
Briery Hill Cottage, Stannington, Morpeth NE61 6ES
info@redsquirrelpress.com
www.redsquirrelpress.com

RETREAT WEST BOOKS ☆

NOVELS, SHORT STORY
COLLECTIONS AND ANTHOLOGIES,
MEMOIRS
news@retreatwest.co.uk
www.retreatwestbooks.com
Editors: Amanda Saint, Sophie Duffy
and Rose McGinty

Established 2017. Primarily
publishes fiction and memoir.
Publications available in major
chain and independent bookshops
nationwide; at national and local
literary events; from Amazon and
other bookshop websites; and
directly through the Retreat West
Books website. Retreat West Books
was shortlisted for Most Innovative
Publisher in the 2019 Saboteur
Awards.
GENRES: Literary fiction; women's
fiction; climate fiction, short stories,
memoir.
SUBMISSIONS: Open to all
worldwide writing in English,
during submissions windows
only. Submit via Submittable
only. Guidelines at www.
retreatwestbooks.com/submissions.
Usually responds in one to three
months. Feedback can be given
on submissions for a fee. Authors
are paid royalties and receive free
copies of their book.
WE SAY: We considered PDFs
of several Retreat West titles,
including anthology *The Word for
Freedom* edited by Amanda Saint
and Rose McGinty, *Soul Etchings*
by Sandra Arnold, and *This is (Not
About) David Bowie* by F J Morris.
Between them, they cover

THEY SAY

Retreat West Books is
a publisher with an
environmental and social
conscience, publishing
beautiful books, discovering
new authors, and raising
funds for good causes. All
titles are print on demand
to make the best use of the
world's finite resources.
Each year, alongside
commissioned titles, it
publishes a charity anthology
featuring emerging and
established authors to
support environmental
and social projects. As well
as traditional prose novels
and short stories Retreat
West Books also publishes
innovative, experimental
work and is particularly
interested in novellas-in-
flash and memoirs-in-flash.

various themes – from the
women's suffrage movement,
to delving into what it means
to be human. The formatting
is clean and professional, and
of note are the cover designs
– they are bold and arresting,
never cluttered and all intriguing
– you'd pick them up from
a crowded shelf. Each has a
neat header banner instantly
marking them as Retreat West
publications.

Editors: Sheila Wakefield
Established 2006. Mainly publishes poetry (see p68). Publications available direct from publisher website; by post and email order; from chain bookshops nationwide; from independent bookshops; at national and local literary events; and from Amazon and other bookshop websites; and from Inpress.com.

Red Squirrel was shortlisted for the Callum Macdonald Memorial Award 2015.

GENRES: Crime/thriller/mystery; wildlife (non-fiction).

SUBMISSIONS: Open to all. Submit by post to Briery Hill Cottage, Stannington, Morpeth NE61 6ES. Guidelines at www. redsquirrelpress.com/submissions. Usually responds in over six months. No feedback offered with rejections. Authors receive free copies of the book.

For more information, see also: poetry publishers p68

ROUTE PUBLISHING LTD

MUSIC / MEMOIR / NOVELS / BIOGRAPHY
01977 793442
info@route-online.com
www.route-online.com
Editor: Ian Daley
Established 2000. Primarily publishes non-fiction above other prose and poetry (see p69). Publications available direct from publisher website; by post and email order; from chain bookshops nationwide; from independent bookshops; at national and local literary events; and from Amazon and other bookshop websites.

Route has been shortlisted for the Pen/Ackerley Prize (2008); the James Tait Black Memorial Prize for Fiction (2011); *NME* Book of the Year (2015); Penderyn Prize (Music Book of the Year) (2015); and Rolling Stone Book of the Year (2018).

GENRES: Literary fiction; biography and true stories; music, stage and screen; and sports and leisure.

SUBMISSIONS: Guidelines at www.route-online.com/ submissions. Usually responds within four to six months, with feedback only if an SAE is provided. No feedback offered with rejections. Authors are paid a flat fee, or royalties only, or an advance/fee plus royalties.

WE SAY: *Rites* by Sophie Coulombeau is a contemporary thriller, looking at the false memories of childhood. A well-written and professionally presented 192-page publication that we saw in hardback. The dust-jacketed cover design is simple and effective, the title made up of embroidered letters, with threads stretched taut across the page. High-quality materials.

See also: poetry publishers p69

ROWMAN & LITTLEFIELD PUBLISHING LTD

NON-FICTION
www.rowmaninternational.com
cservs.uk@rowman.com
Founded in 2012, Rowman & Littlefield International is an independent, interdisciplinary publisher in the Humanities and Social Sciences, publishing for a scholarly audience. It was winner of the Nick Robinson Newcomer Award, Independent Publishers Guild Awards 2015 and shortlisted for Academic, Educational and Professional Publisher of the Year at the British Book Awards 2019.

Open to series and standalone book proposals.

RUBY FICTION
NOVELS / E-BOOKS
Penrose House, Crawley Drive,
Camberley, Surrey GU15 2AB
01276 274920
info@rubyfiction.com
www.rubyfiction.com
Established 2018. Ruby Fiction is an imprint of Choc Lit (see p108). Publishes fiction. Publications available from chain and independent bookshops; and from Amazon and other bookshop websites.
Parent publisher Choc Lit has been the recipient of several awards.
GENRES: Thriller/crime; romance; women's fiction; historical; saga.
SUBMISSIONS: Open to all. Submit by via the website at www.choclitpublishing.com/html/submissions (guidelines at the same address). Responds within one to three months. No feedback included with rejections. Authors royalties.
See also: Choc Lit (prose publisher) p108

RUFUS STONE LIMITED EDITIONS
NON-FICTION
mark@rufuspublications.com
www.rufuspublications.com
Editor: Mark Smith
Established 2011. Publications available direct from publisher website.
GENRES: Art, fashion and photography; music, stage and screen.
SUBMISSIONS: Open to all. Submit by email to mark@rufuspublications.com. Usually responds within four weeks.

Rejections may occasionally include unsolicited feedback. Authors are paid an advance/fee plus royalties.

SACRISTY PRESS
E-BOOKS / NOVELS / NON-FICTION
PO Box 612, Durham DH1 9HT
01913 038313
enquiries@sacristy.co.uk
www.sacristy.co.uk
Editor: Natalie Watson
Established 2011. Also publishes poetry (see p69). Publications available direct from publisher website; from independent bookshops; and from Amazon and other bookshop websites.
GENRES: History; theology; historical fiction.
SUBMISSIONS: Open to all. Guidelines at www.sacristy.co.uk/info/authors. Usually responds within one to three months. Rejections may occasionally include unsolicited feedback. Authors contribute to editorial/publication/marketing costs and are paid royalties only.
WE SAY: We looked at digital editions of novel *The Summer of '39* by David Lowther and non-fiction book *The Evil That Men Do: Faith, Injustice and the Church*, by Marcus K Paul, a defence of the Church's history and ideas. Both are cleanly designed. The contents of *Evil* are easy to follow, and the book ends with clear notes. The cover is standard non-fiction – banded top and bottom, with an illustration framed in the middle. *'39* has a more creative design, using both script and 'typewrite' fonts for chapter titles. The cover features a block colour sketch of Berlin under Nazi Germany.
See also: poetry publishers p69

SALÒ PRESS

NOVELS / SHORT STORY
COLLECTIONS AND ANTHOLOGIES
editorsalopress@gmail.com
www.salopress.weebly.com
Editor: Sophie Essex
Established 2015. Primarily
publishes poetry (see p71) but also
some prose. Publications available
direct from the publisher website.
GENRES: Experimental; literary.
SUBMISSIONS: Open to all.
Submit by post (85 Gertrude
Road, Norwich NR3 4SG) or by
email (editorsalopress@gmail.
com). Guidelines at www.salopress.
weebly.com. Usually responds in
one to three months. No feedback
offered with rejection. Authors and
contributors are paid royalties.
**For more information, including
what We Say, see also: poetry
publishers p71 and *Fur-lined Ghettos*
(mixed-form magazine) p229**

SALT PUBLISHING LTD

E-BOOKS / NOVELS / SHORT STORY
COLLECTIONS AND ANTHOLOGIES
12 Norwich Rd, Cromer NR27 0AX
01263 511011
jen@saltpublishing.com
www.saltpublishing.com
Editors: Jen Hamilton-Emery,
Nicholas Royle
Established 1999. Publishes fiction
and poetry (see p71). Publications
available direct from publisher
website; by post and email order;
from chain bookshops nationwide;
from independent bookshops; at
national and local literary events;
and from Amazon and other
bookshop websites.
Salt title *The Redemption of Galen
Pike* by Carys Davies won the
International Frank O'Connor Short
Story Prize.
GENRES: Literary fiction.

SUBMISSIONS: Agent submissions
only. Guidelines at www.
saltpublishing.com/pages/
submissions. Usually responds
within four to six months. Authors
are paid royalties only, or an
advance/fee plus royalties, and
receive free copies of the book.
WE SAY: A major player in the
indie publishing world, Salt's
perfect-bound paperbacks are of
an exceedingly high quality: cool
crisp cover designs, big-name
blurb quotes and beautifully edited
stories on cream paper. The sleek
website, stellar reputation and
faultless social media presence
(160,000 Twitter followers) put Salt
in the same league as the heavy
hitters of the industry.
See also: poetry publishers p71

SANDSTONE PRESS

FICTION / NON-FICTION / E-BOOKS
Willow House, Stoneyfield Business
Park, Inverness IV2 7PA
info@sandstonepress.com
www.sandstonepress.com
Publishing Director: Moira Forsyth
Established 2002. Publishes
around 50% fiction and 50%
non-fiction. Available direct from
publisher website; from chain and
independent bookshops; at literary
events; and from Amazon and
other bookshop websites.
Sandstone authors have won the
Man Booker International Prize, the
Betty Trask Prize and many others.
GENRES: Literary; speculative;
biography; outdoor.
SUBMISSIONS: Non-fiction open
to all. Fiction submissions currently
accepted only from agents, please
see website for details of open
submission windows. Guidelines at
www.sandstonepress.com/contact/
submissions. Usually responds

within six weeks. Rejected authors may be offered feedback. Authors receive an advance and royalties.
WE SAY: We saw a digital proof of Addison Jones' *Wait for Me, Jack*. With a simple and clean design, the 342-page novel centres around moments in the lives of a long-married husband and wife, reflected in the photo of a swimming couple in old-fashioned garb on the cover.

SAPERE BOOKS

NOVELS / NON-FICTION / E-BOOKS
11 Bank Chambers, 120 High Street, London N8 7NN
07845 685650
caoimhe@saperebooks.com
saperebooks.com
Editor: Amy Durant
Established 2017. Publications available from Amazon (POD).
GENRES: Crime fiction, thrillers and mysteries; historical fiction (general, thrillers, crime and romance); commercial women's fiction and romance; action and adventure (military, naval and aviation fiction); history and historical biography.
SUBMISSIONS: Open to all. Guidelines at www.saperebooks.com/about/submissions. Usually responds within six months. Rejections may occasionally include unsolicited feedback. Authors are paid royalties and receive free copies of their book.
WE SAY: Though they publish a range of genres, we considered a PDF of Sapere Books' historical title *The Catherine Howard Conspiracy* by Alexandra Walsh. As the first book in the Marquess House trilogy, this title crosses the borders between history and thriller through an enticing exploration into the Tudor timeline. With the enthralling framing of these historical events, it's almost easy to forget that they really happened.

SAQI BOOKS

E-BOOKS / NOVELS / SHORT STORY COLLECTIONS AND ANTHOLOGIES / NON-FICTION
26 Westbourne Grove, London W2 5RH
020 7221 9347
elizabeth@saqibooks.com
www.saqibooks.com
Publisher and Managing Director: Lynn Gaspard
Editor: Elizabeth Briggs
Established 1983. Mixed form: also publishes mixed poetry/prose anthologies and collections (see p72), and widely publishes work from and about the Middle East and North Africa. Publications available from chain bookshops nationwide; from independent bookshops; at national and local literary events; and from Amazon and other bookshop websites. Saqi Books won the IPG Diversity Award in 2013, the Arab British Culture and Society Award in 2008 and the British Book Industry Award for Diversity in Literature in 2009.
GENRES: Literary; gender studies; literature in translation; non-fiction; history.
SUBMISSIONS: Open to all. Guidelines at www.saqibooks.com/contact/submissions. Usually responds within one to three months. Rejections may occasionally include unsolicited feedback. Authors are paid an advance/fee plus royalties.
See also: poetry publishers p72

SARABAND

NON-FICTION / NOVELS / E-BOOKS
Digital World Centre, 1 Lowry Plaza,
The Quays, Salford M50 3UB
hermes@saraband.net
www.saraband.net
Editor: Sara Hunt
Established 1994. Available
from chain and independent
bookshops; at literary events;
from Amazon and other bookshop
websites.

Saraband has won and been
shortlisted for several awards,
including Man Booker Prize 2016
(shortlist); IPG Independent
Publisher of the Year 2016
(shortlist); Saltire Society Literary
Awards 2016 (winner Best Fiction
Book and Best First Book, and
shortlisted Best History Book. Also
in shortlisted the Research Book
category in 2014); winner of the
Striding Edge Award (Lakeland
Awards) 2016; and winner of the
Saltire Society Publisher of the Year
2013 (shortlisted 2015 and 2016).
GENRES: Literary fiction; crime
fiction; nature writing; memoir.
SUBMISSIONS: Open to all. Submit
by email to hermes@saraband.net.
Guidelines at www.saraband.net/
about-us. Due to high numbers,
Saraband is unable to respond to
most submissions. Authors are paid
an advance, plus royalties.
WE SAY: We looked at the digital
version of Chitra Ramaswamy's
memoir *Expecting: the inner life
of pregnancy*, which features a
striking red cover with a drawing
of two hands resting over a
pear-shape, signifying a pregnant
woman's body. Well laid out, the
book aims to be an account of
pregnancy that goes 'above and
beyond a manual', and begins
with a dedication and quotes from

Sylvia Plath, Margaret Atwood and
James Joyce, as well as praise for
the book.

SCOTLAND STREET PRESS

NOVELS / NON-FICTION
www.scotlandstreetpress.com
scotlandstreetpress@gmail.com
Publishing a range of prose
work including non-fiction,
memoir, YA, children's as well as
poetry in the form of collections
and verse novels (see p72), this
Edinburgh-based press seeks to
promote Scotland as a distinctive
creative voice in the world, and
redress the balance of women's
voices in Scottish literature. The
press was a regional finalist for
Small Press of the Year, British Book
Awards 2019.
See also: poetry publishers p72

SCRIBE

NOVELS / NON-FICTION /
E-BOOKS
www.scribepublications.co.uk
Operating for nearly 40 years, and
now spanning the globe, Scribe
publishes 'books that matter',
including narrative and literary
non-fiction, and local, international,
and translated fiction. Check
www.scribepublications.co.uk/
about-us/manuscript-policy for
open submissions windows.

SEA LION PRESS

E-BOOKS / NOVELS / SHORT STORY
COLLECTIONS AND ANTHOLOGIES
/ NON-FICTION
tom@sealionpress.co.uk
www.sealionpress.co.uk
Editor: Tom Black
Established 2015. Primarily
publishes fiction, but also some
non-fiction. Publications available
direct from the publisher website,

and from Amazon and other online bookshops.

GENRES: Alternate history; sci-fi.

SUBMISSIONS: Open to all. Submit by email to tom@sealionpress. co.uk. Guidelines at www. sealionpress.co.uk/faq-1. Usually responds within four weeks. Rejections may occasionally include unsolicited feedback. Authors are paid royalties only.

WE SAY: We considered PDFs of *The Boy in the Storm* by Nick Peel and *Fight and Be Right* by Ed Thomas. As publishers of alternative history, this press delves into extreme visions of alternative pasts, reflected in *Fight and Be Right* which implements the genre-specific form of mimicking a history textbook. *The Boy in the Storm*, whilst portraying a more conventional narrative, uses a typewriter-style font to uphold the historical feel present in all of Sea Lion Press' titles.

SEREN BOOKS
NON-FICTION / NOVELS / SHORT STORY COLLECTIONS AND ANTHOLOGIES / E-BOOKS
57 Nolton Street, Bridgend, Wales CF31 3AE
01656 663018
seren@serenbooks.com
www.serenbooks.com
Established 1963. Mixed form: also publishes poetry (see p72). Publications available direct from publisher website; by post and email order; from chain bookshops nationwide; from independent bookshops; at national and local literary events; and from Amazon.

GENRES: Drama and criticism; literary fiction; poetry; art, fashion and photography; biography and true stories; history; travel; books about Wales.

SUBMISSIONS: Non-fiction is open to all; fiction currently open only to authors previously published by Seren (check the website for updates). Submit by post to 57 Nolton Street, Bridgend CF31 3AE. Guidelines at www.serenbooks. com/seren/submissions-policy. Usually responds within one to three months. Rejections may occasionally include unsolicited feedback. Authors are paid an advance/fee plus royalties and receive free copies of the book, as well as other copies at a discount price.

For more information, see also: poetry publishers p72 and *Poetry Wales* (poetry magazine) p281

SHADOW BOOTH, THE
E-BOOKS / SHORT STORY ANTHOLOGIES
dan@theshadowbooth.com
www.theshadowbooth.com
Editor: Dan Coxon
Established 2017. Publishes short fiction in a book-length literary magazine (see also p296). Available direct from the publisher website; by post and email order; at national and local literary events; and from Amazon.

GENRES: Horror; ghost stories; weird fiction; literary.

SUBMISSIONS: During submissions windows only, submit by email to submissions@theshadowbooth. com. Guidelines at www. theshadowbooth.com/submit. Usually responds in one to three months. No feedback offered with rejections. Contributors are paid a flat fee and receive free copies of the issue.

WE SAY: The Shadow Booth publishes eerie and strange fiction in their journal, *Tales from the*

Shadow Booth. We looked at a PDF proof of Volume 2, edited by Dan Coxon, which presents a cover that creates a sinister tone using gory images. This is continued in the tall, bold typeface used throughout the volume, which features a selection of thirteen short stories. Shadow Booth's website reflects this eerie tone, with a dark colour scheme that allows the publisher to fully embody their love of weird and creepy fiction.

See also: *The Shadow Booth* (prose magazine) p296

SHARPE BOOKS ☆

NOVELS / NON-FICTION / E-BOOKS
admin@sharpebooks.com
www.sharpebooks.com
Editor: Richard Foreman
Established 2018. Primarily publishes fiction. Publications available from Amazon.
GENRES: Historical fiction; crime fiction; thrillers; military history; history.
SUBMISSIONS: Open to all. Submit by email to richard@sharpebooks. com. Guidelines at www. sharpebooks.com/submissions. Usually responds within four weeks. Authors are paid royalties only.
WE SAY: On their elegant and appealing website, Sharpe Books provide extensive information on their published works in a professional manner. We viewed a PDF sample of *The Queen's Mary* by Sarah Gristwood, a 200-page historical novel about Mary Queen of Scots. The cover uses a bold photographic image, aligning closely with the other covers they have published.

SHOESTRING PRESS

NOVELS / SHORT STORY COLLECTIONS / NON-FICTION
19 Devonshire Avenue, Beeston, Nottingham NG9 1BS
info@shoestring-press.com
www.shoestring-press.com
Editor: John Lucas
Mainly publishes poetry (see p74), but also some prose. Publications available direct from publisher website; by post and email order; from independent bookshops; at national and local literary events; and from Amazon.
Shoestring titles have been shortlisted for Vondel Prize for Translation and for the Cricket Club Writers' Book of the Year.
GENRES: Historical fiction; literary fiction; biography and true stories.
SUBMISSIONS: Submit by invitation only.
For more information, see also: poetry publishers p74

SILKWORMS INK

E-BOOKS / FICTION / SCRIPT / CHAPBOOKS
www.silkwormsink.com
Established in 2010, Silkworms Ink is 'a digital publisher of eclectica, a purveyor of literary mixtapes, and a weekly-themed quasi-magazine'. They are interested in fiction, non-fiction, poetry, plays and music.
See also: poetry publishers p74 and mixed-form magazines p255

SNOWBOOKS LTD

NOVELS / SHORT STORY ANTHOLOGIES / E-BOOKS
info@snowbooks.com
www.snowbooks.com
Established 2003. Mainly publishes genre fiction. Publications available direct from publisher website; by post and email order; from

chain bookshops nationwide; from independent bookshops; at national and local literary events; and from Amazon and other bookshop websites.

Snowbooks won Futurebook Best Innovation of the Year 2013.

GENRES: Fantasy/sci-fi; horror.

SUBMISSIONS: Open to all. Submit using the online submissions form at snowbooksltd.submittable.com/submit. Guidelines at snowbooks.com/pages/submissions. Requires a small fee of £2, with 50% of each fee going to Save the Children. Usually responds within four to six months or more. No feedback offered with rejections. Authors are paid royalties only, and receive free copies of the book.

SOARING PENGUIN PRESS

E-BOOKS / GRAPHIC NOVELS AND COMICS

Flat 2, 42 Highcroft Villas, Brighton, East Sussex BN1 5PS

07986 995938

submissions@soaringpenguinpress.com

www.soaringpenguinpress.com

Publishers: John Anderson, Tim Pilcher

Established 2012. Publishes graphic novels, both fiction and non-fiction.

Publications available direct from publisher website; by post and email order; from selected/local chain bookshops; from independent bookshops; national literary events; and from Amazon and other bookshop websites. Publications distributed by Turnaround Distribution (UK/Europe) and SCB Distributors (USA/Canada); digital editions available from Comixology and Sequential.

Title *To End All Wars* was nominated for two Eisner Awards: Best Anthology and Best Non-fiction Title. Title *The Black Feather Falls* was nominated for Ignatz for Outstanding Series.

GENRES: Fantasy/sci-fi; graphic/comics; horror; indie fiction.

SUBMISSIONS: Accepts graphic narrative work only, i.e. comics. Submissions open to all, and the press is actively seeking alternative voices. Submit by post (Flat 2, 42 Highcroft Villas, Brighton, East Sussex BN1 5PS) or by email (submissions@soaringpenguinpress.com). Guidelines at www.soaringpenguinpress.com/submissions. Usually responds within four to six months or more. Rejections may occasionally include unsolicited feedback. Authors are paid royalties only, and receive free copies of the books and a discount purchase price on future copies.

WE SAY: We looked at Soaring Penguin's catalogue, which gave us a great overview of the work it produces, particularly the graphic novels. High quality drawing in a range of styles, which bold, striking covers and judicious use of colour in the comics in the inner pages. The work featured includes LGBT YA fiction, politics, time travel and translated work (*Boulet's Notes* is almost meta, chronicling the artist pulling together his first comics collection), all under the umbrella of graphic books. We were captivated and wanted to read more.

See also: *Meanwhile...* (comic anthology magazine) p240

SOLARIS

NOVELS / SHORT STORY COLLECTIONS AND ANTHOLOGIES / NON-FICTION / E-BOOKS

Riverside House, Osney Mead
01865 792201
www.solarisbooks.com
Editors: Michael Rowley and David Thomas Moore
Established 2007. Publications available direct from the publisher website; from chain and independent bookshops; and on Amazon and other bookshops websites.
GENRES: Science fiction; fantasy; horror.
SUBMISSIONS: Submissions from agents only. For unagented submissions see Abaddon Books (p92). Usually responds in one to three months. Rejections may occasionally include unsolicited feedback. Authors are paid an advance fee and royalties, and receive free copies of their book.
WE SAY: As imprints of international games development company and publisher Rebellion, Solaris and Abaddon Books house a vast collection of science-fiction, fantasy and horror, and have been publishing for over ten years. Their website is easy to navigate and clearly presents the titles published by each of these imprints as well as their parent publisher. Overall, they pride themselves on stepping away from airy-fairy fantasy and into clear-cut and captivating writing.
See also: Abaddon Books (prose publisher) p92

SOUTHWORD EDITIONS ☆
CHAPBOOKS
Munster Literature Centre, Frank O'Connor House, 84 Douglas Street, Cork, Ireland
+353 21 431 2955
munsterlit@eircom.net
www.munsterlit.ie
Editor: Patrick Cotter
Established 2001. Publishes poetry (p77) and fiction chapbooks. Publications available direct from publisher website; by post and email order; at national and local literary events; and from Amazon.
SUBMISSIONS: Open to all, during submissions windows – chapbook publication comes as part of the short fiction chapbook competition. Guidelines at www.munsterlit.ie/Fiction%20 Chapbook%20Competition.html. Usually responds within one to three months. No feedback offered with rejections. Authors are paid a flat fee and receive free copies of the book.
See also: poetry publishers p77 and *Southword Journal* **(mixed-form magazine) p258**

SPECULATIVE BOOKS
NOVELLAS / SHORT STORY COLLECTIONS AND ANTHOLOGIES
www.speculativebooks.net
mail@speculativebooks.net
Offer a subscription service to readers – subscribers receive a new book every month. Glasgow-based publisher offering poetry (see p77), fiction, and mixed poetry/prose collections, as well as an annual anthology.
See also: poetry publishers p77

SPLICE
NOVELS / SHORT COLLECTIONS AND ANTHOLOGIES / NON-FICTION / PICTURE BOOKS / E-BOOKS
48 Milner Road, Birmingham B29 7RQ
07783 909469
thisissplice@gmail.com
www.thisissplice.co.uk
Editor: Daniel Davis Wood
Established 2017. Publishes a

range of fiction and non-fiction. Available direct from the publisher website; from independent bookshops; at local literary events; and from Amazon and other bookshop websites. Offers a subscription of £34.99 for three single-author short story collections and one anthology featuring new work by the three authors, plus three more authors of the original authors' choice. Splice was nominated for the 2019 Republic of Consciousness Prize for Small Presses.

GENRES: Literary; experimental.
SUBMISSIONS: Open to all. Submit by email to thisissplice@ gmail.com. Guidelines at www. thisissplice.co.uk/submissions. Usually responds within four weeks. Rejections may occasionally include unsolicited feedback. Authors are paid a flat purchase fee.

WE SAY: This publisher has clearly established their production style despite their fairly recent foundation. We looked at PDFs of short story collections *Our Dreams Might Align* by Dana Diehl and *Flare and Falter* by Michael Conley, as well as the novel *Hang Him When He is Not There* by Nicholas John Turner. These all convey themes of otherworldly activity and experiences of the human psyche, with animals featuring consistently in their vibrant and colourful cover designs.

See also: *Splice* **(mixed-form e-zine) p298**

STAIRWELL BOOKS

NOVELS / SHORT STORY COLLECTIONS AND ANTHOLOGIES / NON-FICTION / AUDIOBOOKS
161 Lowther Street, York YO31 7LZ
01904 733767
rose@stairwellbooks.com
www.stairwellbooks.co.uk
Editors: Rose Drew, Alan Gillott, and assorted guest editors

Established 2005. Publishes prose and poetry (see p77), including poetry-and-prose anthologies – with a slight preference towards novels. Publications available direct from the publisher website; by direct mail and email order; at local and national literary events; and from bookshop websites including Gardners and Neilson.

Stairwell authors have won Saboteur Awards including performance poet, 2015, and publication *Pressed by Unseen Feet* was shortlisted for 2012 Saboteur Award: Best Anthology. Tim Ellis' poetry collection *Gringo on the Chicken Bus* placed number 11 in the Purple Patch Top 20 collections of 2011.

GENRES: Literary fiction; genre fiction including sci-fi, speculative fiction and fantasy; memoirs; children's literature.

SUBMISSIONS: Send synopsis and 30 pages (prose) or ten poems to rose@stairwellbooks. com. Full guidelines at www. stairwellbooks.co.uk. The press publishes 15-20 books per year, but receives hundreds of submissions. It helps if they are familiar with your work, so they suggest also submitting work to *Dream Catcher Magazine* (see p225). 'If you purchase a book, that can create a virtuous circle. Some day someone might purchase yours.' Responds to submissions within one to three months. Rejections include feedback, often with detailed criticism and a few pages edited. Authors are paid

186

royalties and receive free copies of their book.

WE SAY: From Stairwell Books' wide collection of titles, we looked at *Abernathy* by Claire Patel-Campbell. This book's eerie monochromatic cover, displaying a body in the winter snow, marks the start of this dark and twisting plot through a small town with big secrets. *Abernathy*'s vintage-style cover reflects the look of various other Stairwell titles, many with a filmic approach, illustrating a scene from the book.

See also: poetry publishers p77 and *Dream Catcher* (mixed-form magazine) p225

STINGING FLY PRESS, THE ☆
SHORT STORY ANTHOLOGIES AND COLLECTIONS
PO Box 6016, Dublin 1, Ireland
stingingfly@gmail.com
www.stingingfly.org
Editors: Thomas Morris, Declan Meade
Established 1997. Mainly fiction. Publications available direct from publisher website; from selected/local chain bookshops; from independent bookshops; and at national and local literary events. Stinging Fly title *Young Skins* by Colin Barrett won the 2014 *Guardian* First Book Award and the 2014 Frank O'Connor Short Story Award.
GENRES: Irish literary fiction.
SUBMISSIONS: By invitation.
For more information, see also *The Stinging Fly* (mixed-form literary magazine) p260

STONEWOOD PRESS
SHORT STORY COLLECTIONS
Diversity House, 72 Nottingham Road, Arnold, Nottingham NG5 6LF
0845 456 4838
stonewoodpress@gmail.com
www.stonewoodpress.co.uk
Editor: Martin Parker
Established 2011. Also publishes poetry (see p78). Publications available direct from publisher website; from chain bookshops and independent bookshops nationwide; and from Amazon and other bookshop websites.
GENRES: Literary fiction; fantasy/sci-fi.
SUBMISSIONS: See guidelines at www.stonewoodpress.co.uk/about/submissions. Usually responds within four months. Rejections may occasionally include unsolicited feedback. Authors are paid royalties only and receive free copies of the book.
WE SAY: We looked at a digital version of Krishan Coupland's *When You Lived Inside the Walls*, a 41-page book which contains three short stories. The design is well thought out and executed nicely: each chapter starts with a big, illustrated letter, matching the story themes. The inside cover is illustrated with rat traps, the topic of the first story. The type is a relatively big serif style. Different chapters within the story are divided by stars.
See also: poetry publishers p78

STORGY ☆
E-BOOKS / SHORT STORY ANTHOLOGIES
www.storgy.com
Editors: Tomek Dzido, Anthony Self, Ross Jeffery
Established 2013. Anthologies printed as part of the e-zine and competitions.
GENRES: Literary fiction.
SUBMISSIONS: Open to all. Submit by email to submit@storgy.com.

Guidelines on website. Usually responds within one to three months. No feedback offered with rejections. Authors receive free copies of the book. No fee or royalties paid.

WE SAY: We looked at Storgy's anthology *Exit Earth*, which includes short fiction from the 14 winners of its Exit Earth Short Story competition, as well as an additional ten stories from writers including Courttia Newland, Toby Litt, M R Carey and more. It's also bursting with artwork. The over artwork is quite 80s sci-fi, with a neonlight-esque font for the title, and hints at foreboding tales, though the blurb tells us there are utopian as well as dystopian tales within.

See also: *Storgy Magazine* (prose magazine) p298

STRANGE ATTRACTOR PRESS

NON-FICTION / NOVELS / SHORT STORY COLLECTIONS AND ANTHOLOGIES / E-BOOKS
contactee@strangeattractor.co.uk
www.strangeattractor.co.uk
Editors: Mark Pilkington, Jamie Sutcliffe

Established 2004. Primarily publishes non-fiction. Publications available direct from publisher website; from chain bookshops nationwide; at national and local literary events; and from Amazon and other bookshop websites.

GENRES: Fantasy/sci-fi; horror; art and photography; history; popular science and nature; science, technology and medicine; and spirituality and beliefs.

SUBMISSIONS: Open to all. Submit by post (BM SAP, London WC1N 3XX) or by email (proposals@ strangeattractor.co.uk). Usually

responds in up to six months. Rejections may occasionally include unsolicited feedback. Authors are paid royalties only and receive free copies of their book.

STRANGERS PRESS

FICTION / NON-FICTION
www.strangers.press
publishing@uea.ac.uk
Based at the University of East Anglia, Strangers Press is focused on publishing literary translations and international writing in innovative or creative ways. They are particularly interested in the idea of translation as a form of cultural exchange and 'seek to publish in a way that celebrates that'.

STRUCTO PRESS

STORY COLLECTIONS AND NOVELS
editor@structomagazine.co.uk
www.structopress.co.uk
Editor: Euan Monaghan
Established 2015. First book published 2019. Mixed form: also publishes poetry chapbooks (see p79). Publications available direct from publisher website; from bookshops; and from bookshop websites.

GENRES: Literary fiction; literature-in-translation; slipstream; short stories.

SUBMISSIONS: Open to all via email enquiry.

For more information see also: *Structo* (mixed-form magazine) p261 and poetry publishers p79

SWAN RIVER PRESS

NOVELS / SHORT STORY COLLECTIONS AND ANTHOLOGIES
swanriverpress.ie
Editor: Brian J Showers
Established 2003. Publications

188

available direct from publisher website; by post and email order; from independent bookshops; at national and local literary events; and from independent online retailers.

Swan River Press title *Dreams of Shadow and Smoke: Stories for J.S. Le Fanu* won the Ghost Story Award for best book.

GENRES: Supernatural; ghost stories; horror; literary fiction; literary criticism.

SUBMISSIONS: By invitation only. See guidelines at swanriverpress. ie. Usually responds within four weeks. Rejections may occasionally include unsolicited feedback. Authors are paid a flat fee.

See also: *The Green Book* (prose magazine) p294

SWEET CHERRY PUBLISHING

NOVELS / PICTURE BOOKS / E-BOOKS
Unit 36, Vulcan House, Vulcan Road, Leicester LE5 3EF
01162 536796
info@sweetcherrypublishing.com
www.sweetcherrypublishing.com
Editors: Cecilia Bennett, Kellie Jones, Jasmine Allen

Established 2011. Publishes children's books. Publications available direct from the publisher website; at chain and independent bookshops; and from Amazon and other bookshop websites.

In 2017 Sweet Cherry publication *Apley Towers: The Lost Kodas* by Myra King was a finalist in The People's Book Prize.

GENRES: Children's series; teen and YA; picture books.

SUBMISSIONS: Open to all. Submit by email to submissions@ sweetcherrypublishing. com. Guidelines at www.

sweetcherrypublishing.com/ submissions. Usually responds in up to six months. Authors are paid a flat fee or an advance and royalties, and receive free copies of the book.

SYLPH EDITIONS

NOVELS / SHORT STORY COLLECTIONS / NON-FICTION
info@sylpheditions.com
www.sylpheditions.com

Established 2006. Primarily publishes fiction. Publications available direct from publisher website and from independent bookshops.

GENRES: Literary fiction; art, design, photography and culture.

SUBMISSIONS: Open to all. Submit by email to info@sylpheditions. com. Usually responds within four weeks. Authors receive free copies of the book. No fee or royalties paid.

WE SAY: We looked at the Cahiers series, a staple-spine, folded paper series of essay pamphlets. Around 40 pages long, with dust jackets over the thick textured paper covers. The essays are thoughtful and accessible, and illustrated with full-colour images.

TANGENT BOOKS

NOVELS / NON-FICTION / SHORT STORY ANTHOLOGIES
richard@tangentbooks.co.uk
www.tangentbooks.co.uk

Founded in 2004, Tangent's mission statement is 'to publish interesting stuff' and provide 'quality books for the discerning punter' – their range is extensive. Resolutely independent and supportive of local businesses.

TANGERINE PRESS
NOVELS / SHORT STORY
ANTHOLOGIES / NON-FICTION
Unit 18 Riverside Rd, Garratt Business
Park, London SW17 0BA
info@thetangerinepress.com
www.thetangerinepress.com
Editor: Michael Curran

Established 2006. Mainly publishes
fiction, but also some poetry (see
p80). Publications available direct
from publisher website; by post
and email order; from major chain
and independent bookshops; and
at local literary events.
Tangerine Press was longlisted
for *3AM Magazine*'s Publisher of
the Year (2010) and the inaugural
Republic of Consciousness Award
2016. Author Chris Wilson (*The
Glue Ponys*) was longlisted for the
Edgehill Short Story Prize 2017.
GENRES: Autobiographical fiction.
SUBMISSIONS: No feedback
offered with rejections.
See also: poetry publishers p80

TARTARUS PRESS
NON-FICTION / SHORT STORY
ANTHOLOGIES AND COLLECTIONS
/ NOVELS / E-BOOKS
Coverley House, Carlton, Leyburn,
North Yorkshire DL8 4AY
01969 640399
tartarus@pavilion.co.uk
www.tartaruspress.com
Editors: Rosalie Parker, Raymond
Russell

Established 1990. Mainly publishes
fiction. Available direct from
publisher website; by post and
email order; in selected chain
bookshops; and in independent
bookshops.
Tartarus Press won the 2015 World
Fantasy Award (Non-professional).
GENRES: Supernatural; literary.
SUBMISSIONS: Open to all.

Submit by email to rosalieparker@
btinternet.com. Guidelines at
tartaruspress.com/submissions.
html. Usually responds within four
weeks. No feedback offered with
rejection. Authors are paid an
advance and royalties.
WE SAY: We looked at digital
editions of *The Autobiography
Of Arthur Machen: Far Off Things
Near And Far* and *A Country Still
All Mystery* by Mark Valentine. The
covers of the books had a uniform
style: a pale yellow background,
with a small image in the lower
middle of the cover. Both covers
featured a landscape image;
Machen's was a dark church-
like building, with trees in the
foreground and a dark orange sky,
while Valentine's was a high-rise-
style building on a green hill, with a
grey-blue sky. The books supplied
to us were both non-fiction,
but Tartarus Press also accepts
supernatural fiction.
See also: *Wormwood* **(prose
magazine) p298**

TEAM ANGELICA PUBLISHING
E-BOOKS / NOVELS / SHORT STORY
COLLECTIONS AND ANTHOLOGIES
51 Coningham Road, London
W12 8BS
john@teamangelica.com
www.teamangelica.com
Editor: John R Gordon

Established 2011. Predominantly
publishes queer-of-colour centred
fiction. Also produces film and
theatre projects. Publications
available from independent
bookshops; and from Amazon and
other bookshop websites.
Team Angelica title *Fairytales for
Lost Children* by Diriye Osman won
the Polari Prize for Best First Book
(2014). *Tiny Pieces of Skull* by Roz

Kaveney won the Lambda Best Trans Fiction award (2015).

GENRES: Self-help/inspirational; graphic/comics; literary fiction; biography and true stories; health and lifestyle.

SUBMISSIONS: Submissions by invitation only. Email contact john@teamangelica.com. Usually responds within four weeks. No feedback offered with rejections, but they may occasionally include unsolicited feedback. Writers are paid an advance/fee plus royalties.

WE SAY: We looked at the award-winning *Fairytales for Lost Children* by Diriye Osman. A black-and-white image of the author in an Elizabethan gown adorns the cover, which has a slightly rubbery matte laminate feel, and there are ornate drop-cap letters at the beginning of each story, as befits the fairytale title. Set in Kenya, Somalia and South London, the stories explore identity in terms of gender, sexuality, family and country. A prime example of the important work Team Angelica is publishing.

TELOS PUBLISHING LTD

E-BOOKS / NOVELS / SHORT STORY COLLECTIONS AND ANTHOLOGIES / NON-FICTION

david@telos.co.uk
stephen@telos.co.uk
www.telos.co.uk

Editors: David J Howe, Stephen James Walker, Sam Stone

Established 2000. Publications available direct from publisher website; from chain bookshops nationwide; from independent bookshops; and from Amazon and other bookshop websites. In 2006, the founders of Telos Publishing won a World Fantasy Award for the company's work. Telos Publishing also won the British Fantasy Award for Best Publisher in 2010 and 2011.

GENRES: Sci-fi/fantasy/horror; film and television; crime fiction; self-help guides.

SUBMISSIONS: Open to all. Submit by email to david@telos.co.uk or stephen@telos.co.uk. Guidelines at www.telos.co.uk/submissions-3/. Usually responds within four weeks. No feedback offered with rejections. Authors are paid either: an advance plus royalties; or a flat fee depending on the project. All authors receive free copies of their book.

WE SAY: We looked at a digital version of *Nights of Blood Wine* by Freda Warrington: a 215-page collection of fifteen vampire stories. It contains formerly published stories as well as new ones. The first part is made up of ten 'Blood Wine' stories, where the second part covers five further pieces, such as a journal extract and a sequel to a previous publication. The design is plain: black and white print, serif type and justified text. The stories are intriguing, sometimes elaborating on earlier stories with the same characters.

TENEBRIS BOOKS

NOVELS / SHORT STORY COLLECTIONS

www.grimboldbooks.com

The dark fiction imprint of Grimbold Books (see p131), publishing work including, but not limited to, dark fantasy, modernsations of fairy and folk tales, weird fiction and ghost stories. Check for open submissions before sending your manuscript.

For more information, see also: Grimbold Books (prose publisher) p131

THISTLE PUBLISHING

E-BOOKS / PAPERBACKS / NOVELS / NON-FICTION
02072227574
info@thistlepublishing.co.uk
www.thistlepublishing.co.uk
Editors: David Haviland, Andrew Lownie
Established 1996. Publications available direct from publisher website; from chain bookshops nationwide; from independent bookshops; at national and local literary events; and from Amazon and other bookshop websites.
Thistle Publishing won the People's Book Prize 2017 with *A Life in Death* by Richard Venables. *The Warehouse Industry* by William Macbeth was longlisted for the Not the Booker Prize 2018, and *The Unrivalled Transcendence of Willem J. Gyle* by J D Dixon was shortlisted for the Somerset Maugham Prize 2018.
GENRES: Crime; thriller; literary; reading group; women.
SUBMISSIONS: Open to all. Submit by email to info@thistlepublishing.co.uk. Non-fiction authors should provide a synopsis, author profile, sample chapter, and brief chapter summaries. Fiction authors should provide a synopsis and three sample chapters. Guidelines at www.thistlepublishing.co.uk/about.html. Usually responds within four weeks. Rejections may occasionally include unsolicited feedback. Authors are paid an advance/fee plus royalties.
WE SAY: We looked at a digital version of *Rickshaw*, a 260-page book by David McGrath, about a homeless Irish character who rides a rickshaw in London. This is a fascinating, sharp and humorous story from the very first page. The writing is direct and to-the-point, and the design simple with a classical font and justified text. The cover design is a pen-and-ink style drawing in black and white, against a striking yellow background.

THREE HARES PUBLISHING

NOVELS / NON-FICTION / E-BOOKS
submissions@threeharespublishing.com
www.threeharespublishing.com
Editor: Yasmin Kane
Established 2018. Mainly publishes fiction. Publications available from Amazon.
GENRES: Historical; crime; thrillers; military history; history.
SUBMISSIONS: Open to all. Submit by email to submissions@threeharespublishing.com. Guidelines at www.threeharespublishing.com. Does not provide feedback due to time constraints. If authors do not hear back within 12 weeks, their submission has been unsuccessful. Authors are paid royalties only, or an advance fee and royalties.

THUNDERPOINT PUBLISHING

NOVELS / SHORT STORY COLLECTIONS / E-BOOKS
Bryn Heulog, Talley, Llandeilo, Carmarthenshire SA19 7YH
01558 685860
info@thunderpoint.co.uk
www.thunderpoint.scot
Editor: Seonaid Francis
Established 2012. Publishes fiction. Publications available from chain and independent bookshops; and from Amazon and other bookshop websites.
Thunderpoint Publishing was shortlisted for the 2019 Bloody Scotland McIlvanney Prize in Début Scottish Crime.
GENRES: Crime; historical; humour; literary; mystery/thriller.

SUBMISSIONS: Open to all, during submissions windows only. Submit by email to submissions@thunderpoint.co.uk. Guidelines at www.thunderpoint.scot/contact.html. Usually responds within one to three months. Rejections may include unsolicited feedback. Authors are paid royalties only.
WE SAY: Thunderpoint Publishing embrace the strange and radical, publishing texts that challenge readers' thoughts and feelings. We looked at a PDF of *The Peat Dead* by Allan Martin, a gory tale of murder and mystery that entices readers with an ominous cover graphic. With similarly intriguing designs on their other books, Thunderpoint are clearly publishers of all things extraordinary and thrilling.

TINY OWL PRESS

PICTURE BOOKS
www.tinyowl.co.uk
info@tinyowl.co.uk
Founded in 2014, Tiny Owl's editors publish children's books designed to introduce children in the UK to other cultures, and commission work from writers around the world. The Tiny Owl editors are not currently accepting unsolicited submissions.

TINY TREE CHILDREN'S BOOKS

CHILDREN'S PICTURE BOOKS / CHILDREN'S FICTION
Unit 46, Goyt Mill, Marple, Stockport SK6 7AW
01614 278329
james.shaw@
            matthewjamespublishing.com
www.matthewjamespublishing.com
Editor: James Shaw
Established 2016. Imprint of

Matthew James Publishing Ltd. Publications available direct from publisher website; by direct mail and email orders; from selected/local chain bookshops; from independent bookshops; at national and local literary events; and from Amazon and other bookshop websites.
GENRES: Children's fiction.
SUBMISSIONS: Open to all. Submit by email to submissions@matthewjamespublishing.com. Guidelines at www.matthewjamespublishing.com/submissions-and-permissions/. Usually responds within four weeks. Rejections may occasionally include unsolicited feedback.

TRAMP PRESS

E-BOOKS / NOVELS / CREATIVE NON-FICTION / SHORT STORY COLLECTIONS AND ANTHOLOGIES
info@tramppress.com
submissions@tramppress.com
www.tramppress.com
Publishers/editors: Lisa Coen and Sarah Davis-Goff
Established 2014. Publications available direct from publisher website; at chain and independent bookshops nationwide and internationally; at national and local literary events; and from Amazon and other bookshop websites and e-book providers. Some online content freely available to all. Tramp Press authors have won the Goldsmiths Prize, four Irish Book Awards, the Rooney Prize, the Geoffrey Faber Memorial Award, the Waterstones Book of the Year and the Kate O'Brien Award. They've been nominated for many others including the Kerry Group, the IMPAC, the Republic of Consciousness Prize, the Costa, the

Warwick Prize, the Guardian First Book Award, the Man Booker and the Desmond Elliot Prize.
GENRES: Crime/thriller/mystery; fantasy/sci-fi; horror; literary fiction; YA.
SUBMISSIONS: Open to all. Submit by email to submissions@

TIRGEARR PUBLISHING
E-BOOKS / NOVELS / SHORT STORY COLLECTIONS AND ANTHOLOGIES / NOVELLAS
info@tirgearrpublishing.com
www.tirgearrpublishing.com

Established 2012. Commercial adult and cross-genre fiction. Publications available by post and email order, and from Amazon and other bookshop websites, and by request from most bookshops.
GENRES: Commercial adult genre and cross genre fiction: mystery; horror; thrillers; suspense; detective/PI; police procedurals; romance; romantic suspense; erotic romance; historical fiction; historical romance; sci-fi/fantasy.
SUBMISSIONS: Open to all. Submit via online form at www.tirgearrpublishing.com/submissions (guidelines at the same address). Usually responds within one to three months, and provides feedback with all rejections. Authors are paid royalties only and receive free copies of book.
WE SAY: An e-book-only publisher, Tirgearr has an extensive list of genre fiction. Their online catalogue shows cover designs that echo those of big commercial print publishers (passionate gazing-into-the-distance for romance; chrome and planets for sci-fi, etc), and the stories are well edited and entertaining.

THEY SAY

Tirgearr Publishing is a small independently-owned publishing company of commercial adult genre fiction. We offer full-circle services, working with authors on a one-on-one basis through editing and cover design states, to ensure each book we publish is of the highest quality. Using our expertise from more than twenty years in the publishing business, we work side-by-side with our authors to develop effective marketing plans and promotional programs, advising on career choices and forward career planning, and assist in setting up the author's overall image.

194

tramppress.com. Guidelines at www.tramppress.com/submissions. Usually responds within four weeks. Rejections may occasionally include unsolicited feedback. Authors are paid an advance/fee plus royalties.

WE SAY: The perfect-bound paperbacks we saw feel like Big Five titles – indeed Mike McCormack's *Solar Bones* was longlisted for the Man Booker Prize. The covers are eye-catching, such as the droplet-strewn feathers of a blue bird featured on Sara Baume's *A Line Made by Walking*. The novel follows a young artist who, having dropped out of college and moved in with her grandmother in rural Ireland, begins a series photographing everything from roadkill to kitchen curios, documenting the beauty and destruction around her.

TRIGGER PUBLISHING
NON-FICTION
The Foundation Centre, Navigation House, 48 Millgate, Newark, Nottinghamshire NG24 4TS
01636 600825
beth@triggerpublishing.com
www.triggerpublishing.com
Editor: Beth James

Established 2016. Publishes non-fiction. Publications available direct from the publisher; from chain and independent bookshops; at local literary festivals; and from Amazon and other bookshop websites.
GENRES: Mental health; wellbeing
SUBMISSIONS: Open to all, during submissions windows. Submit by email to submissions@triggerpublishing.com. Complete guidelines at www.triggerpublishing.com/submissions. Usually responds in one to three months.

WE SAY: Wholly dedicated to acting as a voice for mental health welfare, Trigger Publishing is a refreshing voice for the modern world. We looked at a PDF proof of *Within the White Lines: How the Beautiful Game Saved My Life* by Ruth Fox; a non-fiction memoir in Trigger's Inspirational Stories series. Conveying a raw and honest account of surviving mental illness, this title focuses on football just as many of their books tell stories of mental health in fundamental human experiences.

TTA PRESS
E-BOOKS / NOVELS / SHORT STORY COLLECTIONS AND ANTHOLOGIES / NOVELLAS
5 Martins Lane, Witcham, Ely, Cambridgeshire CB6 2LB
www.ttapress.com
Editor: Andy Cox

Established 1994. Fiction. Publications available direct from publisher website; by post and email order; from chain bookshops nationwide; from independent bookshops; at national and local literary events; and from Amazon and other bookshop websites. All online content available to all.
GENRES: Crime/thriller/mystery; fantasy/sci-fi; horror; literary fiction.
SUBMISSIONS: Open to all. Submit via tta.submittable.com/submit. Usually responds within four weeks. Rejections may occasionally include unsolicited feedback. Authors are paid a flat fee and receive free copies of the book.
See also: *Interzone* (sci-fi prose magazine) p294, *Black Static* (horror prose magazine) p289, and *Crimewave* (crime prose magazine) p290

TURAS PRESS
NOVELS / SHORT STORY
COLLECTIONS
6-9 Trinity Street, Dublin D02 EY47
+353 1 818 3176
admin@turaspress.ie
www.turaspress.ie
Editor: Liz McSkeane
Established 2016. Primarily
publishes poetry (see p81), but
also some fiction. Publications
available direct from the publisher
website, and from independent
bookshops.
GENRE: Fiction.
SUBMISSIONS: Open to all, within
specified submissions windows
twice a year. Submit by email to
admin@turaspress.ie. Guidelines
at www.turaspress.ie/submissions.
Usually responds in one to three
months. Rejections may very
occasionally include a small amount
of feedback. Authors are paid an
advance/fee plus royalties, and
receive free copies of the book.
See also: poetry publishers p81

TWO RIVERS PRESS
NON-FICTION
7 Denmark Road, Reading RG1 5PA
tworiverspress@gmail.com
www.tworiverspress.com
Editor: Sally Mortimore
Established 1994. Publishes mainly
non-fiction. Publications available
direct from publisher website; by
post and email order; from selected/
local chain bookshops; from
independent bookshops; at local
literary events; and from Amazon
and other bookshop websites.
GENRES: Books about Reading and
the Thames Valley; art books.

UKAUTHORS/UKAPRESS
NOVELS / SHORT STORY
ANTHOLOGIES / NON-FICTION
ukauthors@ukauthors.com
www.ukapress.com
Fiction and non-fiction unrestricted
by genre or style. Looking for
quality writing with 'originality,
sparkle and the promise of
something unexpected'.

UNBOUND
NOVELS / SHORT STORY
COLLECTIONS AND ANTHOLOGIES
/ NON-FICTION / E-BOOKS
Unit 18, Waterside, 44-48 Wharf Road,
London N1 7UX
020 7253 4230
www.unbound.co.uk
Established 2011. Mixed form:
also publishes poetry (see p81).
Publications available direct
from publisher website; by
post and email order; at chain
and independent bookshops
nationwide; at national and local
literary events; and through
Amazon and other bookshop
websites. Publications are
subsidised by crowdfunding.
Multi-award-winning: Unbound title
The Wake won Book of the Year
at the 2015 Bookseller Industry
Awards and the 2014 Gordon Burn
Prize; was shortlisted for the 2014
Goldsmiths Prize; and longlisted
for the Man Booker Prize 2014, the
Desmond Elliott Prize 2014, and
the Folio Prize 2014. Unbound won
Best Publisher Website 2014 at the
FutureBook Innovation Awards and
British Book Design and Production
Awards, and Best Start-Up at
the 2011 FutureBook Innovation
Awards. Also won the Literature
Award 2013 for *26 Treasures* at the
British Book Design and Production
Awards.
GENRES: Crime/thriller/mystery;
fantasy/sci-fi; graphic/comics;
historical fiction; literary fiction;

biography and true stories; food and drink; history; popular science and nature; society, education and politics.

SUBMISSIONS: Open to all. Submit via the online form at unbound. co.uk/authors/work-with-us. Guidelines at the same address. Usually responds within one to three months. Rejections may occasionally include unsolicited feedback. Authors are paid royalties: a 50/50 profit share from crowdfunding.

WE SAY: We looked at *The Wake* by Paul Kingsnorth: a prime example of an indie taking a punt on a risky book. *The Wake* is a post-apocalyptic novel, set in 1066, and written in a version of Old English. The production values on this book are impressive, from the textured cover to the wonderfully thick paper. Unbound's crowdfunding approach to publishing means it can afford to get the best materials possible, knowing future readers have already covered the cost. And with *The Wake* already a modern classic, the editors clearly have an eye for the market.

See also: poetry publishers p81

UNIFORMBOOKS

NON-FICTION
info@uniformbooks.co.uk
www.uniformbooks.co.uk
Editor: Colin Sackett
Established 2011. Mixed form: also publishes poetry (see p82). Publications available direct from publisher website; by direct mail and email orders; from chain bookshops nationwide; from independent bookshops; and from Amazon.

GENRES: Visual and literary arts; cultural geography and history;

music and bibliographic studies.

SUBMISSIONS: Open to all. Submit by email to info@uniformbooks. co.uk. Usually responds within four weeks. Rejections may occasionally include unsolicited feedback. Authors are paid royalties only and receive free copies of the book.

See also: poetry publishers p82

UNSUNG STORIES

E-BOOKS / NOVELS / SHORT STORY COLLECTIONS AND ANTHOLOGIES / NON-FICTION
info@unsungstories.co.uk
www.unsungstories.co.uk
Editor: George Sandison
Established 2014. Publications available direct from publisher website; from chain bookshops nationwide; from independent bookshops; and from Amazon and other bookshop websites. Unsung Stories titles have been nominated for the John W Campbell Award, Shirley Jackson Award, James Tiptree Jr Awards, BSFA Awards, BFS Awards, Saboteur Awards and the *Guardian*'s Not the Booker.

GENRES: Speculative fiction; sci-fi; fantasy; horror; weird fiction.

SUBMISSIONS: Open to all, during submission windows. Submit online at www.unsungstories.co.uk/ submissions. Guidelines at www. unsungstories.co.uk/submissions. Usually responds within four to six months. Rejections may occasionally include unsolicited feedback. Authors are paid royalties on sales and receive free copies of the book.

WE SAY: Unsung publish a number of short stories on their website, which is where we looked to get a feel for its publications. The site certainly gives enough information on their books to pique interest. Cover designs are professional: all fit the Unsung template (a jagged slice of colour across the bottom containing the author/title). The cover images are disquieting: almost ordinary at first glance, only for the viewer to be unsettled by an out-of-the-ordinary detail, as is fitting for an imprint specialising in high quality speculative fiction.

UNTHANK BOOKS

E-BOOKS / NOVELS / SHORT STORY COLLECTIONS AND ANTHOLOGIES / NON-FICTION
PO Box 3506, Norwich NR7 7QP
information@unthankbooks.com
www.unthankbooks.com
Editor: Ashley Stokes
Established 2010. Publications available direct from publisher website; by direct mail and email orders; from chain bookshops nationwide; from independent bookshops; at local literary events; and from Amazon and other bookshop websites.
Unthank Books was shortlisted in the Saboteur Awards 2017 for Most Innovative Publisher and Best Anthology.
GENRES: Literary.
SUBMISSIONS: Open to all. Submit by post (PO Box 3506, Norwich NR7 7QP) or email (robin.jones@unthankbooks.com). Guidelines at www.unthankbooks.com/contacts.html. Usually responds within one to three months. Rejections may include occasional unsolicited feedback. Authors are paid royalties only and receive free copies of the book.
WE SAY: We looked at *Some of us glow more than others: stories* by Tania Hershman, though looking through the book Hershman's work

blurs the story/poetry line (as many good short stories do). The cover is thick, good quality material featuring an ethereal image of jellyfish and marked with 'As heard on Radio 4' – which should give an indication as to the high quality of writing Unthank looks for. The contents split the featured stories into groups under different titles 'Fight or Flight', 'Grounded' etc, which for this reader encouraged a feeling that you could pick a batch of stories to pick a mood – and the title pages of each batch feature poetry. A lovely collection.

V. PRESS

COLLECTIONS, ANTHOLOGIES AND CHAPBOOKS/PAMPHLETS
vpresspoetry@hotmail.com
vpresspoetry.blogspot.co.uk
Editor: Sarah Leavesley
Established 2013. Publishes poetry and flash fiction. Publications available direct from publisher website; at national and local literary events; and from Amazon.
SUBMISSIONS: Submit by email to vpresspoetry@hotmail.com, but only when the submissions window is open. Guidelines at vpresspoetry.blogspot.co.uk/p/submissions.html. Usually responds within three months. Rejections may occasionally include feedback. Authors receive initial free copies of the book, followed by copies at a discount rate.
WE SAY: As with their poetry entry (p82) V. Press shared a favourite piece of fiction with us, with the caveat that their 'tastes are quite eclectic'. 'Wild green fig jam' is taken from Jude Higgin's flash fiction pamphlet *The Chemist's House* – the cover of which is in black and white, and features a

photo within a photo. The piece is evocative and almost poetic in its use of repetition and the senses, even as it relays the harsh realities of illness and loss. As an example of the standard published by V. Press, this is setting the bar very high indeed.
See also: poetry publishers p82

VAGABOND VOICES
FICTION
www.vagabondvoices.co.uk
info@vagabondvoices.co.uk
Glasgow-based press publishing novels, poems and polemics. They are committed to introducing new titles from Scottish authors and translating fiction from other languages. They only accept submissions during their open submission window.
See also: poetry publishers p83

VALLEY PRESS
NOVELS / SHORT STORY COLLECTIONS AND ANTHOLOGIES / NON-FICTION
Woodend, The Crescent, Scarborough YO11 2PW
07806 765524
jo@valleypressuk.com
www.valleypressuk.com
Editor: Jamie McGarry
Established 2008. Mainly publishes poetry (see p83). Publications available direct from publisher website; from chain bookshops nationwide; from independent bookshops; at national and local literary events; and from Amazon and other bookshop websites.
In 2019, Valley Press title *High Spirits: A Round of Drinking Stories* won the Saboteur Award for Best Anthology.
GENRES: Short stories; literary fiction; anthologies; memoir.

SUBMISSIONS: Open to all. Submit online at www.valleypressuk.com/submissions. Usually responds within one to three months. Rejections may occasionally include unsolicited feedback. Submitters are required to buy a magazine/book from the press. Authors are paid a flat fee and royalties only and receive free copies of the book.
See also: poetry publishers p83

VANE WOMEN PRESS
SHORT STORY PAMPHLETS AND ANTHOLOGIES
low.down@vanewomen.co.uk
www.vanewomen.co.uk
Editors: SJ Litherland, Marilyn Longstaff (assistant editor), Pat Maycroft (art editor)
Established 1993. Mainly publishes poetry (see p83). Publications available direct from publisher website; by post and email order; at local literary events; and at Vane Women events and workshops. Vane Women title *The Spar Box* by Pippa Little was the 2006 Poetry Book Society Pamphlet choice.
SUBMISSIONS: Open to previously unpublished women in North East England. Contact by email (submissions@vanewomen.co.uk) in the first instance, and a postal address to send poems and short stories to will be provided if appropriate. Full submission guidelines at www.vanewomen.co.uk/submissions.html. Usually responds in up to six months. Rejections may occasionally include unsolicited feedback. Authors receive free copies of their book.
For more information, see also: poetry publishers p83

VANGUARD EDITIONS
SHORT STORY COLLECTIONS AND
ANTHOLOGIES
Apt 18, Triangle Court,
315 Camberwell New Road,
London SE5 0AT
vanguardeditions@gmail.com
richardskinner.weebly.com/vanguard-
editions
Editor: Richard Skinner
Established 2014. Mixed form:
also publishes poetry (see p84).
Publications available direct from
publisher website; by post and
email order; from independent
bookshops; and at local literary
events.
SUBMISSIONS: Submissions
by invitation only to
vanguardeditions@gmail.com.
Usually responds within four
weeks. Rejections may occasionally
include unsolicited feedback.
Authors receive free copies of the
book.
See also: poetry publishers p84

VERTEBRATE PUBLISHING
E-BOOKS / NOVELS / NON-FICTION
/ ANTHOLOGIES
Omega Court, 352 Cemetery Road,
Sheffield S11 8FT
0114 267 9277
info@v-publishing.co.uk
www.v-publishing.co.uk
Editor: John Coefield
Established 2004. Primarily
publishes non-fiction. Publications
available direct from the publisher
website; by direct mail and
email orders; from chain and
independent bookshops; at
national and local literary events;
from Amazon and other bookshop
websites; and from specialist shops
(e.g. climbing, cycling, outdoor).
Vertebrate Publishing publication
Tides by Nick Bullock won the

2018 Mountain Literature Award
(BANFF Mountain Book Festival).
GENRES: Biography; guidebooks;
adventure; children's books.
SUBMISSIONS: Open to all. Submit
by post (Vertebrate Publishing,
Omega Court, 352 Cemetery
Road, Sheffield S11 8FT) or email
(submissions@v-publishing.co.uk).
Sometimes charges a reading fee.
Guidelines at www.v-publishing.
co.uk/submissions. Usually
responds in one to three months.
Rejections may occasionally include
unsolicited feedback. Authors are
paid a flat fee or royalties, or an
advance plus royalties. Contracts
vary.
WE SAY: We fawned over
*Waymaking: An Anthology Of
Women's Adventure Writing,
Poetry, and Art* (and fell deeply in
love). A true coffee table book,
this stunning anthology has a
bold, intriguing cover and lovingly
curated contents. The book itself is
chunky and almost square-shaped,
with full colour photography and
art, gorgeous writing and effortless
design. Printed on the highest
quality materials and edited by
industry juggernauts, it's a class
act.

VERVE BOOKS
NOVELS / E-BOOKS
theeditors@vervebooks.co.uk
www.vervebooks.co.uk
Editors: Katherine Sunderland and
Clare Quinlivan
Established 2018, sister company
to No Exit Press. Publishes digital
fiction. Publications available direct
from the publisher website and
from e-book retailers.
GENRES: Crime and thriller;
women's fiction; commercial fiction.
SUBMISSIONS: Open to all. Submit

via the website at www.vervebooks.
co.uk/submit.php. Guidelines
at the same address. Usually
responds in four to six months.
Rejections include feedback only
if requested. Authors are paid an
advance fee and royalties.
WE SAY: Priding themselves as a
'dynamic digital publisher', Verve
Books publish a variety of books
with the primary requirement
of being page-turning and
entertaining. We looked at PDF
proofs of *The Righteous Spy*
by Merle Nygate, a spy thriller
that transgresses borders in an
international plot. The book's
cover image shows a mysteriously
silhouetted individual, surely
reflecting the books contents,
which also gives a fascinating
exploration into life as a spy.
**See also: No Exit Press (prose
publisher) p160**

VICTORINA PRESS
NOVELS / NON-FICTION /
CHILDREN'S BOOKS
www.victorinapress.com
victorinapress@gmail.com
Established in 2017, Victorina
Press is based in Staffordshire, and
rooted strongly in Chilean and
British cultures courtesy of founder
Consuelo Rivera-Fuentes. The
press is focused on bibliodiversity
– which is to say it looks for books
engaging with society in a range
of styles and genres rather than
for books fitting a certain brand.
Submissions guidelines are
available on the website.
See also: poetry publishers p84

VOIDERY APERTURE, THE
NOVELS
information@thevoideryaperture.com
www.thevoideryaperture.com

Editor: Christopher Pickard
Established 2016. Mixed form:
also publishes poetry (see p84).
Publications available from chain
bookshops nationwide; from
independent bookshops; and
from Amazon and other bookshop
websites.
GENRES: Literary; experimental.
SUBMISSIONS: Submissions by
invitation only. Rejections may
occasionally include unsolicited
feedback. Authors are paid
royalties only.
WE SAY: We looked at the Voidery
Aperture website, where cover
images and extracts from its
publications can be accessed.
Cover designs are simple –
plain colour backgrounds, with
contrasting title-and-author text in
a serif font, and the publisher logo
clearly displayed. The inner page
design is clean and professional.
The types of writing seems to err
on the side of experimental, for
example Neil Godsell's *Crump
Redivivus*, which is fiction written
almost as script, but without any
stage directions.
See also: poetry publisher p84

WALKER BOOKS
PICTURE BOOKS
www.walker.co.uk
marketing@walker.co.uk
Founded in 2008, Walker Books
is one of the world's leading
independent publishers of books
and content for children. They
accept submissions year-round
and are especially interested in
illustrated picture-book stories, as
well as illustration samples.

WARD RIVER PRESS
NOVELS
info@poolbeg.com

www.poolbeg.com
The literary imprint of Poolbeg Press, one of Ireland's most established presses (since 1976), which is particularly known for nurturing new women's writing.
See also: Poolbeg Press (prose publisher) p171

WARD WOOD PUBLISHING

E-BOOKS / NOVELS / SHORT STORY COLLECTIONS / MIXED-FORM ANTHOLOGIES
6 The Drive, Golders Green, London NW11 9SR
07504 863024
adele@wardwoodpublishing.co.uk
www.wardwoodpublishing.co.uk
Editor: Adele Ward

Established 2010. Mixed output – also publishes poetry (see p84), as well as the Bedford Square MA Anthology from Royal Holloway, University of London, with work by graduates of the poetry and fiction courses. Publications available direct from publisher website; from major chain and independent bookshops; at literary events; and from Amazon and other bookshop websites.

Ward Wood author Joe Stein was on the longlist of 10 for the Crime Writers' Association Dagger in the Library award 2016.

GENRES: Literary; crime; comedy; LGBT.

SUBMISSIONS: By invitation only, to adele@wardwoodpublishing. co.uk. Please check www. wardwoodpublishing.co.uk/ manuscripts.htm for submissions information. Usually responds within one to three months. Rejections may occasionally include unsolicited feedback. Authors are paid royalties.

WE SAY: Of the digital versions we saw, *Mr Oliver's Object of Desire* by V G Lee had the most interesting cover, with a watercolour-styled outline of the London skyline. Lee's novel, along with *Through Another Night* by Joe Stein and the collection by Royal Holloway Creative Writing Programme, *Bedford Square 10*, were clearly formatted for print, but translated well to PDF form. *Bedford Square 10*, which leads with a description of the programme, sets out the varied work of its students, ranging from fiction time-travel from the 1930s to psychological mystery, encompassing prose and poetry.

See also: poetry publishers p84

WAYWISER PRESS ☆

NOVELS / SHORT STORY COLLECTIONS / ILLUSTRATED WORKS
Christmas Cottage, Church Enstone, West Oxfordshire OX7 4NN
01608 677492
info@waywiser-press.com
www.waywiser-press.com
Editors: Philip Hoy, Joseph Harrison, Dora Malech, V Penelope Pelizzon, Eric McHenry, Greg Williamson, Clive Watkins, Matthew Yorke

Established 2001. Mainly publishes poetry (see p85). Publications available direct from publisher website; by post and email order; at chain bookshops and independent bookshops nationwide; and via Amazon and other bookshop websites, including Inpress Books.

GENRES: Biography, memoir, literary criticism, literary history.

SUBMISSIONS: Prose can be submitted year round. Submit by

post to Christmas Cottage, Church Enstone, Chipping Norton OX7 4NN. Guidelines at waywiser-press.com/about-us/submissions. Usually responds within one to three months, no feedback offered if rejected. Authors receive royalties and receive free copies of the book.
For more information, including what We Say, see also: poetry publishers p85

WHITTRICK PRESS
SHORT STORY COLLECTIONS / CHILDREN'S BOOKS / E-BOOKS
www.whittrickpress.com
An 'innovative and independent' press based in Northern Ireland, founded in 2012. Very small stable of authors.

WILD THINGS PUBLISHING
NON-FICTION
www.wildthingspublishing.com
hello@wildthingspublishing.com
Publishes lifestyle books and apps to 'get people out, experiencing and enjoying nature, and our wonderful (often local) world'. Their product lines include walking guides, wild swimming guides, bothying, bikepacking etc. The editors are open to pitches.

WILD WOLF PUBLISHING
NOVELS
editor@wildwolfpublishing.com
www.wildwolfpublishing.com
'Fiction with teeth.' Looks for full-length fiction of a dark nature: thriller, horror or sci-fi.

WORDWELL BOOKS
NON-FICTION
www.wordwellbooks.com
Founded in 1986, Wordwell Ltd is a Dublin-based publisher producing high-quality specialist non-fiction books about Irish culture and history, and a range of culturally significant magazines, including *Archaeology Ireland*, *Books Ireland*, and *History Ireland*.

WRECKING BALL PRESS ☆
E-BOOKS / NOVELS / SHORT STORY COLLECTIONS AND ANTHOLOGIES / NON-FICTION
5 Theatre Mews, Egginton Street, Hull HU2 8DL
01482 211499
editor@wreckingballpress.com
www.wreckingballpress.com
Editors: Shane Rhodes, Russ Litten
Established 1997. Mainly publishes poetry (see p85). Publications available direct from publisher website; by post and email order; at chain and independent bookshops nationwide; at literary events; and on Amazon. Some online content available to all. Wrecking Ball Press title *The Scene of My Former Triumph* by Matthew Caley was nominated for Best First Collection, The Forward Prize 2005.
GENRES: Drama and criticism; fantasy/sci-fi; literary fiction; biography and true stories.
SUBMISSIONS: Open to all. Submit by post (Wrecking Ball Press, 5 Theatre Mews, Egginton Street, Hull HU2 8DL) or by email (editor@wreckingballpress.com). Guidelines on the website. Usually responds within one to three months. Rejection may occasionally include unsolicited feedback. Authors are paid royalties and receive free copies of the book.
See also: poetry publishers p85

WUNDOR EDITIONS
FICTION / NON-FICTION
www.wundoreditions.com
enquiries@wundoreditions.com
Publishing fiction, non-fiction, art
and poetry (see p86), London-
based Wundor welcomes fiction
submissions. It publishes literary
fiction only, but considers
innovative genre fiction to be
literary fiction. They are 'committed
to publishing innovative and
challenging literature and images,
working with new and established
writers'.
See also: poetry publishers p86

Y LOLFA
E-BOOKS / NON-FICTION
Talybont, Ceredigion, Wales SY24 5HE
01970 832304
ylolfa@ylolfa.com
www.ylolfa.com
Editors: Carolyn Hodges,
Lefi Gruffudd, Eirian Jones
Established 1967. Mainly publishes
non-fiction. Publications available
direct from publisher website; by
post and email order; at chain
and independent bookshops; at
local literary events; and through
bookshop websites.
Titles from Y Lolfa have been
shortlisted for British Sports Book
of the Year and won Welsh Book of
the Year.
GENRES: Welsh interest; biography
and true stories; history; sports and
leisure; travel.
SUBMISSIONS: Open to all.
Submit by post (Y Lolfa, Talybont,
Ceredigion SY24 5HE) or email
(edit@ylolfa.com). Guidelines at
ww.ylolfa.com/en/cyhoeddi.php.
Usually responds within four
weeks. Rejections may occasionally
include unsolicited feedback.
Authors are paid royalties or an
advance/fee plus royalties. Some
titles may require crowdfunding or
author contribution.
WE SAY: We looked at *The
Shadow of Nanteos* by Jane
Blank, a weighty perfect-bound
paperback publication that
connects the matte finish of the
professional design to the dark
plot within the novel. The quality
continues within with high-quality
cream paper. This dark historic
novel provides a gripping
Gothic chill and oozes Welsh
history: a great read for anyone
who wants to find more about
Welsh heritage.

YLVA PUBLISHING
E-BOOKS / NOVELS / SHORT STORY
COLLECTIONS AND ANTHOLOGIES
astrid.ohletz@ylva-publishing.com
www.ylva-publishing.com
Editor: Astrid Ohletz
Established 2012. Publisher of
lesbian and bi fiction. Publications
available direct from publisher
website; from chain bookshops
nationwide; from independent
bookshops; at local literary events;
and from Amazon and other
bookshop websites.
Two Ylva Publishing titles have
been finalists in the 2016 and
2017 Lambda Awards: Andrea
Bramhall's *Collide-O-Scope*
and Lee Winter's *Requiem for
Immortals*. Ylva have also won
several other awards over the past
five years with the GCLS and the
Rainbow Awards.
GENRES: Lesbian or bi: romance;
crime/mystery; sci-fi/fantasy; YA;
erotica.
SUBMISSIONS: Women writers
only. Submit by email to astrid.
ohletz@ylva-publishing.com.
Guidelines at www.ylva-publishing.

com/submissions-guidelines/. Usually responds within one to three months. No feedback offered with rejections. Authors are paid royalties only.

WE SAY: We saw a variety of examples, from *Collide-o-Scope* by Andrea Bramhall, featuring a misty photo of a lake on its matte cover, and containing the tale of a murder mystery set on the North Norfolk Coastal Path; to the larger *Defensive Mindset* by Wendy Temple, which features a line drawing of two female football players tussling on its glossy cover, and is a drama focused on a footballer/businesswoman who must learn to play with her foil. Quality materials, with the lesbian focus of Ylva writ proudly in the cover designs.

YOLK PUBLISHING

NOVELS / NON-FICTION / E-BOOKS
www.yolkpublishing.co.uk
editorial@yolkpublishing.co.uk

Publishing high quality fiction and non-fiction, ranging from the serious to the humorous. The editors welcome submissions from 'new and previously unpublished authors as well as those who have been previously published to submit manuscripts for consideration'. They are committed to reading any unsolicited work.

ZED BOOKS

NON-FICTION
editorial@zedbooks.net
www.zedbooks.co.uk
Editors: Ken Barlow, Kim Walker, Kika Sroka-Miller

Non-fiction only. An independent, scholarly publishing house, Zed Books caters to academics and students, and more widely, activists and policy-makers. It promotes diversity, alternative voices and progressive social change through critical and dynamic publishing.

GENRES: Politics and international; relations; economics; development studies; gender studies; area studies (Africa, the Middle East, Asia and Latin America); environment.

SUBMISSIONS: Open to all. Extensive guidelines are available at www.zedbooks.net/publishing-with-zed.

ZENOPRESS

ANTHOLOGIES
zenopress.info@gmail.com
www.zenopress.com
Editor: Christian Patracchini

Established 2017. Mixed form: also publishes poetry, including mixed prose/poetry anthologies (see p86). Publications available direct from the publisher website.

GENRES: Literary fiction.

SUBMISSIONS: Open to all. A reading fee may apply. Submit by email to zenopress.info@gmail.com. Guidelines at www.zenopress.com/submissions. Usually responds in one to three months. No feedback offered with rejection. Authors receive free copies of the book.

For more information, including what We Say, see also: poetry publishers p86

ZUNTOLD

CHILDREN'S NOVELS / NON-FICTION
www.zuntold.com

Manchester-based press primarily publishing fiction for children and young people, ranging from MG to

205

YA and crossover. Also interested
in some non-fiction with a focus
on the environments we live in
or books on emotional wellbeing
and mental health. Authors should
contact the editors through the
'Contribute' page on the website.

Part 2:
Literary magazines
and e-zines

Llenyddiaeth Cymru Literature Wales

Canolfan Ysgrifennu Tŷ Newydd Writing Centre

An idyllic, creative escape in stunning north west Wales.

For further information, visit:
www.tynewydd.wales

Literary magazines: ebbs and flows

The world of independent book publishers and literary magazines is a precarious one, and our research for this Guide has revealed that magazines, in particular, are especially apt to appear and disappear – due to the lack of retail outlets and the extra commitment required to maintain a regular publication schedule.

Though the absolute number of presses featured in this third edition of the Guide has increased by 20 per cent, the number of magazines has dropped by 11 titles compared with the second edition. But despite these closures, we're happy to say that 45 entries in this edition are completely new to us, and many of the titles that appeared in the very first edition of the Guide are continuing to thrive.

Why the turnover? Running a literary magazine is a labour of love. Editors' evenings and weekends are spent sifting through submissions, laying out pages, untangling code, talking to printers, marketing – and editing, of course. When you add in the need for a day job to pay the bills, plus working on their own writing (many editors are writers too), and spending time with family and friends, it's not surprising that some editors eventually start to feel ground down.

Very few are able to survive on income from subscriptions and single sales alone. True, some publishers are supported by regional Arts Councils and local government or generous benefactors, but the vast majority are subsidised by the free labour of their own staff.

So bear this in mind when submitting to magazines. The editors love good writing, and want to share it with the world, but they are almost certainly working for nothing and can afford to pay very little, if at all, for the writing they publish – though there are some high payers in these listings. They rarely have time to tailor individual rejection letters – don't underestimate just how many submissions even the smallest publication receives.

As a writer, you can help by sticking to submission guidelines, ensuring your work matches their aesthetic, and being patient as you wait for a reply (see p11). If you do receive a rejection, take it on the chin (or go and have a little cry), but don't lash out at the poor editor.

As a reader, you can help by actually supporting the magazines you are submitting to. Buy a single copy at least. If you love it, take out a subscription. If it's an online-only publication, share the love. Spread the word about items you've enjoyed and alert people when there's a new issue out. In particular, try to share beyond your immediate circle and help break the cycle of writers who only read in order to be published. There are some amazing stories, heart-stopping poems and beautiful accessible e-zines and magazines out there, and they deserve to be read by everyone.

As Debbie wrote in her introduction to the first edition of this Guide, 'Independent presses are literature's Amazon rainforest, the oxygen that sustains new voices and helps them rise to the top of the mainstream's slush pile. Yet many presses teeter constantly on the brink of extinction, sustained mainly by the hard work and self-sacrifice of those who run them. If we don't buy what they publish, they will disappear. They need us as much as we need them. It's as simple as that.'

By 'mixed form', we mean magazines that publish both poetry and prose (fiction and/or non-fiction), as opposed to focusing exclusively on either poetry or prose, as in the later sections of this Guide. We also mean magazines that may, for instance, branch out into graphic fiction or poetry. Some magazines may have a bias towards one form, such as poetry, but also mix in a few short stories and/or reviews – or vice versa. And some feature poetry and prose in a particular genre, such as fantasy or science fiction. Whatever you write, you're sure to find a place to submit here.

3:AM MAGAZINE
DIGITAL
www.3ammagazine.com
Co-Editor-In-Chief: Andrew Gallix.
Editors: Jospehine Schreiber (criticism
and non-fiction); SJ Fowler (poetry);
Sylvia Warren and Isabella Streffen
(contributing)
Publishes a wide range of fiction,
flash fiction, poetry, interviews
and criticism, all to-the-point,
funny and whip-smart. Writers
are urged to contact the relevant
editor according to the subject
field of their submission. Tagline:
'Whatever it is, we're against it'.

404 INK
PRINT, DIGITAL AND E-ZINE
hello@404ink.com
www.404ink.com
Editors: Heather McDaid, Laura Jones
Established 2016. Mixed form. $15
subscription per issue, via Patreon,
or available via the publisher
website at £10 per single issue.
Only subscribers/purchasers can
read all content, though some
pieces are made available to all via
the website.
GENRES: Fiction; non-fiction; poetry.
SUBMISSIONS: Open to all. Submit
by email to submissions@404ink.
com. Guidelines are available
www.404ink.com/submissions.
Usually responds in one to three
months. Rejections are to a
standard template and include an
overview of main points as to why
pieces were not published in the
issue. Contributors are paid a set
rate, and receive free copies of the
magazine.

WE SAY: We looked at a PDF of
Issue 5 – the first to be produced
in *404 Ink*'s newly revamped style.
On the theme of Space, it features
a truly eclectic range of work that
interprets the prompt in all ways
ranging from inclusive spaces in
publishing, to an insight into how
it feels to be a NASA astronaut
(yes, Adriana Ocampo features).
The cover is stunning – a brightly
illustrated alien who appears to be
made up of a collage of elements
of the work in the magazine.
**See also: 404 Ink (prose publishers)
p91**

A3 REVIEW, THE ☆
PRINT
PO Box 65016, London N5 9BD
020 7193 7642
a3@writingmaps.com
www.thea3review.com
Editor: Shaun Levin
Established 2014. Mixed output,
including fiction, poetry and art.
Available direct from the publisher
website.
GENRES: Literary fiction; flash
fiction; poetry; graphic stories;
comics.
SUBMISSIONS: Open to all, during
submissions windows. Submit via
thea3review.submittable.com/
submit, where full guidelines are
also available. A reading fee is
charged. Usually responds in one
to three months. Rejections do
not include feedback unless paid
for. Authors are paid a flat fee and
receive free copies of the issue.
WE SAY: Microfiction, poetry and
illustrations printed on both sides

of one piece of thick, coloured A3 paper, with the creases acting as page dividers. The bright illustrations pull the page as a whole together. It's an ingenious design idea, very striking; the fiction and poetry are nuggets of strong writing, whole narratives in just a few words.
See also: prose publishers p91 and poetry publishers p15

A NEW ULSTER ☆
PRINT AND DIGITAL
g.greig3@gmail.com
anuanewulster.wixsite.com/anewulster
Editors: Amos Greig, Arizahn, E V Greig
Established 2012. Print copies available direct from publisher website. All online content is freely available to all.
GENRES: Literary; humour; fiction.
SUBMISSIONS: Open to all. Submit by email to anu.anewulster@gmail.com. Guidelines at anuanewulster.wixsite.com/anewulster/submission-guidelines. Usually responds within four weeks. Feedback on request. Contributors receive a digital copy of the magazine.
WE SAY: We looked at a digital version of *A New Ulster* (Issue 83), which champions the work of Northern Irish writers, as well as welcoming global writers. Also available in print, it has a neatly presented design – stylish and clean, with minimal artwork – and includes biographies of its featured writers. It showcases their work well, allowing for a good number of poems for each poet, interspersed with stories. Clearly dedicated and filling the gaps left by *The Honest Ulsterman* and *Fortnight* magazines.

A VOID
PRINT
www.morbidbooks.net
info@morbidbooks.net
Based in South London, *A Void* is an annual magazine published by Morbid Books. They pride themselves on being a 'Temple of Surrealist Literature' and welcome enquires and proposals for their upcoming issues.
See also: Morbid Books (prose publishers p155 and poetry publishers p54)

AFRICAN WRITING
PRINT AND E-ZINE
editor@african-writing.com
www.african-writing.com
Editor: Chuma Nwokolo
Mixed form, including poetry, essays, fiction, memoir and other prose. Its 'natural constituency of writers and material are African or Diasporan' but 'any writer who writes into the African Condition' will be considered – a description, they say, to 'interpret boldly'.

ALL-NEW SWIMMERS CLUB, THE
E-ZINE
www.all-new.swimmersclub.co.uk
Editors: Victoria Brown, Richard Brammer
Established 2015. Mixed form. Free access – all online content available to all.
GENRES: Short stories; literary interviews.
SUBMISSIONS: Open to all. Submit by email to email.swimmersclub@gmail.com. Guidelines at www.all-new.swimmersclub.co.uk/submissions. Usually responds within four weeks. Unpaid.
WE SAY: This is a graphics-led site, with the home page contents

a grid of linked photographic images leading to articles and stories. Each photo includes a subhead with the author or subject name and a category header (e.g. Subterraneans are interviews within subcultures and independent culture; Treading Water leads to short fiction). Offerings include audio as well as text, and the photographic images add a lot to the experience. Biographies are short, with author/interviewee info offered as a 'factfile'. There's much to explore here.

See also: Dostoyevsky Wannabe (poetry publishers p31 and prose publishers p118)

ALL THE SINS
E-ZINE
allthesinssubmissions@gmail.com
www.allthesins.co.uk
Editors: Lisa Davison, Sinéad Keegan
Established 2016. Mixed form, published quarterly, with additional long and short features on arts-related topics published on the website. All online content is available to all, with additional editorial feedback and behind-the-scenes information available to patrons (see the magazine's Patreon page at www.patreon.com/allthesins).
GENRES: Literary; experimental; slipstream; collaborative.
SUBMISSIONS: Open to all. Submit via email to allthesinssubmissions@gmail.com. Guidelines at www.allthesins.co.uk/submissions. Usually responds in one to three months. To date the editors have been able to offer basic feedback to every submitter, and offer extended, guaranteed feedback to patrons. Unpaid.
WE SAY: We looked at Issue 2 of *All the Sins*, as well as two standalone features. The Issue 2 'cover page' consisted of a beautiful smudge line drawing illustrating the title text (Issue 2: Movement) on the left side of the screen. This same layout is used for the standalone essays. The contents page and editorial note are to the right, and each issue item has its own page, whether that item be writing, video, photography etc. This is a magazine that appreciates art, and its power to effect change. We particularly loved the editors' piece 'Why theatre shouldn't be safe'.

AMBIT MAGAZINE ☆
PRINT AND DIGITAL
Staithe House, Main Road, Brancaster Staithe, Norfolk PE31 8BP
07715 233221
contact@ambitmagazine.co.uk
www.ambitmagazine.co.uk
Editors: Briony Bax, Kate Pemberton, André Naffis-Sahely
Established 1959. Mixed form. Subscription £29.99 per annum. Available direct from publisher website; by post and email order; from selected/local chain bookshops; from independent bookshops; and at local literary events. Only subscribers/purchasers can access online content.
GENRES: Drama and criticism; literary fiction; poetry.
SUBMISSIONS: Open to all, during submissions windows. Submit by post (Staithe House, Main Road, Brancaster Staithe, Norfolk PE31 8BP) or through Submittable (ambit.submittable.com/submit). Guidelines available at www.ambitmagazine.co.uk/submit. Usually responds within one to three months. Rejections may include occasional unsolicited

feedback. Contributors can choose between receiving payment (set rate), a discount subscription, or print copies.

WE SAY: Clocking in at a little larger than A5, this weighty tome comes in a funky jacket sleeve with cut-out lettering. A name that bears significant industry gravitas, family-owned *Ambit* has been making waves since its launch in 1959, and remains lovingly curated from unsolicited submissions. Each edition feels like an experience; we loved how the artwork and photography was intermingled with the collection of diverse writing. An appearance in *Ambit* is a worthy notch on your writerly CV.

AMORIST, THE

PRINT AND DIGITAL
Moray House, 23-31 Great Titchfield Street, London W1W 7PA
07811 990250
belinda@theamorist.co.uk
www.theamorist.co.uk
Editor: Rowan Pelling

Features, fiction and poetry, articles and reviews, exploring sexual love. Looking for discursive, romantic, philosophical writing, with historical perspective and touching on science and technology.

ARCHIPELAGO

PRINT
PO Box 154, Thame OX9 3RQ
info@clutagpress.com
www.clutagpress.com/archipelago
Non-fiction prose and verse.
An occasional magazine – no fixed publication dates.
See also: Clutag Press (poetry publishers) p27

ARETÉ MAGAZINE

PRINT
8 New College Lane, Oxford OX1 3BN
01865 289194
aretebooks@gmail.com
www.aretemagazine.com
Editor: Craig Raine

Established 1999. Mixed form. Annual subscription costs: £27 UK individual; £30 library; $65 overseas; $85 overseas library. Issues available direct from the publisher website; in selected/local chain bookshops; in independent bookshops; and on Amazon. Some online content available to all.

GENRES: Drama and criticism; literary fiction; poetry; art, fashion and photography; biography and true stories; music, stage and screen.

SUBMISSIONS: Open to all. Submit by post to *Areté*, 8 New College Lane, Oxford, OX1 3BN. Guidelines at www.aretemagazine. co.uk/about-arete. Usually responds within one to three months. Rejections may include occasional unsolicited feedback. Contributors receive a print copy of the magazine.

WE SAY: We looked at Issue 43, which is a beautifully produced perfect-bound paperback: 157 thick, bright white pages contained in a dark grey matte, French-flap cover with a smart wraparound design and a pink cardboard inner cover. The brightly coloured titles look appropriately sophisticated and scholarly. The quantity of closely-typed text inside is rather daunting, but the reviews, poetry and fiction are actually very accessible.

See also: Areté Books (poetry publishers) p18

BANGOR LITERARY JOURNAL, THE ☆

DIGITAL
Bangor, Northern Ireland
thebangorliteraryjournal@hotmail.com
www.thebangorliteraryjournal.com
Editors: Amy Louise Wyatt and Paul Daniel Rafferty
Established 2018. Mixed output, publishing poetry, flash fiction, art, photography and reviews. Free access – all online content available to all.
SUBMISSIONS: Submit work only during the submissions windows, by email to thebangorliteraryjournal@hotmail.com. Guidelines at www.thebangorliteraryjournal.com/submissions. Usually responds within four weeks. Rejections may occasionally include unsolicited feedback. Unpaid.
WE SAY: We viewed Issue 6, which can be downloaded online free of charge. This winter issue creates a seasonal theme through its decorative cover, adding a personal touch with their Editors' Welcome, composed by Amy Louise Wyatt and Paul Daniel Rafferty. What follows is a nearly 100-page mixed-form publication, covering a variety of themes and introducing each piece with an author bio.

BANIPAL (MAGAZINE OF MODERN ARAB LITERATURE)

PRINT AND DIGITAL
1 Gough Square, London EC4A 3DE
editor@banipal.co.uk
www.banipal.co.uk
Editor: Samuel Shimon
Established 1998. Mixed output of work in translation. For subscription information, see www.banipal.co.uk/subscribe. Print issues available direct from the publisher website, and by direct mail and email order. Only subscribers/purchasers can read all digital content.
Banipal Publishing won the 2016 Sheikh Hamad Award for Translation and International Understanding, Doha, Qatar.
GENRES: Literary.
SUBMISSIONS: Editors usually select the authors and texts and content they want in each issue, and then commission the contributors, book reviewers, and translators. Full information at www.banipal.co.uk/submissions. Contributors are paid a set rate.
See also: prose publishers p100 and poetry publishers p21

BANSHEE

PRINT
bansheelit@gmail.com
www.bansheelit.com
Editors: Laura Cassidy, Claire Hennessy, Eimear Ryan
Established 2015. Mixed form. Subscriptions: €21 for one year (€25 international) or €38 for two years (€45 international). Issues available direct from publisher website; from independent bookshops; and at national and local literary events. Some online content available to all. One of Banshee's published stories was longlisted for www.writing.ie's Short Story of the Year.
GENRES: Literary fiction; memoir and personal essays.
SUBMISSIONS: Open to all, but only during submissions windows in March and October. Submit by email to bansheelit@gmail.com. See guidelines at bansheelit.tumblr.com/submissionsguidelines. Usually responds within one to three months. Rejections may occasionally include unsolicited

feedback. Contributors are paid a set rate and receive a print copy of the magazine.

WE SAY: We looked at Issue 8 of *Banshee*. Now 132 pages long (up from 98 pages in its earlier issues) this A5 magazine is beautifully designed – the cover image of bright yellow umbrellas against a blue, cloudy sky is certainly eye-catching. The materials used are of high quality: a thick, matte cover and heavy cream pages. The design is clean and neatly presented, alternating stories with poems. The writing is bold and engaging – we recognised several emerging names in the contributors list.

See also: Banshee Press (poetry publishers p21 and prose publishers p100)

BI'AN: THE UK CHINESE WRITERS' NETWORK
E-ZINE
www.bi-an.org
hello@bi-an.org

A section of the Bi'an Network website is dedicated to publishing writing by Chinese heritage writers. They accept poetry, fiction, life-writing and script, including work that has been previously published.

BLUE NIB, THE ☆
PRINT AND E-ZINE
Ecklands, Carnhill, Loughshinny, Skerries, Co Dublin
+353 858 513 376
info@thebluenib.com
www.thebluenib.com
Editors: Shirley Bell (poety and EOC), Mimi Gladman (fiction) and Dave Kavanagh (online editor)

Established 2016. Quarterly, publishing poetry, short fiction, essays, reviews and articles. Available direct from the publisher website, from independent bookshops, and from Amazon. Online content is accessible to all. *The Blue Nib* was longlisted for the 2018 Saboteur Awards Best Literary Magazine.

SUBMISSIONS: Open to all. Guidelines at www.thebluenib. com/submission-guidelines. Usually responds in one to three months. Rejections may occasionally include unsolicited feedback. Contributors receive a digital copy of the issue.

WE SAY: We reviewed the second-ever print edition of *Blue Nib* – a chunky, perfect-bound volume in a square-ish shape. The overall style is plain and simple, with few bells and whistles; there's a strict house style of single-spaced Times New Roman 12pt (although every effort will be made to reflect the author's original intention with their pieces).

See also: prose publishers p103 and poetry publishers p23

BRITISH JOURNALISM REVIEW
PRINT AND E-ZINE
SAGE Publications, 1 Oliver's Yard, 55 City Road, London EC1Y 1SP
020 7324 8500
editor@bjr.org.uk
www.bjr.org.uk
Editor: Kim Fletcher

Non-fiction magazine with a focus on society, education and politics. According to its website, it is 'designed as a forum of analysis and debate, to monitor the media, submit the best as well as the worst to scrutiny, and to raise the level of the dialogue'.

BRITTLE STAR ☆
PRINT AND DIGITAL
Diversity House 72 Nottingham Road, Arnold Nottingham NG5 6LF

0845 456 4838
brittlestarmag@gmail.com
www.brittlestar.org.uk
Editors: Martin Parker, Jacqueline Gabbitas

Established 2000. Poetry and short stories, articles and reviews of first full collections. Subscription £15 (UK) or £25 (world) for two issues. Available direct from publisher website, and by post and through bookshops. Digital edition available at www.0s-1s.com/brittle-star. Some online content available to non-subscribers.

GENRES: Literary fiction; poetry.
SUBMISSIONS: Open to all new and emerging writers (no established writers from major presses, please). Submit by post to *Brittle Star*, Diversity House 72 Nottingham Road, Arnold Nottingham NG5 6LF. Guidelines at www.brittlestar.org.uk/submissions. Usually responds within one to six months, no feedback offered on rejections. Contributors receive a print copy and a discount purchase price. Please refer to website for up-to-date information.
WE SAY: *Brittle Star* is a bit smaller than A5 and perfect bound. The PDF issue we looked at (Issue 37) was 86 pages long. The cover is striking – *Brittle Star* seems to go for images with texture, in this case a repeated pattern of grey cells (or are they pebbles?). Detailed line drawings are placed at the start of each story. The writing is punchy and in some cases rather experimental, blurring the line between poetry and prose.

BURNING HOUSE PRESS
E-ZINE
www.burninghousepress.com
infoburninghousepress@gmail.com

Open periodically to themed submissions of poetry, short stories, flash fiction, prose poems, essays, reviews, commentary, features, interviews – and all hybrids, fragments and cross-forms. Each theme is chosen and curated by a guest editor.

BURNT ROTI
PRINT
sharan.dhaliwal@burntroti.com
www.burntroti.com
Editor: Sharan Dhaliwal

Established 2016. Primarily publishes non-fiction pieces. Publication available direct from the publisher website.
Burnt Roti was a finalist for Media Platform of the Year, in the 2019 Precious Lifestyle Awards, and was nominated for the Community Organisation Award in the 2018 National Diversity Awards.
TOPICS: Culture; race; history; religion.
SUBMISSIONS: Open to all. Submit by email to sharan.dhaliwal@burntroti.com. Usually responds within four weeks. Feedback offered only if requested. Unpaid.
WE SAY: One look at *Burnt Roti*'s website shows this publisher's passion for writing that promotes inclusion and identity, grounded within the South Asian community. We looked at a PDF proof of Issue 2, which is filled with vibrant photography and writing on sexuality, race, love, and culture. This insightful publication speaks from its own community whilst speaking to universal experiences with diverse forms.

CABINET OF HEED, THE
E-ZINE
cabinetofheed@hotmail.com

www.cabinetofheed.com
Editor: Simon Webster
Established 2017. Mixed form. Free access – all online content available to all.
SUBMISSIONS: Open to all. Submit by email to cabinetofheed@hotmail.com. Guidelines at www.cabinetofheed.com/submission-guidelines. Usually responds within four weeks. Unpaid.
WE SAY: This literary journal's playful website presents each issue as a cabinet of drawers, each containing a unique piece of writing. We looked at Issue 19, which presents a range of poetry and fiction, all exploring different themes. Above anything, this is a journal that proclaims itself as being 'hungry' for good writing of any kind, although it does love a bit quirkiness.

CAMBRIDGE LITERARY REVIEW
PRINT
Trinity Hall, Cambridge CB2 1TJ
cambridgeliteraryreview@gmail.com
www.cambridgeliteraryreview.org
Editors: Lydia Wilson, Rosie Snajdr, Jocelyn Betts, and Paige Smeaton
Established 2009. Mixed form. Subscription £25/€40/$60. Available direct from publisher website and in independent bookshops. Some content is available to view as a taster online.
GENRES: Drama and criticism; literary fiction; poetry; history; and essays on a variety of subjects but mostly in the humanities, and mostly on some aspect of literature.
SUBMISSIONS: Follow Twitter @camlitrev for themed calls for submissions. Submit to these calls by post (Trinity Hall,

Cambridge CB2 1TJ) or by email (cambridgeliteraryreview@googlemail.com). Usually responds within four to six months. Rejections may include occasional unsolicited feedback. Contributors receive a print copy of the magazine.
WE SAY: *Cambridge Literary Review* is a fairly high-brow affair, which warrants attention from the likes of *TLS*. We looked at the available online content (the website reflects the print design and is easy to navigate), which includes poetry, short fiction, essays and criticism. The creative work is contemporary and accessible; the essays and criticism weighted with theoretical knowledge, but not so intellectual as to be alienating.

CARDIFF REVIEW, THE
PRINT, DIGITAL AND BLOG
John Percival Building, Colum Dr, Cardiff CF10 3EU
hello@cardiffreview.com
www.cardiffreview.com
Editors: Jamie Gillingham, Rebecca Lawn, Callum McAllister
Established 2015. Mixed form. Subscription £25/year for four issues. Publications available direct from publisher website; from selected/local chain bookshops; and from independent bookshops. Free access – all online content available to all.
GENRES: Literary.
SUBMISSIONS: Precedence given to students currently on a related postgraduate course (i.e. Creative Writing, English Literature or Journalism) or, alternatively, who have recently graduated and have yet to publish a major work. Submit by email to submissions@

cardiffreview.com. Guidelines at www.cardiffreview.com/submit. Usually responds within one to three months. Rejections may occasionally include unsolicited feedback. Contributors are paid a set rate and receive a print copy.
WE SAY: The 72-page, A5, perfect-bound eighth instalment of *The Cardiff Review* begins with two poems printed vertically down the pages, rather than horizontally, to preserve long line length. Prose pieces are headed by a large-font title set low from the top of the page, with the text beginning in single-column width in the bottom third. The magazine is stylish, wrapped in a high quality, coloured matte cover.

CATERPILLAR, THE ☆
PRINT
Ardan Grange, Belturbet, Co Cavan, Ireland
editor@thecaterpillarmagazine.com
www.thecaterpillarmagazine.com
Editor: Rebecca O'Connor
Sibling magazine to *The Moth* (see p242). Mixed form: poetry, stories and art aimed at children between the ages of 7 and 11. Annual subscription €28.
SUBMISSIONS: Open to all. See guidelines at www.thecaterpillarmagazine.com/a1-page.asp?ID=4150&page=5.
WE SAY: Slightly less than letter-sized, this saddle-stitched magazine includes various styles of colourful art, including collage, pencil drawing and digital art. In 27 pages of matte paper, the copy we saw of Issue 17, showcased such work as a fun poem rhyming eight lines with 'octopus' and another about a sheep feeling better after 'a good baaaa' with his friend.

See also: *The Moth* **(mixed-form magazine) p242**

CHAPMAN
PRINT
www.chapman-pub.co.uk
chapman-pub@blueyonder.co.uk
Established in 1970, *Chapman* prides itself on being Scotland's leading literary magazine. Based in Edinburgh, they publish a range of poetry, fiction, criticism, review and debate in each issue. They welcome a range of unsolicited submissions, with their focus being on Scotland; however *Chapman* has 'a long history of publishing international literature, both in English by non-Scots and in translation from other languages'.

CLEARING, THE
E-ZINE
jon@littletoller.co.uk
www.littletoller.co.uk/the-clearing
Mixed-form e-zine, accepting new writing in a range of forms, including essays, poetry and spoken-word, which explores and celebrates the landscapes we live in. Free access – all online content available to all.
GENRES: Travel; natural landscape and place writing.
SUBMISSIONS: Open to new and established writers, during submissions windows. The editors welcome original submissions in all written, audio and visual genres. Submissions should reflect *The Clearing*/Little Toller's concern with the natural environment – full guidelines at www.littletoller.co.uk/the-clearing.
See also: *Little Toller Books* **(prose publishers) p150**

CLOVER AND WHITE MAGAZINE
E-ZINE
editor@cloverandwhite.com
cloverandwhite.wordpress.com
An online magazine looking for short stories, flash fiction and poetry by under-represented and emerging writers, *Clover and White* publishes new work every Sunday. The editors are looking for writing that 'does something that feels fresh'.

CŌNFINGŌ
PRINT AND DIGITAL
249 Burton Road, Didsbury, Manchester M20 2WA
0161 445 0546
www.confingopublishing.uk
Editors: Tim Shearer, Zoe McLean
Established 2014. Fiction and poetry focus. Subscription £12 per annum. Available direct from publisher website; from selected/local chain bookshops; from independent bookshops; and at local literary events. Some online content available to all.
GENRES: Literary fiction; poetry; art.
SUBMISSIONS: Open to all, during submissions windows. Submit by email to tim@confingopublishing.uk. Guidelines at www.confingopublishing.uk/#!form/cry1. Usually responds within one to three months. Rejections may occasionally include unsolicited feedback. Contributors are paid a set rate and receive a print copy of the magazine.

CRANNÓG
PRINT
editor@crannogmagazine.com
www.crannogmagazine.com
Editors: Sandra Bunting, Ger Burke, Jarlath Fahy, Tony O'Dwyer
Established 2002. Fiction and poetry. Annual subscription €22.50 for three issues. Publication available at major bookshops nationwide; at independent bookshops; on bookshop websites; direct from the publisher 's website; and from Amazon (including by Kindle).
GENRES: Literary.
SUBMISSIONS: Open to all, during submissions windows. Submit via email only to editor@crannogmagazine.com. Guidelines at www.crannogmagazine.com/submissions.htm. Usually responds in eight weeks from closing date. No feedback offered with rejection. Contributors are paid a set rate and receive a print copy of the magazine.
WE SAY: A 96-page A5 perfect-bound magazine with a matte cover. In Issue 45, the titles of the pieces are framed by an upper and lower line the width of the text area; prose pieces are also started with a large, dropped letter. Although the page margins are somewhat smaller than usual, the design remains stylish. The cover image's artist is also given attention, with an artist's statement included just before the writers' biographies.

CRYSTAL MAGAZINE ☆
PRINT
3 Bowness Avenue, Prenton, Birkenhead CH43 0SD
0151 608 9736
christinecrystal@hotmail.com
christinecrystal.blogspot.com
Editor: Christine Carr
Established 2001. Mixed output – stories, articles and poetry. £18 per year for six issues, or £22 overseas. Print issues available to order via

the publication website (use Paypal button) or by direct mail (send a cheque payable to Mrs C Carr).

GENRES: Literary; nature; romance; horror; travel.

SUBMISSIONS: Submissions accepted from subscribers only (see above). Submit by post (3 Bowness Avenue, Prenton, Birkenhead CH43 0SD) or email (christinecrystal@hotmail.com). Usually responds within four weeks. No feedback offered with rejections. Unpaid.

WE SAY: A 42-page wiro-bound monthly zine with a homemade feel. We looked at Issue 112. The editor's letter often includes personal news about the founder's family, as well as remarks about that month's content. In terms of design, *Crystal* is very simple and low-key, making heavy use of Word Art and Clip Art. Readers' letters policy: kind comments or none at all.

CURLY MIND, THE

E-ZINE

reubenwoolley52@gmail.com
thecurlymindblog.wordpress.com
Editor: Reuben Woolley
Established 2014. Mixed form – mainly poetry but includes artwork and reviews. Free access – all online content available to all.

GENRES: Exploratory poetry.

SUBMISSIONS: Open to all. Submit via email to reubenwoolley52@gmail.com. Guidelines at thecurlymindblog.wordpress.com. Usually responds within four weeks. Rejections may occasionally include unsolicited feedback. Unpaid (no money is involved for anyone, including the editor).

WE SAY: Describing themselves as a blogzine, *The Curly Mind*

editors pride themselves on the avant-garde, experimentalist variety of work they publish. In their own words, 'it is definitely not mainstream!'. Looking through their published issues, this is confirmed: we saw highly obscure and experimental work that plays with space and structure.

See also: *I Am Not A Silent Poet* **(mixed-form e-zine) p232**

DAWNTREADER MAGAZINE, THE

PRINT

24 Forest Houses, Halwill, Beaworthy, Devon EX21 5UU
publishing@indigodreams.co.uk
www.indigodreams.co.uk
Editor: Dawn Bauling
Established 2007. Mainly poetry, some stories and articles under 1,000 words. Subscription £17/year for four issues. Available direct from publisher website; and by post and email order.
Indigo Dreams' editors won the Ted Slade Award for Services to Poetry 2015 (organised by Poetry Kit).

GENRES: Myth; legend; in the landscape; nature; spirituality and love; the mystic, the environment.

SUBMISSIONS: Open to all. Submit by post (IDP, 24 Forest Houses, Halwill, Beaworthy, Devon EX21 5UU) or by email (dawnidp@gmail.com). Guidelines at www.indigodreams.co.uk. Usually responds within four weeks. No feedback offered with rejection.

WE SAY: One of the Indigo Dreams' publications, *The Dawntreader* is an A5, 52-page monthly magazine, perfect bound with a (rare, these days) glossy full colour cover. We looked at Issue 039. IDP encourage comment on the included work, and welcome environmental, spiritual, folklorish etc work, which is described by one reader as 'poetry for the soul'. The magazine has an international readership and IDP foster a community of readers. **For what They Say, see Indigo Dreams Publishing Ltd (poetry publisher) p46. See also: *Sarasvati* (mixed-form magazine) p253 and *Reach Poetry* (poetry magazine) p282**

DISSECTIONS

E-ZINE
CLT, University of Brighton, Falmer, Brighton BN1 9PH
01273 643115
www.simegen.com/writers/dissections/
Editors: Gina Wisker, Michelle Bernard
Established 2006. Mainly fiction. Free access – all online content available to all.
GENRES: Fantasy/sci-fi; horror; literary fiction; poetry; non-fiction (horror, literary criticism).
SUBMISSIONS: Open to all. Submit by post (CLT, University of Brighton, Falmer, Brighton BN1 9PH, to Gina Wisker) or by email (ginwskr@aol.com and michelle. bernard64@gmail.com). Usually responds within three to four months. Rejections do not include feedback. Unpaid.
WE SAY: An annually updated e-zine that focuses on the horror genre. Line drawings illustrate each piece, and it has a dark palette. It's easy to navigate to poems, short stories and reviews, which are contemporary and must have a fresh take on any horror tropes. The poetry we saw was mainly narrative and lyrical in style, and the prose was gripping. No writer biographies were offered.

DNA MAGAZINE

DIGITAL
hello@dnamag.co.uk
www.dnamag.co.uk
Editor: Katie Marsden
Established 2017. Only accepts non-fiction prose. Free access – all online content available to all.
GENRES: Twitterature; creative flash non-fiction; poetry.
SUBMISSIONS: Open to all, during submission windows. Submit by email to submissions@dnamag. co.uk. Guidelines at www.dnamag. co.uk. Usually responds within one to three months. Rejections may occasionally include unsolicited feedback. Unpaid.
WE SAY: We looked at Issue 2, digitally available through Issuu. The cover features an arresting photograph with a bright yellow background. The inner pages make strong use of graphics, sometimes provided by contributors, to accentuate the writing. Items are rarely over one page long, and include 'twitterature' (flash non-fiction) and experimental non-fiction; as well as straightforward autobiographical texts. Each piece is a glimpse into someone else's life. An engaging and stylish magazine, we loved 'Divine Delivery': twitterature about a package, styled to appear in the 'bottom' of a box.

DODGING THE RAIN

E-ZINE
alwaysdodgingtherain@gmail.com (for general queries only)
dodgingtherain.wordpress.com
Established 2016. Mainly publishes poetry, but also drama, fiction, features, art and non-fiction. Free access – all online content available to all.

GENRES: Contemporary; literary.
SUBMISSIONS: Open to all. Follow the guidelines at dodgingtherain. wordpress.com/submissions. Usually responds in one to three months. Rejections may occasionally include unsolicited feedback. Unpaid.
WE SAY: An art and literary journal, *Dodging the Rain* platforms new and emerging voices on their colourful, tiled website. From viewing the plethora of writing they publish on a regular basis, it is clear that *Dodging the Rain* care deeply about maintaining a steady stream of content. Their published pieces are all presented through vibrant and detailed images, making their website genuinely appealing.

DREAM CATCHER
PRINT

161 Lowther Street, York YO31 7LZ
01904 733767
dreamcatchersubmissions@gmail.com
www.dreamcatchermagazine.co.uk
Editor: Wendy Pratt
Established 1996. Mixed output. Subscriptions cost £15 for two issues annually. Publications available direct from the publisher website; by direct mail and email order; at local and national literary events; and from bookshop websites including Gardners and Neilson. Back issues of the magazine soon to be available as PDFs.
Work from *Dream Catcher* was shortlisted for the Forward Prize in 2011.
GENRES: Poetry; short stories; book reviews; art; essays/criticism.
SUBMISSIONS: Open to all. Submit by post (161 Lowther Street, York YO31 7LZ) or email (dreamcatchersubmissions@gmail.

com). Guidelines available at www. dreamcatchermagazine.co.uk. Responds to submissions within one to three months. Rejections may include unsolicited feedback. Contributors are offered a discount purchase price on copies of the issue.
WE SAY: We looked at a PDF of Issue 39, a 100-page eclectic mix of poetry, prose, artwork and reviews. This diverse publication is introduced with an abstract, vintage cover graphic interspersed with modern elements, encapsulating the adventurous nature of the magazine. On their website, *Dream Catcher* describes itself as an ever-evolving publication, particularly looking to engage further with the performing arts as it grows.
See also: Stairwell Books (prose publishers p185 and poetry publishers p77)

ELEMENTUM
PRINT

www.elementumjournal.com
Published twice a year, *Elementum* is an independent literary journal based in Dorset with a focus on nature writing and visual story telling. They are periodically open to submissions and commission work from both established and emerging writers and artists who offer differing perspectives and new insights.

ÉPOQUE PRESS EZINE
E-ZINE

info@epoquepress.com
www.epoquepress.com/ezine
Editor: varies from issue to issue
Established 2018. Mixed form. Free access – all online content available to all.

GENRES: Short stories, poetry, spoken word, essays, photography, visual art and music.
SUBMISSIONS: Open to all. Submit by email to submissions@epoquepress.com. Guidelines at www.epoquepress.com/submissions. Usually responds in one to three months. Rejections may occasionally include unsolicited feedback. Unpaid.
WE SAY: *époque press'* webzine, with white text against a dark background, certainly reflects their latest theme, 'departures'. The zine celebrates almost every art form, from spoken word to photography. Every piece interprets the theme differently, leading to a range of styles and approaches. The editors appear to favour creativity and individual exploration.
See also: époque press (prose publishers) p120

EROTIC REVIEW
E-ZINE
editorial@ermagazine.org
www.eroticreviewmagazine.com
Editor: Jamie Maclean
Aims to 'take a lively, intelligent approach to erotica and sexuality', and publishes fiction, articles, photography, art portfolios and reviews, as well as videos and podcasts.

FIREWORDS
PRINT AND DIGITAL
info@firewords.co.uk
www.firewords.co.uk
Editors: Dan Burgess and Jen Scott
Established 2014. Mainly fiction. Publication available direct from publisher website and at independent bookshops.
GENRES: Short stories and poetry; artwork. No non-fiction.

SUBMISSIONS: Open to all during submissions windows. Submit via online submissions form at www.fireworks.co.uk/submit (guidelines found at the same place). Responses take up to three months, with feedback only if requested. Contributors receive a copy of the magazine.
WE SAY: You'd never guess this perfect-bound, full-colour literary magazine wasn't produced by a full-time team. Smaller than A5 and full of bold design, it's an innovative 48-page affair printed on matte paper. The writing is thought-provoking, unique and contemporary, but it was the unexpected design quirks that had us hooked, from the striking illustrations to the contents laid out on the back cover like a rock album.

FIVE DIALS
DIGITAL
80 Strand, London WC2R 0RL
hamish@hamishhamilton.co.uk
fivedials.com
Editor: Craig Taylor
Established 2008. Mixed output. Free access – all online content available to all. *Five Dials* is part of Penguin Books.
GENRE: General interest.
WE SAY: *Five Dials* has a modern, experimental style. We looked at Issue 51, The Body, which uses simple graphics of bodies throughout as well as curtains at the start and end of its contents, adding a theatrical quality. With some texts portraying the everyday experience and others delving into more abstract visions, *Five Dials* appears to be a press that favours variety and playfulness in its publications.

FLASHBACK FICTION ☆
E-ZINE
flashback@flashbackfiction.com
www.flashbackfiction.com
Editors: Ingrid Jendrzejewski, Kellie
Carle, Emily Devane, Anita Goveas,
Damhnait Monaghan, Sharon Telfer,
and Judi Walsh
Established 2018. Publishing flash
fiction, prose poetry and hybrid
writing. The editors publish one
story and one author interview
most weeks. Free access – all
online content available to all.
The editors have nominated stories
for various awards, and *Flashback
Fiction*'s authors have won places
in anthologies *Best Small Fictions*
and *Best Microfictions*.
GENRES: Historical.
SUBMISSIONS: Open to all,
during submissions windows only.
Submit by email to submissions@
flashbackfiction.com. Guidelines at
www.flashbackfiction.com/index.
php/submit. Usually responds in
one to three months. Rejections
may occasionally include
unsolicited feedback. Unpaid.
WE SAY: We viewed a range
of publications from *FlashBack
Fiction*, all engaging with historical
ideas. Their website displays their
published works in the authentic
format of a timeline, with each
text's setting placing it in historical
context. With texts spanning
from the 2000s to the Stone Age,
Flashback Fiction's texts cover vast
periods of time, whilst individually
portraying a closeness to home
through familial and community
focused writing.

FLY ON THE WALL WEBZINE ☆
DIGITAL AND PRINT
isabellekenyon@hotmail.co.uk
www.flyonthewallpoetry.co.uk

Editor: Isabelle Kenyon
Established 2018. Mainly publishes
poetry, but also prose, including
flash fiction. As of 2019, in paid
digital and print form.
GENRES: Political; literary.
SUBMISSIONS: Open to all. Submit
by email to isabellekenyon@
hotmail.co.uk. Guidelines at www.
flyonthewallpoetry.co.uk/webzine-
guidelines. Usually responds
within four weeks. Rejections may
occasionally include unsolicited
feedback. Contributors receive
a digital copy of the issue and
royalties.
WE SAY: We looked at Fly on
the Wall's *Webzine 2: Change
and New Beginnings*, edited by
Isabelle Kenyon with artwork by
Amy Alexander. The webzine
boasts extensive poetry on a
variety of themes, printed in a
simple black and white typeface.
The cover page presents an
obscure illustration of the human
body, acting as the only image
in this publication. The back of
the issue also provides interviews
with authors from Fly on the Wall's
anthology, *Persona Non Grata*.
**See also: prose publishers (p128)
and poetry publishers (p37)**

FOR BOOKS' SAKE
E-ZINE
jane@forbookssake.net
www.forbookssake.net
Editor: Jane Bradley
Mainly fiction, reviews, interviews,
articles. Free access – all online
content available to all.
GENRES: Literary fiction; poetry;
YA; biography and true stories;
music, stage and screen; society,
education and politics.
SUBMISSIONS: Submit during
submissions windows. Open

to self-identifying women and especially encouraged from women of colour, disabled women, queer women, trans women and women from low-income backgrounds. Submit through Submittable at forbookssake.submittable.com/submit. Pitches for reviews/features can be emailed to reviews@forbookssake.net / features@forbookssake.net. Guidelines at forbookssake.submittable.com/submit. Usually responds within four weeks.

For a fuller description of this press, see also: poetry publishers p38 and prose publishers p129

FOXTROT UNIFORM
PRINT

2 Sowell Street, Broadstairs, Kent CT10 2AT
foxtrotuniformpoetry@gmail.com
foxtrotuniformblog.wordpress.com
Editors: Joshua Cialis and Reece D Merrifield

Established 2017. Mixed output. Annual subscription £7 for two issues. Available by direct mail and email order, from independent bookshops and at local literary events.
GENRES: Literary; experimental; spontaneous; modern; political.
SUBMISSIONS: Open to all. Submit by email to foxtrotuniformpoetry@gmail.com. Guidelines at foxtrotuniformblog.wordpress.com/2019/01/10/submissions-for-publication. Usually responds within four weeks. Rejections may occasionally include unsolicited feedback. Contributors receive free copies of the magazine.
WE SAY: Set up by four literature students, *Foxtrot Uniform* prides itself on seeking out the unseen

and providing fresh new options for writers and readers. We looked at the first four issues of their magazine in PDF format. They celebrate poetry and prose on a variety of topics – and there is also a continual development in cover design, showing the growth and character that this publisher is gaining with each new issue.
See also: poetry publishers p39

FROM GLASGOW TO SATURN
PRINT AND DIGITAL

fromglasgowtosaturn@glasgow.ac.uk
glasgowtosaturn.com
Editors: Suki Hollywood, Daniel Gee Husson, Erin MacDonald, Erin Morin, and Siobhan Mulligan

Established 2007. Mixed output. Print copies available by direct mail and email order and at local literary events. All online content is available to all.
SUBMISSIONS: Submitters must be affiliated with the University of Glasgow and may submit work only during the submissions windows, by email to fromglasgowtosaturn@glasgow.ac.uk. Guidelines at glasgowtosaturn.com/submit-work/guidelines. Usually responds within one to three months. No feedback is offered with rejections. Contributors receive print copies of the issue and a select few are invited to read at the launch party.
WE SAY: Produced within the University of Glasgow, *From Glasgow to Saturn* is anything but confined to the vibrant Scottish city. We considered a PDF of Issue 42 of the magazine, containing more than 70 pages of diverse poetry and prose. The editors' introduction immediately sets the global identity of this publication, with the members of staff spanning

the globe. What follows is a vast array of written pieces including both traditional forms and structural experimentation, all embedded with personality and voice.

FUR-LINED GHETTOS

PRINT
editorflg@gmail.com
www.fur-linedghettos.weebly.com
Editor: Sophie Essex
Established 2012. Mixed output. Available direct from the publisher website.

GENRES: Experimental; literary; weird; surreal.

SUBMISSIONS: Open to all. Submit by email to editorflg@gmail.com. Usually responds in one to three months. No feedback offered with rejection. Contributors receive free copies of the magazine.

See also: Salò Press (prose publishers p178 and poetry publishers p71)

GOLD DUST MAGAZINE

PRINT AND DIGITAL
55 Elmsdale Road, Walthamstow, London E17 6PN
mailtallulah@gmail.com
www.golddustmagazine.co.uk
Editors: Omma Velada (founder), Adele Geraghty (poetry), David Gardiner (prose)
Established 2004. Mixed form. Also releases 'best of' anthologies containing the best short stories and poetry. Available direct from publisher website. All online content is freely available to all.

GENRES: Literary fiction; drama; reviews; features; fantasy; sci-fi; romance; graphic fiction; photography; artwork.

SUBMISSIONS: Open to all. Content selected solely on merit, regardless of the age, gender, reputation or prior publication history of the writer. Submit by email to sirat@davidgardiner.net (prose) or bramwith22@aol.com (poetry). Usually responds within one to three months. Includes feedback with rejection. Unpaid.

WE SAY: *Gold Dust* offers its 50-page magazine in three formats: as digital (free), black-and-white print (cheapish), and full-colour print (less cheap). We looked at the digital version of Issue 28 on issuu.com. Alternating features, reviews, stories and poems throughout, the magazine is liberally scattered with photo illustrations. Its layout is closer to a lifestyle magazine than your average literary magazine. The contents are well curated – we think most people would find something to enjoy here.

GORSE

PRINT AND E-ZINE
info@gorse.ie
gorse.ie
Established 2014. Mixed form. Subscription: two issues €35 (Ireland); €45 (rest of the world). Available direct from the publisher website; from independent bookshops; and at local literary events, with some online content available to all, updated on a rolling basis.
Gorse was shortlisted for the Association of Illustrators awards, Book Category, 2014.

GENRES: Literary fiction; poetry; essays; interviews.

SUBMISSIONS: During submissions windows, submit by email to info@gorse.ie. Usually responds within one to three months, with a standard rejection (no feedback). Contributors are paid a set rate, and receive a print copy and a discount purchase price on the magazine.

WE SAY: Thick enough to be an anthology, *Gorse* – which is a very occasional publication – features beautiful matte covers with regular artist Niall McCormack's bold, textured paintings. Containing essays, poems and stories, this is a high quality publication in every sense of the word. The writing is sharp, sometimes traditional, sometimes experimental (see the poems from Kimberly Campanello in Issue 4, available online).

GRANTA MAGAZINE
PRINT AND DIGITAL
12 Addison Avenue, London W11 4QR
020 7605 1360
info@granta.com
www.granta.com
Editor-in-Chief: Sigrid Rausing
Established 1979. Mixed form. Annual subscription £34 (print and digital); £12 (digital only). Available direct from publisher website; by post and email order; at chain bookshops nationwide; in independent bookshops; on newsstands; at national literary events; at local literary events; and from Amazon and other bookshop websites.

Only subscribers/purchasers can access all of the online content, but some online content is freely available to all.

GENRES: Literary fiction; poetry; biography and true stories; history; popular science and nature; society, education and politics; travel; photography.

SUBMISSIONS: During submissions windows, submit via Submittable to granta.submittable.com/

submit (guidelines at the same address). Agented submissions also welcome. Usually responds within one to three months. A rejection may occasionally include unsolicited feedback. Contributors are paid a set rate.

WE SAY: We saw a copy of the 40th birthday edition of *Granta* magazine, a bumper collection of writing from their archives with a cheerful, celebratory cover using overlapping prime colours. The production quality is, as with all Granta publications, high. It contains some of the best writing from *Granta*'s 40 years, including work by Angela Carter, Raymond Carver, Mary Gaitskill, Binyavanga Wainaina and many other heavyweight names.

See also: Granta Books (prose publisher) p131

GUTTER MAGAZINE
PRINT AND DIGITAL
Gutter Magazine Ltd, 0/2, 258 Kenmure Street, Glasgow G41 2QY
contactguttermagazine@gmail.com
www.guttermag.co.uk
Editors: Henry Bell, Kate MacLeary, Colin Begg (lead editors). Board includes Ryan Vance, Calum Roger, Katy Hastie, Laura Waddell, Robbie Guillory
Established 2011, reformed as a co-operative in 2017. Mainly fiction. Annual subscription £14. Available direct from publisher website; from some chain and independent bookshops; and at literary events. Some online content is available to all.

GENRES: Scottish literature; literary fiction; prose; poetry.

SUBMISSIONS: Open to all. Submit by via the website at www.guttermag.co.uk/submit

(guidelines at the same address). Usually responds in six months; feedback unavailable. Contributors receive a print copy of the magazine and £25 payment.

WE SAY: We're big fans of this bold, trail-blazing magazine. We looked at Issue 20. The stark A5 covers are edgy and eye-catching – they clearly know their graphic design stuff – and the page count is chunky at 155. Cleanly laid out on thick cream pages, the writing is varied and thought-provoking, and though the contributors must have some connection to Scotland, the appeal is global in its scope.

HAVERTHORN
PRINT
haverthorn@gmail.com
www.hvtn.co.uk
Editor: Andrew Wells
Established 2014. Mixed-form magazine. Available direct from publisher website; and at local literary events.

SUBMISSIONS: Open to all. Submit by email to haverthorn@gmail.com. Guidelines at www.hvtn.co.uk/submission. Usually responds within four weeks, but please note that response times are usually faster in January and August. Feedback offered only if requested. Contributors receive a print copy of the magazine.

HERE COMES EVERYONE
PRINT AND DIGITAL
ICE, Parkside, Coventry CV1 2NE
raef@herecomeseveryone.me
matt@herecomeseveryone.me
herecomeseveryone.me
Editors: Raef Boylan, Matthew Barton
Established 2012. Mixed form. Publication available by direct post and email order; local literary events; and from independent bookshops and bookshop websites.

GENRES: No fixed genres. (Poetry, short stories, creative non-fiction, visual artwork.)

SUBMISSIONS: Open to all. Submit through HCE website at: herecomeseveryone.me/submit/. Usually responds within four to six months. Rejection may occasionally include unsolicited feedback. Unpaid.

WE SAY: We looked at The Rituals Issue – Volume 7, Issue 3 of *Here Comes Everyone*'s biannual magazine. This publication presents a thrilling blend of mixed-form writing and visual pieces, using ritualistic typefaces and graphics to bind the issue's theme. Each issue clearly makes equal effort to follow its chosen theme, with futuristic fonts and digital themed graphics on the cover of The Tomorrow Issue, paying testament to the publisher's creative ambition.

HOTEL
PRINT
07532 128558
editors@partisanhotel.co.uk
www.partisanhotel.co.uk
Editors: Dominic Jaeckle, Thomas Chadwick and Jon Auman
Established 2016. Publishes poetry, essays, literary fiction, art writing and photography. Annual subscription £16 for two issues. Available direct from the publisher website; by post and email order; at local literary events; and from independent bookshops.

SUBMISSIONS: Open to all. Submit by email to editors@partisanhotel.co.uk. Guidelines at www.partisanhotel.co.uk/submissions.

Usually responds in one to three months. Offers feedback on rejected work only if requested. Contributors receive a copy of the issue.

HYPNOPOMP
E-ZINE
hypnopompblog.wordpress.com
hypnopompmag@gmail.com
Looks for 'strange and/or experimental short fiction', as well as poems, essays and articles for publication online.

I AM NOT A SILENT POET
E-ZINE
reubenwoolley52@gmail.com
iamnotasilentpoet.wordpress.com
Editor: Reuben Woolley
Established 2014. Mixed form – mainly poetry but includes artwork and reviews. Free access – all online content available to all. *I Am Not A Silent Poet* was shortlisted for the Saboteur Awards in 2017 and 2018, and came second in both years.
GENRES: Protest poetry.
SUBMISSIONS: Open to all. Submit via email to reubenwoolley52@gmail.com. Guidelines at iamnotasilentpoet. wordpress.com/about. Usually responds within four weeks. Rejections may occasionally include unsolicited feedback. Unpaid (no money is involved for anyone, including the editor).
WE SAY: On a simply-structured website, *I Am Not A Silent Poet* publishes protest poetry, focusing on themes surrounding the broad experience of abuse in modern life. Underneath the bold and eye-catching header image, their equally bold poems are published in full form, boasting

an enticing variety of structure and style.
See also: *The Curly Mind* (mixed-form e-zine) p223

IDLE INK
ZINE
idleink@outlook.com
www.twitter.com/_idleink_
Editor: J L Corbett
Established 2017. Mixed form. Publication available at local literary events and on Etsy (link on Twitter page).
GENRES: Literary; sci-fi; horror; introspective.
SUBMISSIONS: Open to all, during submission windows. Submit by email to idleink@ outlook.com. Guidelines at www.twitter.com/_idleink_/ status/881103424728817664. Acknowledgement of submission within 24 hours. Usually responds with a decision within one to three months, with feedback only if requested. Contributors receive print copies.
WE SAY: Issue 1 of *Idle Ink* has the the title 'Madness'. The publishing style is simple: staple spine, folded green cardboard cover reminiscent of pamphlets; 20 thick white paper inner pages. The front cover is illustrated with a pen-and-ink drawing of a face made up of four different characters; the issue contains four stories, and the back cover gives a tagline for each story, though there is a standard contents page as well. Every story is also illustrated with a line drawing. The stories in this issue skirt the edges of genre fiction: madness, aliens, horror, psychic gifts and robots abound. It's a quick read, but a satisfying one.

INK SWEAT & TEARS ☆
E-ZINE
www.inksweatandtears.co.uk
Editor: Helen Ivory
Established 2007. Primarily poetry. Free access – all online content available to all.
GENRES: Poetry; word and image work; flash and short fiction (under 750 words); reviews of poetry books.
SUBMISSIONS: Open to all. Guidelines at www.inksweatandtears.co.uk/pages/?page_id=23. Usually responds within one to three months. No feedback with rejection. Unpaid, but readers vote for Pick of the Month and the winning writer receives a £10 gift card.
WE SAY: Clearly signposted and publishing new content each day. The magazine focuses mainly on poetry and reviews and takes a contemporary approach to its content, with a fair amount of free verse and prose-poetry, but without stepping into the realms of the wildly experimental. There's a clear sense of curation and selection. Each piece of creative writing includes a brief biography of the contributor. This is a good site for a poet's CV, and a welcoming way for readers to discover your work.
See also: Ink Sweat & Tears Press (poetry publishers) p47

INTERPRETER'S HOUSE, THE
ONLINE
6/12 Commercial Wharf, Edinburgh EH6 6LF
editorinterpretershouse@gmail.com
theinterpretershouse.org
Editors: Georgi Gill (managing editor), Annie Rutherford (fiction editor), Andrew Wells (reviews editor)
Established as a print journal in 1984. Online publication since June 2018. Mainly poetry, but also short fiction and reviews.
GENRES: Poetry; short stories on all subjects; reviews.
SUBMISSIONS: Open to all, during submissions windows (though past contributors are asked to wait three issues after appearing in the magazine before submitting again). Submit by email (interpretershousesubmissions@gmail.com). Guidelines at theinterpretershouse.org/submissions. Usually responds within one to three months.
WE SAY: We considered Issue 79 of *The Interpreter's House*. This magazine is presented dynamically yet simply – the website is uncluttered and easy to navigate, with clear links to each featured piece. A wide range of themes are covered in this issue, from childbirth to languages to technology, with a mixture of both traditional and experimental writing structures.

IRIS
PRINT
www.hurststreetpress.co.uk
Editors: Beth Sparks, Shoshana Kessler
Established 2016. Mixed form. Publication available direct from publisher website; from selected/local chain bookshops and independent bookshops.
GENRES: No fixed genres.
SUBMISSIONS: Open to all. Usually responds within four weeks. Rejection may occasionally include unsolicited feedback. Contributors receive a print copy of the magazine.
For a fuller description of this press see Hurst Street Press (poetry publishers p45 and prose publishers p140)

IRISH LITERARY REVIEW
E-ZINE
editor@irishliteraryreview.com
www.irishliteraryreview.com
Editor: Catherine Higgins-Moore
A mixed-form magazine,
publishing poetry, flash fiction,
short stories and interviews.
Welcomes submissions from
Ireland and around the world.

ISLAND REVIEW, THE
E-ZINE
mail@theislandreview.com
www.theislandreview.com
Editors: Jordan Ogg, Malachy Tallack
Established 2013. Mixed form.
All online content freely available
to all.
GENRES: Crime/thriller/mystery;
fantasy/sci-fi; historical fiction;
literary fiction; poetry; art, fashion
and photography; biography
and true stories; history; popular
science and nature; travel.
SUBMISSIONS: Open to all.
Submit through Submittable at
theislandreview.submittable.
com/submit/ (guidelines at same
address). Usually responds in up
to six months. Usually no feedback
if rejected, but may include
occasional unsolicited feedback.
Unpaid.
WE SAY: A clean, heavily illustrated
website, featuring writing inspired
by islands. It's a niche subject with
great potential. One story we
particularly liked imagines Glasgow
as a city of islands. The site is
updated regularly, with work well
curated and presented.

JOTTERS UNITED LIT-ZINE ☆
E-ZINE
unitedjotters@gmail.com
jottersutd.wix.com/jotters-united
Editor: Nick Gerrard

Established 2014. Mainly fiction.
Free access – all online content
available to all.
GENRES: Literary fiction; poetry;
biography and true stories; travel.
SUBMISSIONS: Open to all. Submit
by email to unitedjotters@gmail.
com. Guidelines at jottersutd.
wixsite.com/jotters-united/submit.
Usually responds within four
weeks. Rejections may occasionally
include unsolicited feedback.
Unpaid.
WE SAY: Bold and bright, *Jotters
United* combines bright illustration
and surreal artwork with videos,
music, slideshows and, of course,
writing. The menu starts at Issue
1, so it's a bit of a scroll to get to
the most recent work, but once
you find it, it's clearly laid out, with
six writers per issue. The writing
itself is in a clear large-ish font; the
stories very much slices of life.

JUNCTION BOX
E-ZINE
goodiebard2@googlemail.com
www.glasfrynproject.org.uk/w/
category/junction-box
Editor: Lyndon Davies
Established 2015. Publishes poetry,
prose and criticism. All online
content is available to all.
SUBMISSIONS: Submissions by
invitation only.
WE SAY: Issues of *Junction Box*
are presented with a succinct Issue
home page introduction, and a
menu to the right of the screen.
Presentation of the articles vary:
sometimes selecting an item
from the menu will take you to
an introductory paragraph and
biography of the writer, with a
link to a clearly presented PDF,
complete with images where
necessary and easier on the eyes

than a website page. Others lead to videos or articles presented directly in the browser, in slightly smaller font than is used for the PDF presentations. The writing is critical, well-argued and often quite academic in tone.

See also: Aquifer Books (poetry publishers) p17

KHIDR COLLECTIVE ZINE
PRINT
69 Uxbridge Road, Shepherds Bush, London W12 8NR
07852 337369
khidrcollective@googlemail.com
www.khidrcollective.co.uk
Editors: Zain Dada, Raeesah Akhtar, Zainab Rahim and Nishat Alam

Established 2017. Publishes prose and poetry. Available direct from the publisher; by direct mail and e-mail orders; from independent bookshops; and at local literary events.

GENRE: Literary.

SUBMISSIONS: Open to all. Submit by email to khidrcollective@ googlemail.com. Guidelines at www.khidrcollective.co.uk. Usually responds in one to three months. No feedback offered with rejections. Contributors are paid a flat fee.

WE SAY: *Khidr Collective*'s website is a sleek and stylish presentation of their vast, multidisciplinary works. As well as their biannual publication featuring the work of Muslim writers, *Khidr Collective* also digitally publish written and visual projects including photography and comics, all spiritually grounded in the origin of their name; the religious figure 'Khidr'.

See also: prose publishers p144 and poetry publishers p48

LABLIT.COM
E-ZINE
editorial@lablit.com
www.lablit.com
Editor: Dr Jennifer Rohn

Mixed lab-lit genre writing – fiction, non-fiction, reviews, interviews etc. Note: lab-lit is not sci-fi. The magazine is 'dedicated to real laboratory culture and to the portrayal and perceptions of that culture', so stick to realistic science, please, written to inform, entertain and surprise non-scientists as well as scientists.

LAMPETER REVIEW, THE
DIGITAL
The Journal of the Lampeter Creative Writing Centre
info@lampeter-review.com
www.lampeter-review.com

The online magazine of Lampeter Creative Writing Centre (part of the University of Wales, Trinity St David), this publication accepts submissions of prose, poetry and screenplays/ plays. Contributors receive a hard copy of the magazine.

LEARNED PIG, THE
E-ZINE
tom@thelearnedpig.org
www.thelearnedpig.org
Editor: Tom Jeffreys

Established 2013. Mixed form. Free access – all online content available to all.

GENRES: Art; nature writing; philosophy; poetry; creative non-fiction.

SUBMISSIONS: Open to all. Submit by email to tom@ thelearnedpig.org. Guidelines at www.thelearnedpig.org/contact. Usually responds within four weeks. Individual feedback is provided in all rejections. Unpaid.

WE SAY: This is a graphics-heavy zine, with every article heralded by a photo banner. As this Guide went to press, the zine's approach to editorial was in the process of changing. Having found themed editorial approaches proved successful, work now appears under the editorial sections 'Fields', 'Rhythm', 'Root Mapping', and 'Rot', with the reasoning behind these themes fully and eloquently explained, and a separate editor for each section. Previously selected work for *The Learned Pig* has included eye-catching art and intense reading, and we expect this tradition will continue.

LETTERS PAGE, THE
DIGITAL
School of English, University of Nottingham, Nottingham NG7 2RD
editor@theletterspage.ac.uk
www.theletterspage.ac.uk
Editor: Jon McGregor
Established 2013. Mixed form. Available direct from publisher website, with all online content freely available to all.
GENRES: Literary and poetry correspondence.
SUBMISSIONS: Open to all. Submit by post to *The Letters Page*, School of English, University of Nottingham, Nottingham NG7 2RD. Guidelines at www.theletterspage.ac.uk/letterspage/submissions.aspx. Usually responds within one to three months. No feedback is offered with rejections. Contributors are paid a set rate.
WE SAY: The art of letter writing turned into a lit-zine, The Letters Page consists of handwritten letters that have been transcribed into a simple and effective layout. These letters appear in the magazine 'illustrated' by scanned images of the original letter. There's something voyeuristic and satisfying about the resulting reading experience. The tone varies – sad, humorous, matter-of-fact – and it's almost impossible to distinguish between memoir, essay and invention. A unique idea, presented well.

LIARS' LEAGUE
E-ZINE & LIVE EVENT WITH VIDEO AND PODCAST
07808 939535
liars@liarsleague.com
www.liarsleague.com
Editor: Katy Darby
Established 2007. Fiction suitable for performance. Free access – all online content available to all. Liars' League won the 2014 Saboteur Award for Best Regular Spoken Word Event and was named one of the *Guardian*'s Ten Great Storytelling Nights.
GENRES: Crime/thriller/mystery; fantasy/sci-fi; horror; historical fiction; literary fiction; romance. No YA or children's fiction.
SUBMISSIONS: Open to all. Submit by email to liars@liarsleague.com. Guidelines at www.liarsleague.com/liars_league/writers.html. Usually responds within eight weeks. Offers feedback only on shortlisted stories. Contributors are offered payment in kind (books, and/or free ticket and drinks).
WE SAY: Including *Liars' League* in this Guide is something of an anomaly, as they are primarily known for performances. Submitted stories are chosen to be performed by a professional actor in front of an appreciative audience; those same stories are also published on the website in

an easy-to-browse archive, along with the performances on videos and audio (there are podcast and youtube channels). The League is noted for great taste in fiction and looks for surprising, unique work that fits themes that are announced well in advance. A great way to get your name known and your work performed.

LIGHTHOUSE
PRINT
32 Grove Walk, Norwich NR1 2QG
admin@gatehousepress.com
www.gatehousepress.com/lighthouse
Editors: Meirion Jordan, Andrew McDonnell, Julia Webb, Philip Langeskov, Anna de Vaul, Jo Surzyn, Angus Sinclair, Scott Dahlie, Molly-Sue Moore, Sharlene Teo
Established 2012. A journal for new writers. Poetry and short fiction. Subscription £22.50 per year (four issues); single issue £5 plus postage. Available direct from publisher website; at selected/local chain bookshops and independent bookshops; and at national and local literary events.
Lighthouse won the Saboteur Award for Best Magazine 2015.
GENRES: Literary fiction; poetry, art. Essays by request.
SUBMISSIONS: Submit during submissions windows by email to submissions@lighthouse.gatehousepress.com. Usually responds within one to three months. No feedback offered on submissions. Contributors receive a print copy of the magazine, and a discount purchase price on further copies.
WE SAY: We looked at a PDF of Issue 9, a 96-page A5 quarterly magazine is printed in a font that reminded us of old novels (in a

good way). Stories are laid out as if in a standard book, without much white space, and both stories and poems are interspersed with artwork that looks like line drawings of slanted sunlight. Poetry, prose and prose poetry is gathered here, all very high quality. Features are saved for last, and are very in-depth.
See also: Gatehouse Press (poetry publishers p39 and prose publishers p130)

LITRO MAGAZINE
PRINT AND DIGITAL
020 3371 9971
info@litro.co.uk
www.litro.co.uk
Editors: Eric Akoto, Precious Williams
Established 2005. Mainly publishes fiction, in print, online and as a podcast. For subscription information see www.litro.co.uk/join. Available direct from publisher website; at chain bookshops nationwide; at independent bookshops; and at national and local literary events. Only subscribers/purchasers can access all online content, although some is available as a preview. Litro has been shortlisted for awards.
GENRES: Crime/thriller/mystery; drama and criticism; literary fiction; poetry; art, fashion and photography; food and drink; music, stage and screen; science, technology and medicine; society, education and politics; travel.
SUBMISSIONS: Submit across all of *Litro*'s platforms via Submittable. Guidelines and link at www.litro.co.uk/submit.
WE SAY: Perfect-bound 40-page magazine featuring fiction, essays, interviews and culture. Matte finish, striking cover design (we looked

238

at Issue 144: 'Transgender'), and full-colour inside, printed on thick quality paper. *Litro* has its roots in the city, and this is reflected in its aesthetic, which is contemporary and edgy. The expansive website features a large number of articles, interviews, weekly flash fiction etc, as well as the contents of the print version of the magazine. The sheer scale of the site was somewhat difficult to navigate – there's a lot going on – but the content is interesting and well-written.
See also: Litro Magazine Ltd (prose publishers) p149

LONDON MAGAZINE, THE ☆
PRINT AND DIGITAL
11 Queen's Gate, London SW7 5EL
020 7584 5977
admin@thelondonmagazine.org
www.thelondonmagazine.org
Editor: Steven O'Brien
Established 1732. Mixed form. Annual subscription £33. Available direct from publisher website; by post and email order; from chain bookshops; and from independent bookshops. Some online content is freely available to all.
GENRES: Literary fiction; poetry; art, fashion and photography; biography and true stories; history; music, stage and screen; society, education and politics; travel.
SUBMISSIONS: Open to all. Submit by post (to 11 Queen's Gate, London SW7 5EL), by email (admin@thelondonmagazine. org) or through Submittable (thelondonmagazine.submittable. com/submit). Sometimes charges a reading fee. Usually responds within one to three months. Rejections may occasionally include unsolicited feedback. Contributors are paid (rate by negotiation) and receive print copies and a digital copy of the magazine.
WE SAY: A long-established perfect-bound 118-page magazine with a contemporary aesthetic. The cover design is eye-catching; the materials high quality. The publication takes an intellectual, literary approach in its critical essays and reviews, and is strict about the quality of the free verse it publishes – the poems must have a purpose and no word should be wasted. The creative writing is engaging and tightly written, somewhat traditional and often London-focused.

LONELY CROWD, THE
PRINT AND DIGITAL
62 Kings Road, Cardiff CF11 9DD
johnlavin@thelonelycrowd.org
www.thelonelycrowd.org
Editor: John Lavin
Established 2015. Mixed-form magazine publishing poetry and prose. Print and digital subscriptions at £25 for three issues. Available direct from the publisher website; from independent bookshops; and at local literary events.
The Lonely Crowd was shortlisted for Best Magazine in the 2017 Saboteur Awards, and longlisted in 2018.
GENRE: Literary.
SUBMISSIONS: Open to all. Guidelines at www.thelonelycrowd. org/submissions. Usually responds in four to six months. No feedback included with rejections. Authors receive a free three-issue subscription, plus an author copy.
WE SAY: Every issue of *The Lonely Crowd* is more a book than a journal. We looked at Issue 11, which features a bright but atmospheric cover, with shadows

stretching across deep blue walls. The Issue clocks in at more than 200 pages, in part because the pages are laid out in a large-ish font, making the work easy to read and follow. Contributors include recognisable names such as Robert Minhinnick and Polly Atkin. The poetry and short stories are followed by 'The Lonely Crowd Essay' in this case a thoughtful piece by Catrina Davies and Grahame Williams entitled 'And we still send each other books'.

See also: The Lonely Press (poetry publishers p52 and prose publishers p151)

LOSSLIT MAGAZINE

DIGITAL MAGAZINE / E-ZINE
losslituk@gmail.com
www.losslit.com
Editors: Kit Caless, Aki Schilz, Jonny Keyworth
Established 2014. Welcomes poetry, short stories, and creative non-fiction. All online content freely available to all.
LossLit was shortlisted for the Saboteur Awards: Best Collaborative Work 2015 and runs alongside the #LossLit digital literature project on Twitter.
GENRES: Literary; genre; poetry; short story; creative non-fiction (essay).
SUBMISSIONS: Open to all. No fee. Submit by email to losslituk@gmail.com during submission periods: January (for April issue), May (for August issue) and September (for December issue). Aims to respond within two months and will always get in touch if interested in seeing more work, or if they have feedback. However may not always be able to get back to everyone. Unpaid.

WE SAY: *LossLit* consists of an easily navigated website, the home page of which takes you straight to the most recent issue. It's a plain, almost austere site, appropriate for its content, which focuses on all forms of loss. In addition to the website, there is the collaborative *LossLit* Twitter project, on the first Wednesday night of the month. Writers share microfiction about loss (#LossLit) and respond to each other's work. The result is archived to be read at leisure. *LossLit* is an interesting read, with a truly original use of social media.

LOW LIGHT MAGAZINE

PRINT
contact@hi-vispress.com
www.hi-vispress.com/low-light-magazine
Editors: Sophie Pitchford, Jim Gibson, Ben Williams
Established 2017. Mixed form. Publications available direct from publisher website; from selected/local chain bookshops; from independent bookshops; and at national literary events.
GENRES: Social realism; literary fiction; working class writing; experimental form poetry and prose.
SUBMISSIONS: During submission windows only. Submit by email to contact@hi-vispress.com. Guidelines at www.hi-vispress.com/low-light-magazine. Usually responds within one to three months, with feedback only if requested. Contributors receive a free print copy and prize money is awarded for best prose/poetry contribution and best photography contribution.
WE SAY: *Low Light* is beautifully designed, with plenty of gorgeous,

soft light, darkly emotive photography (in black and white and colour), accompanying poetry and prose laid out with an eye to space. The occasional splash of bold red is used judiciously. All attributions include the writers'/artists' twitter handle or website. At 82 pages, there's plenty to read, including interviews, in-depth essays, experimental poetry, and it even includes a Lit Zine round-up. We looked at a PDF proof, but in our dreams, this is printed on textured, matte paper.

See also: Hi Vis Press (poetry publishers p44 and prose publishers p135)

LUNE
PRINT
www.lunejournal.org
thelunejournal@gmail.com
Publishes memoir, essay, review, interview, fiction, biography, criticism, manifesto and poetry. They are curious about the community building potential of small press publishing and welcome submissions for their upcoming themed issues.

MANCHESTER REVIEW, THE
E-ZINE
Centre for New Writing, Samuel Alexander Building, University of Manchester M13 9PL
0161 2753167
manreviewsubmissions@gmail.com
www.themanchesterreview.co.uk
Editors: John McAuliffe, Lucy Burns
Established 2007. Mixed form. Two issues a year, plus rolling reviews. All online content available for free.
GENRES: Literary fiction; poetry; creative non-fiction.
SUBMISSIONS: Open to all during submissions windows. Submit by

email to manreviewsubmissions@gmail.com. Usually responds within four to six months. Rejections may occasionally include unsolicited feedback. Contributors are paid (by negotiation).
WE SAY: The front page of this online magazine is very sleek and minimal in design. At the top of the page, we have a gallery of the images to scroll through, with links to each story. Then, moving down, the images appear again as thumbnails accompanying the first paragraph of each story. The art varies in style, but is always eye-catching. The aim of the magazine is to feature international writers, both established and up-and-coming, and to '[document] the constantly evolving cultural landscape of our beloved Manchester'.

MAYBE LATER PRESS
E-ZINE
maybelaterpress@gmail.com
www.maybelaterpress.com
Maybe Later is a small press based in Newcastle upon Tyne. It publishes a zine of poetry, short fiction and creative non-fiction responding to a theme, with regular call outs for submissions on social media, or check the website for the most recent prompt.

MEANWHILE...
PRINT AND DIGITAL / E-BOOKS
Flat 2 42 Highcroft Villas, Brighton, East Sussex BN1 5PS
07986 995938
submissions@soaringpenguinpress.com
www.soaringpenguinpress.com
Editor: John Anderson
Established 2012. Graphic narrative fiction. Annual subscription £39.99 (UK). Available direct from

publisher website; by post and email order; at selected/local chain and independent bookshops; at national literary events; and via Amazon and other bookshop websites (including Diamond Comics Distributors). Digital editions available from Comixology and Sequential.

GENRES: Fantasy/sci-fi; graphic/comics; horror; indie fiction.

SUBMISSIONS: Accepts graphic narrative work only, i.e. comics. Submissions open to all, and the press is actively seeking alternative voices. Open to all. Submit by post (4 Florence Terrace, London SW15 3RU) or by email (submissions@soaringpenguinpress.com). Usually responds within four to six months or more. Rejections may occasionally include unsolicited feedback. Contributors are paid (set rate or by negotiation), and receive print copies and a discount purchase price on the magazine.

See also: Soaring Penguin Press (prose publisher) p183

MECHANICS' INSTITUTE REVIEW, THE

E-ZINE
editor@mironline.org
mironline.org

Established 2010 (previously Writers' Hub). Mixed form. Free access – all online content available to all.

GENRES: Literary fiction; poetry; features; reviews; biography and true stories.

SUBMISSIONS: Open to all, during submissions windows. Submit by email to editor@mironline.org. Guidelines at mironline.org/submissions. Usually responds within four to six months. Rejections may include occasional unsolicited feedback. Unpaid.

WE SAY: *MIRonline* is the online publication from Birkbeck University, which also produces the high-quality MIR print publication (which contains work only by Birkbeck students and well-known authors). The site is clean and easy to navigate – fiction, poetry, features and reviews are all separately signposted, so readers in the mood for a long read can just work their way down the backlist or easily search the archives. There's even some audio, if you prefer your poetry to go straight to the ear. It's a professional, organised, easy-on-the-eye site – and as the student editorial staff rotates annually, never a place to cross off as 'not for my work', because the tastes and design change with the staff.

MINOR LITERATURE[S]

E-ZINE
www.minorliteratures.com
Editors: Fernando Sdrigotti, Tomoe Hill, Kevin Mullen, Eli Lee, Martin Dean, Thom Cuell, Yanina Spizzirri, Daniela Cascella

Established 2013. Published three times a week. Free access – all online content available to all.

GENRES: Literary fiction; essays; poetry; experimental prose; book reviews.

SUBMISSIONS: Open to all, must be anonymous. Submit via minorliteratures.submittable.com/submit – guidelines available at the same address. Usually responds within one to three months. No feedback offered with rejection.

WE SAY: The *Minor Literature[s]* zine website is simple to navigate, with bold photography and large serif font headers announcing the work. Essays, features, fiction, experimental prose and poetry, all are available. We particularly looked at the evocative essay 'Cocktail napkin: Chateau Marmont' by Liska Jacobs, an exploration of family and heredity as explored through the doors of Hotel Chateau Marmont in Los Angeles, combining imagined glamour with memories.

MONSTROUS REGIMENT
PRINT
editor@monstrous-regiment.com
www.monstrous-regiment.com/
submissions
Editors: Lauren Nickodemus, Ellen Desmond
Established 2017. Mixed form. Publications available direct from publisher website; by direct mail and email orders; and at local literary events.
GENRES: Short literary fiction; poetry; creative non-fiction; illustrations/photography; short genre fiction.
SUBMISSIONS: Open to all, during submission windows. Submit by email to editor@monstrous-regiment.com. Guidelines at www.monstrous-regiment.com/submissions. Usually responds within four weeks, with feedback only if requested. Contributors are paid a set rate and receive print copies.
For further information, including what They Say, see also Monstrous Regiment Publishing (poetry publishers p54 and prose publishers p155)

MOTH, THE ☆
PRINT
Ardan Grange, Belturbet, County Cavan, Ireland

editor@themothmagazine.com
www.themothmagazine.com
Editor: Rebecca O'Connor
Established 2010. Mixed form. Annual subscription €28. Available direct from publisher website; by post and email order; at independent bookshops; and in Eason and newsagents in Ireland. *The Moth* features work from new writers as well as from the likes of Billy Collins, John Boyne and Sara Baume; a poem published in *The Moth* was shortlisted for the Forward Prize for Best Single Poem. They also publish a children's version called *The Caterpillar* (see p221).
GENRES: Literary fiction; poetry; interviews.
SUBMISSIONS: Open to all. Submit by post (*The Moth*, Ardan Grange, Belturbet, County Cavan, Ireland) or by email (editor@themothmagazine.com). Guidelines at www.themothmagazine.com/a1-page.asp?ID=1972&page=18. Usually responds within four to six months. Rejections may occasionally include unsolicited feedback. Contributors receive a print copy of the magazine.
WE SAY: Aesthetically striking, this 35-page magazine features literature, interviews and art. Contents are published on high quality matte paper with artwork throughout and a cover image that continues onto the back. We looked at Issue 29, which showcased compelling fiction and a high-quality array of poetry ('Brezhenv's Daughter' by Carole Braverman was particularly captivating).
See also: *The Caterpillar* **(mixed-form magazine) p221**

MOVING WORLDS: A JOURNAL OF TRANSCULTURAL WRITINGS

PRINT

School of English, University of Leeds, Leeds LS2 9JT

mworlds@leeds.ac.uk

www.movingworlds.net

Editors: Shirley Chew, Stuart Murray

Established 2001, and published both by University of Leeds and Nanyang Technological University, Singapore. Mixed-form output. Subscriptions £32/year for two issues (individuals); £14/year (students/unwaged); £62/year (institutions). Available direct from publisher website; by post and email order; and from bookshop websites including Neilsens and EBSCO.

SUBMISSIONS: Open to all. Submit by email to mworlds@leeds.ac.uk. Guidelines at www.movingworlds. net/submissions. Usually responds within one to three months. Rejections may occasionally include unsolicited feedback. Contributors receive print copies of the magazine and a discount purchase price on further copies. Creative work (poetry) is paid.

NEON LITERARY MAGAZINE

PRINT AND DIGITAL

info@neonmagazine.co.uk

www.neonmagazine.co.uk

Editor: Krishan Coupland

Established 2006. Mixed form. Annual subscription £12 (three issues). Publications available direct from publisher website; by direct mail and email orders; from independent bookshops; at national literary events; and from Amazon and other bookshop websites. Only subscribers/ purchasers can access all online content, although some content is available to read freely.

GENRES: Sci-fi; horror; slipstream; magical realism; literary fiction.

SUBMISSIONS: Open to all, during submission windows. Submit by email to subs@neonmagazine. co.uk. Guidelines at www. neonmagazine.co.uk/guidelines. Usually responds within four to six months. Rejections may occasionally include unsolicited feedback for a fee. Submissions hold a tip-jar option, but this does not affect publisher's decision. A reading fee is required for expedited response times. Contributors are paid a set rate and receive a free digital copy, print copy and discount purchase price on further copies.

WE SAY: We saw a digital version of Issue 43, which featured a black-and-white photo of patterned fabric on the front and back cover, with further black-and-white photos throughout the publication. The design is simple and crisp, the photos used for atmospheric purposes alongside each piece of work. There is a mix of poetry and prose in this issue – the tone is dark and melancholic, presented in a very stylish magazine.

See also: Neon (poetry publishers p56 and prose publishers p158)

NEW WELSH REVIEW ☆

PRINT AND DIGITAL

PO Box 170, Aberystwyth SY23 1WZ

01970 628410

editor@newwelshreview.com

www.newwelshreview.com

Editor: Gwen Davies

Established 1988. Subscriptions available for £16.99 a year (direct debit) or £20.99 (by other payment methods). Available direct from

the publisher website; by post and email order; from selected major chain bookshops and independent bookshops; at local literary events; and from www.gwales.com. Only subscribers can access all online content, although some content is available to read for free.
GENRES: Fiction; non-fiction; poetry; opinion; essays.
SUBMISSIONS: Open to all. Submit by post (Submissions,

MSLEXIA ☆

PRINT AND DIGITAL
PO Box 656, Newcastle upon Tyne
NE99 1PZ
0191 204 8860
postbag@mslexia.co.uk
www.mslexia.co.uk
Editor: Debbie Taylor

Established 1999. Mixed form. Subscription £34.75 (UK) a year for four issues. Available direct from publisher website; by post and email order; at selected chain bookshops and independent bookshops; and at national and local literary events. Only subscribers/purchasers can access all of the online content, although some content is available to read freely.
GENRES: Literary fiction; poetry; features; biography and true stories; history; society, education and politics.
SUBMISSIONS: Open to all. Submit by post (PO Box 656, Newcastle upon Tyne NE99 1PZ), by email (submissions@mslexia.com) or via online form. Guidelines at mslexia. co.uk/submit-your-work. Usually responds within one to six months. Feedback overview of all entries offered with rejections (for creative work). Contributors are paid a set rate and may receive a copy of the magazine.

They say

No other magazine provides *Mslexia*'s unique mix of debate and analysis, advice and inspiration; news, reviews, interviews; competitions, events, courses, grants. All served up with a challenging selection of new poetry and prose. *Mslexia* is read by top authors and absolute beginners. A quarterly masterclass in the business and psychology of writing, it's the essential magazine for women who write. We are a vibrant, ambitious and growing organisation, and we aim to provide a high-profile platform for new and established voices with every copy of the magazine.

PO Box 170, Aberystwyth SY23 1WZ) or by email (editor@ newwelshreview.com). Guidelines at www.newwelshreview.com/ submissions.php. Usually responds within one to three months. No feedback offered with rejections. Contributors are paid a set rate.

WE SAY: We looked at a copy of Issue 120 of the *New Welsh Reader*, New Welsh Review's magazine, which publishes writing from Wales and beyond. The magazine is A5, perfect-bound and printed on high-quality gloss paper, lending it a professional edge. The cover is made from pleasingly heavy card. It features short fiction, poetry and non-fiction pieces, many of which are illustrated with striking black-and-white and colour photographs. There are some well-known names alongside emerging writers.

See also: New Welsh Review (prose publishers) p159

NEW WRITING SCOTLAND

PRINT
ASLS, 7 University Gardens, Glasgow G12 8QH
0141 330 5309
office@asls.org.uk
www.asls.org.uk
Editors: Susie Maguire, Samuel Tongue
Established 1983. Fiction, non-fiction and poetry. Subscription: annual anthology – copies can be purchased direct from the publisher or from booksellers.
GENRES: Any and all genres of short fiction; prose work on all topics; poetry.
SUBMISSIONS: Open to works by writers resident in Scotland or Scots by birth, upbringing or inclination. During submissions window (1 May to 30 September),

submit by post to *New Writing Scotland*, ASLS, 7 University Gardens, Glasgow G12 8QH. Guidelines at asls.arts.gla.ac.uk/ NWSsubs.html. Usually responds within four to six months. No feedback offered with rejection. Contributors are paid £20 per published page and receive a print copy and a discount purchase price on the magazine.

WE SAY: We looked at a digital extract from Issue 34: Talking About Lobsters. It presents an interesting and fascinating story about a Ukrainian woman on her way to Scotland, crossing borders. The pages are quite full, with justified text and long paragraphs. As the writer is a professor in Eastern Europe studies, it aims to introduce the world beyond the western borders. It also includes poetry and short fiction from Scotland-based award-winning authors and authors who are just beginning their careers.

See also: ASLS (poetry publishers p19 and prose publishers p97)

NORTHWORDS NOW

PRINT AND DIGITAL
Easter Brae, Culbokie, Dingwall, Ross-shire IV7 8JU
editor@northwordsnow.co.uk
www.northwordsnow.co.uk
Editor: Kenny Taylor
Established 2005. Mixed form. Available by post and email order; from selected/local chain bookshops and independent bookshops; at national and local literary events; from other bookshop websites; and at libraries, galleries and other outlets in Scotland. Free access – all online content is available to all.

246

GENRES: Literary fiction; poetry; short stories (strictly no novel extracts); biography and true stories; travel; literary essays.
SUBMISSIONS: Open to all. Submit by post to The Editor, *Northwords Now*, 6 Kippendavie Lane, Dunblane, Perthshire FK15 0HL, or via the submission form at www.northwordsnow.co.uk (guidelines at the same address). Usually responds within four to six months. Rejections may occasionally include unsolicited feedback. Contributors are paid (a set rate and by negotiation) and receive a print copy of the magazine.
WE SAY: We looked at a PDF of this 32-page literary magazine, which is printed in newspaper format. A bold and striking cover announces the contents, which are laid out across four columns per page for prose, and three columns for poems. The effect is one of immediacy and freshness. Work appears in English and in Scottish Gaelic, and always embraces Scotland as landscape and culture.

NOTTINGHAM REVIEW, THE
DIGITAL AND E-ZINE
thenottinghamreview@gmail.com
www.thenottinghamreview.com
Editor: Spencer Chou
Established 2015. Mainly fiction, recently expanding to include poetry. All online content freely available to all.
GENRES: Literary. Strictly no non-fiction.
SUBMISSIONS: Open to all. Submit by email to thenottinghamreview@gmail.com. Guidelines at www.thenottinghamreview.com/submit. Usually responds within four weeks. Rejections may include occasional unsolicited feedback. Unpaid.

WE SAY: *The Nottingham Review* is a beautiful-looking digital magazine available in multiple formats. The design is simple – professional and contemporary. There are no images in the inner pages, just text with plenty of white space. The cover is uncluttered: one large, simple image. Where possible, there are live links to information on contributing writers, so readers can easily find out more. Each issue has a theme, and the stories are engaging nuggets of the everyday, followed by enthusiastic comments on the web-browser version.
See also: prose publishers p161

OGHAM STONE, THE
PRINT AND DIGITAL
School of Culture and Communication, University of Limerick
+353 21 202336
oghamstoneul@gmail.com;
oghamstone@ul.ie
www.theoghamstoneul.com
Editors: MA Students of Creative Writing and English
Established 2013. Mixed-form output. Some online content is freely available to all.
GENRES: Literary; visual.
SUBMISSIONS: Open to all, during submissions windows only. Submit via www.theoghamstoneul.com/submit/ (guidelines at the same address). Usually responds within four to six months. No feedback offered with rejection. Contributors receive print copies of the magazine.
WE SAY: We looked at a digital version of the Spring 2017 issue. A full-colour, painted cover image is taken from a Richard Smyth painting, which is shown in full in the inner pages. We feel the

top-page margins of the inner pages run a little narrow, but the overall design is a pleasure, with the text regularly interspersed with beautiful colour illustrations in a range of styles, and the complete writer biographies on the final page.

ORBIS QUARTERLY INTERNATIONAL JOURNAL ☆
PRINT
17 Greenhow Avenue, West Kirby, Wirral CH48 5EL
carolebaldock@hotmail.com
www.orbisjournal.com
01516 251446
Editor: Carole Baldock
Established 1969. Mainly publishes poetry, but also some prose and short stories. Subscription £18 for four issues per year. Available direct from the publisher website; by direct mail and email order; and at national and local literary events. Some online content is available to all.
GENRES: All.
SUBMISSIONS: Open to all. Submit by post to 17 Greenhow Avenue, West Kirby, Wirral CH48 5EL. Overseas submissions ONLY accepted by email to carolebaldock@hotmail.com. Guidelines at www.orbisjournal. com/about-orbis. Usually responds in one to three months. Feedback: contributors receive proofs with editorial suggestions. Contributors may win the £50 Readers' Award; a further £50 is divided between the runners-up.
WE SAY: We viewed a PDF proof of Issue 185 of this quarterly journal. The magazine features mixed form writing, providing an extensive selection of poems interjected with reviews, ultimately spanning

to nearly 100 pages. Illustrations are sparse, and the absence of clearly divided sections makes the issue slightly hard to navigate. Nevertheless, the quality of the writing itself is high.

PAPER AND INK
PRINT
paperandinkzine@outlook.com
www.paperandinkzine.co.uk
Editor: Martin Appleby
Established 2013. Mixed form. Available direct from the publisher website and from independent bookshops.
Longlisted for Best Magazine in the 2017 Saboteur Awards.
GENRES: Drama and criticism; literary fiction; poetry. No non-fiction.
SUBMISSIONS: Open to all. Submit by email to paperandinkzine@ outlook.com. Guidelines at www.paperandinkzine.co.uk/ submissions. Usually responds within one to three months. Rejections may occasionally include unsolicited feedback. Contributors receive a print copy of the magazine.

PENNY DREADFUL, THE ☆
PRINT
Clonmoyle House, Coachford, Cork
The.P.Dreadful@Gmail.com
thepennydreadful.org
Editors: Marc O'Connell, John Keating
Mixed form. Annual subscription £26. Available direct from publisher website, selected/local chain bookshops, independent bookshops and at local literary events.
GENRES: Drama and criticism; graphic/comics; literary fiction; poetry; and reviews, specifically

literary pieces that can include elements of biography.
SUBMISSIONS: Open to all. Submit through Submittable via thepennydreadful.org/index.php/ submit (guidelines in the same place). Usually responds within four weeks. Rejection may occasionally include unsolicited feedback. Unpaid.
WE SAY: A perfect-bound magazine, with a professional design on high-quality paper – and a particularly dark ethos. The Issue we checked out (No. 5) had a cover featuring a woman with blank, black eyes, a knowing smile and a red hood with horns – fair warning about the edgy, occasionally humorous writing inside. Contemporary, Irish and living up to its name, the work featured well-written stuff – but it's not a comfort read.

PEOPLE'S FRIEND, THE
PRINT
peoplesfriend@dcthomson.co.uk
www.thepeoplesfriend.co.uk
A very popular magazine for readers aged from around 30 to 'well over 80'. Accepts a range of work, including poetry, short stories and articles, all in a very distinctive style for popular readership. Clear guidelines are available on the website.

PIXEL HEART LITERARY MAGAZINE
DIGITAL
pixelheartmag@gmail.com
pixelheartmag.wordpress.com
Editor: Chloe Smith
Established 2018. Mixed output. Free access – all online issues are available to all.
GENRES: Poetry; flash fiction; short stories.

SUBMISSIONS: Open to all. Submit by email to pixelheartmag@gmail. com. Guidelines at pixelheartmag. wordpress.com/submissions. Usually responds within four weeks. No feedback is offered with rejection. Currently unpaid.
WE SAY: Issue 1 of *Pixel Heart Literary Magazine*, titled 'Love', opens with a warm introduction from editor Chloe Smith. What follows is a 50-page spread of poems and short fiction, all of varying length and style. What makes this issue refreshing is the breadth of diversity in its contents, with some pieces using experimental structures, whilst others follow a traditional format. The issue closes with a bio for each featured author, making this a personal publication which truly platforms its authors.

PLANET AND PLANET EXTRA
PRINT AND E-ZINE
PO Box 44, Aberystwyth, Ceredigion SY23 3ZZ
01970 611 255
submissions@planetmagazine.org.uk
website@planetmagazine.org.uk
www.planetmagazine.org.uk
Publishes articles, poetry and reviews (with a focus on Wales, as this journal is 'The Welsh Internationalist'). Paid.

PLATFORM FOR PROSE
ONLINE SHOWCASE
editor@platformforprose.com
www.platformforprose.com
Established 2015. Mixed form: shorts, flash and poetry. Available direct from publisher website. Forthcoming anthologies (e-books) will be available from Amazon. Some online content freely available to all.

GENRES: Contemporary short fiction. No children's or young adult fiction, sci-fi or fantasy.
SUBMISSIONS: During submissions windows, submit by email to editor@platformforprose.com. Guidelines at www.platformforprose.com/submissions. Usually responds within four weeks. No feedback currently offered with rejections. Unpaid.
WE SAY: Despite the name, this showcase does include some poetry. It's an easy to navigate, good-looking site with a healthy mixture of short stories, flash fiction and poems. It also branched out into audio presentation and includes comment sections under the content so that readers can express their pleasure at the work.

POPSHOT MAGAZINE
PRINT AND DIGITAL MAGAZINE
hello@popshotpopshot.com
www.popshotpopshot.com
Editor: Matilda Battersby
Established 2008. Fiction and poetry. Annual subscription £20 (for four issues) from 2018. Publication available direct from publisher website; in chain bookshops nationwide; and from bookshop websites.
GENRES: Literary fiction; poetry. No non-fiction.
SUBMISSIONS: Open to all. Submit at www.popshotpopshot.com/submit (guidelines at same address). Usually responds within four weeks – no feedback unless requested. Contributors receive print copies of the magazine.
WE SAY: An A5, 64-page literary magazine printed on matte paper. We looked at Issue 14. The modern formula of contemporary illustration mixed with poetry,

short stories and flash fiction feels fresh and original. Each illustration is quirky and unique, specifically commissioned to appear alongside each piece of writing. Our favourite was 'Through the Flowers', a short story complemented by pop-art flowers with eyeballs at their centre. Wonderfully weird. The magazine has taken off in 18 countries around the world.

PROLE ☆
PRINT AND DIGITAL
01204497726
admin@prolebooks.co.uk
www.prolebooks.co.uk
Editors: Brett Evans, Phil Robertson
Established 2010. Mixed form. Annual subscription £15 (three issues). Publications available direct from publisher website and by direct mail and email orders.
Prole won the Saboteur award for Best Literary Magazine in 2016.
GENRES: Literary; engaging; accessible; challenging; entertaining.
SUBMISSIONS: Open to all. Submit by email to submissionspoetry@prolebooks.co.uk or submissionsprose@prolebooks.co.uk. Guidelines at www.prolebooks.co.uk/submissions.html. Usually responds within four weeks. Rejections may occasionally include unsolicited feedback. Contributors are paid royalties only.
See also: Prolebooks (poetry publishers p65 and prose publishers p171)

PROTOTYPE
PRINT
71 Oriel Road, London E9 5SG
admin@prototypepublishing.co.uk
www.prototypepublishing.co.uk
Editor: Jess Chandler

Established 2019. Annual anthology/magazine published in July each year. UK subscriptions £10. Publications available direct from publisher website; via distributor NBN International; from a selection of independent and chain bookshops nationwide;

PORRIDGE MAGAZINE

E-ZINE AND PRINT
porridgemagazine@gmail.com
www.porridgemagazine.com
Editors: Georgia Tindale, Nora Selmani, Kitty Howse, Chris Rowse

Established 2016. Mixed form. Free access – all online content available to all. Print publication available from publisher's website.
GENRES: Literary; academic; multimedia; interdisciplinary; current affairs.
SUBMISSIONS: Open to all. Submit by email to porridgemagazine@gmail. com. Guidelines at www. porridgemagazine.com/ submissions. Usually responds within four weeks. Rejections may occasionally include unsolicited feedback. Unpaid. Print submissions open biannually and announced on website.
WE SAY: We viewed Issue 3 of *Porridge*, a mixed-form magazine covering a wide range of topics. While their online publication includes articles on current affairs and cultural pieces as well as creative writing, Issue 3 of their print magazine also includes abstract graphics and experimentally structured writing. With a highly sophisticated website, *Porridge Magazine* has a modern feel, and projects a youthful, ambitious message.

THEY SAY

Founded by university graduates in 2016, *Porridge* is a free, volunteer-run, international, interdisciplinary online and print magazine. We love supporting new and emerging writers from all around the world and publish a diverse range of work including critical essays, short fiction, photography, poetry, illustration, essays on contemporary culture, recipes and much more. We are especially proud of our print issues and their launch events which are free to attend and bring together our contributors from all over the world through readings, live performances, research talks, workshops and more. In short, *Porridge* is all about community, creativity and interconnectedness.

and at local literary events and book fairs.

GENRES: Poetry; fiction; some artwork.

SUBMISSIONS: Open year-round. Submit by post (71 Oriel Road, London E9 5SG) or by email (admin@prototypepublishing. co.uk). Guidelines at www. prototypepublishing.co.uk/ submissions. Responses within three months. Contributors receive two free print copies.

WE SAY: We looked at a PDF proof of *Prototype*'s first issue. It's a smart and sleek design, with a list of contributors printed in bold white sans serif type on the back cover, and the front cover's black background lifted by the overlay of an illustration taken from the magazine's contents in warm grey, under the magazine title. Full contact details are included on the inner cover pages. All art in the inner pages is in greyscale on white paper. The final four pages list the contributor biographies, which include the likes of Rebecca Tamás, Emily Berry and Eley Williams.

See also: poetry publishers p65 and prose publishers p172

PUSH – THE WRITING SQUAD

ONLINE PLATFORM
steve@writingsquad.com
www.sqpush.com
Editor: Steve Dearden
Established 2001. Mixed form. Free access – all online content available to all.

GENRES: Literary fiction; poetry; travel; new journalism.

SUBMISSIONS: Submissions from members only or by invitation only.

WE SAY: An online magazine that features articles and creative writing for young adults. The design is contemporary, the colour scheme bright but not overwhelming, and the work is clearly laid out. Content includes poetry and prose, lyrical and contemporary.

PUSHING OUT THE BOAT

PRINT AND DIGITAL
info@pushingouttheboat.co.uk
www.pushingouttheboat.co.uk
Established 2000. Creative writing with visual art. Print format available by direct mail and email, from major chain and independent bookshops, and at local literary events. All online content of the digital format is available to all.

GENRES: Accepts every form of creative writing (including playscript etc) on any theme.

SUBMISSIONS: Submissions are open to all, during submissions windows only. To submit follow the instructions at www.pushingouttheboat.co.uk, where a link is made available during open submission windows. Additional guidelines at www.pushingouttheboat.co.uk/ hints-and-tips. Usually responds in four to six months, with the selection decision made available to writers in their record on the online submission system. Contributors receive free copies of the magazine.

WE SAY: We viewed Issue 13 of this literary and arts magazine using their online viewing tool. Spanning to 100 pages, this magazine presents a wide variety of poetry, prose and visual arts. All forms are integrated throughout the issue rather than segregated by section, so each page leads fluidly onto the

next, and the reader feels taken on a journey.
See also: prose publishers (p173) and poetry publishers (p66)

READER, THE
PRINT
magazine@thereader.org.uk
www.thereader.org.uk/getinvolved/magazine
Editor: Philip Davis
Literary mix magazine, published quarterly since 1997. Showcases writing from well-known names and new voices side by side. Welcomes submissions of poetry, fiction, essays, readings and thoughts.

RIGGWELTER
DIGITAL
Editor: Amy Kinsman
riggwelterpress@gmail.com
riggwelter.wordpress.com
Established 2017. Mixed output: poetry, prose and script, with non-fiction and reviews posted on an as-and-when basis. All online content is freely available. *Riggwelter* was shortlisted for the Saboteur Awards Best Magazine in 2018.
GENRES: Experimental; literary; philosophical; queer; surreal; confessional.
SUBMISSIONS: Open to all. Submit by email to riggwelterpress@gmail.com. Guidelines at riggwelter.wordpress.com/submissions. Responds within four weeks, offering feedback only if requested. Unpaid.
WE SAY: Charmingly named after a piece of northern rural dialect, Riggwelter Press uses a simple website with an image of a herd of sheep in its header. In stark contrast, the individual issues available on their website use bold, abstract graphics. This mixed-form publication integrates prose, poetry and graphics throughout, often tied together by a subtle theme. In this way, *Riggwelter* embraces individual work that collaborates to form a cohesive publication.

RIPTIDE JOURNAL
PRINT
Dept of English, Queen's University of Exeter, Exeter, Devon EX4 6QH
07895 012300
editors@riptidejournal.co.uk
www.riptidejournal.co.uk
Editors: Dr Virginia Baily, Dr Sally Flint
Established 2006. Literary fiction (i.e. short stories and poetry). Available direct from publisher website; by post and email order; from independent bookshops; and at local literary events. Stockists listed on the website. Some content available online to all.
GENRES: Children's fiction; drama and criticism; erotica; fantasy/sci-fi; graphic/comics; horror; romance. No non-fiction.
SUBMISSIONS: Open to all. Submit by email to editors@riptidejournal.co.uk. Guidelines at www.riptidejournal.co.uk/contribute/. Usually responds within four to six months. No feedback offered. Contributors are paid a set rate and receive a print copy and discount purchase price on the magazine.
WE SAY: Only technically a journal, *Riptide* is a series of anthologies published as volumes as opposed to issues. Each volume contains a healthy amount of work (23 pieces in Vol 10: 'The Suburbs', which is the one we looked at), and has a gloss laminate cover. The inside is pure book: (no illustrations, a

prelims page, contents, thanks, and the work), but the cover design is very much that of a journal, with a single piece of art in a wide, white frame, and brief information about the contents below. This volume had an introduction from Michael Rosen, and some recognisable names in the contributors' list.
See also: Dirt Pie Press (poetry publishers p30 and prose publishers p116)

SABLE
PRINT AND E-ZINE
editorial@sablelitmag.org
www.sablelitmag.org
Managing editor: Kadija Sesay
An established and important publication, *Sable* is a showcase magazine for writers of colour, featuring work from internationally renowned and new writers. The magazine also offers training and support, and created the Writer's HotSpot: the first international creative writing residencies for people of colour. Originally solely a literary magazine, Sable has been recreated as a cultural magazine, 'underwritten by literary factors'. Types of work accepted include fiction, poetry, in translation, memoir, travel narratives (Blackpackers), essays, classic review and more. Online only slots include reviews, listings and microfiction.
SUBMISSIONS: Open to all writers of colour. Submit by email to editorial@sablelitmag.org. Full guidelines at www.sablelitmag.org/submissions.

SALOMÉ
DIGITAL AND PRINT
salomeliterature@gmail.com
www.salomelit.com

Editor: Jacquelyn Guderley
Established 2017. Mixed form. Annual digital subscription £13 (four issues); digital and print subscription £40 (four issues in both digital and print format). Print publication available direct from publisher website. While only subscribers/purchasers can read complete issues (in print and digital download formats), free samples of pieces from each issue are available online.
GENRES: Literary; feminist; mixed theme.
SUBMISSIONS: Open to self-identifying women only, during submission windows. Submit online at www.salomelit.com/submissions. Guidelines at www.salomelit.com/submissions-guide. Usually responds within one to three months. Rejections include feedback for all work submitted during submissions windows. Contributors are paid a set rate and receive free print and digital copies.
WE SAY: A magazine for emerging female writers, *Salomé* Issues 1 and 2 both have cover art featuring paintings of strong women in bold colours and thoughtful, but galvanising editor's letter. The use of art continues within, with gorgeous paintings set between each story and poem, usually challenging the convention of the 'model' woman. Full biographies of both writers and artists appear in the last few pages. The writing is set to theme (e.g. 'Body') and with an eye to including as many different voices as possible.

SARASVATI
PRINT
24 Forest Houses, Halwill, Beaworthy, Devon EX21 5UU

254

publishing@indigodreams.co.uk
www.indigodreams.co.uk
Editor: Dawn Bauling
Established 2008. Mainly poetry,
some prose under 1,000 words.
Subscription £17/year for four
issues. Available direct from
publisher website; and by post and
email order. Indigo Dreams' editors
won the Ted Slade Award for
Services to Poetry 2015 (organised
by Poetry Kit).
GENRES: All styles considered.
SUBMISSIONS: Open to all. Submit
by post (IDP, 24 Forest Houses,
Halwill, Beaworthy, Devon EX21
5UU) or by email (publishing@
indigodreams.co.uk). Guidelines at
www.indigodreams.co.uk. Usually
responds within four weeks. No
feedback offered with rejection.
WE SAY: An A5 quarterly
publication by Indigo Dreams,
showcasing poetry and prose.
Looking at Issue 45, most
contributors have three or more
pieces of writing featured, giving
the sense of a series of mini
collections. This allows each writer
to display their style more clearly,
making for a diverse as well as
engrossing publication. The glossy
full-colour design is appealing and
vibrant, encasing a simple black
and white interior.
**For what They Say, see Indigo
Dreams Publishing Ltd (poetry
publishers) p46. See also *The
Dawntreader* (mixed-form magazine
p223) and *Reach Poetry* (poetry
magazine) p282**

SCORES, THE
DIGITAL
School of English, Castle House, The
University of St Andrews, St Andrews
KY16 9AL
scorespoetry@st-andrews.ac.uk

www.thescores.org.uk
Editors: Patrick Errington and Rosa
Campbell
Established 2016. Mixed form.
Free access – all online content
available to all.
GENRES: Poetry; short prose
(nonfiction and fiction); translation;
reviews.
SUBMISSIONS: Open to all,
during submissions windows.
Submit through Submittable at
thescores.submittable.com/submit.
Guidelines at www.thescores.org.
uk/submit. Usually responds in one
to three months. Rejections may
occasionally include unsolicited
feedback. Unpaid.
WE SAY: Despite their name
reflecting the origins of this
publisher in the town of St
Andrews, *The Scores* embraces
an international outlook in their
biannual issues that cover a range
of themes. We looked at Issue 5
on their classy and sophisticated
website, which displays links to
each written piece. Grouped into
numbered sections, the pieces are
also integrated with visual art.

SCRITTURA MAGAZINE
DIGITAL
scrittura.magazine@gmail.com
scritturamagazine.tumblr.com
Editors: Valentina Terrinoni and
Yasmin Rahman
Established 2015. Mixed output –
poetry, prose, script. Free access –
all online content available to all.
GENRES: Literary; romance; horror;
fantasy; thriller.
SUBMISSIONS: Open to all. Submit
by email to scrittura.magazine@
gmail.com. Guidelines at static.
tumblr.com/cwmgztm/r7Qno773j/
submission_guidelines.pdf. Usually
responds in one to three months.

No feedback offered with rejection. Unpaid.

WE SAY: We looked at Issue 12 of *Scrittura Magazine*, featuring a bold and colourful cover image of glamorous circus horses. The form and structure of this publication is incredibly playful and bright, using colourful text, backgrounds and graphics in accordance with the theme of each piece. Even the header fonts are in constant flux, painting this magazine as one that celebrates vibrant variety, both in content and style.

SELKIE, THE
DIGITAL
www.theselkie.co.uk
Editor: Huriyah Taliha Quadri
Established 2018, and now a registered non-profit community interest company (The Selkie Publications CIC). Mixed form. Free access – all online content available to all, direct from the publisher website or at Apple Books and Issuu.

GENRES: All welcome except fan fiction and erotica.

SUBMISSIONS: *The Selkie* is committed to working with marginalised and/or under-represented voices and will only accept work by/concerned with: individuals identifying as women; people of colour; minorities in predominantly white nations; refugees and first-generation immigrants; LGBTQIA+; those living with mental illness, or physical or other disabilities; those persecuted for their political or religious beliefs; victims of violence, or domestic or sexual abuse; and those without access to higher education degrees, living below the poverty line, or

who are/have been homeless or incarcerated. Submit via email – full guidelines and addresses at www.theselkie.co.uk/submissions. Usually responds within four weeks. Rejections may occasionally include unsolicited feedback. Unpaid.

WE SAY: Issue 1 of *The Selkie*, themed 'transformation', makes a bold statement on social and political change, dedicating themselves to platforming marginalised voices. The dark and obscure cover image conveys human transformation, and the collection presents poetry and prose that delves into the human experience. With bold titles and the absence of any graphics, this publication is professional and powerful in its content.

SENTINEL LITERARY QUARTERLY
PRINT AND E-ZINE
www.sentinelquarterly.com
Published at the end of January, April, July and October, online and in limited print. Mixed form, it accepts poetry, short stories, novel extracts, reviews and interviews, plays and essays. Note that a different email address applies for each area of submission.

SILKWORMS INK
E-ZINE
www.silkwormsink.com
Established in 2010, *Silkworms Ink* is 'a digital publisher of eclectica, a purveyor of literary mixtapes, and a weekly-themed quasi-magazine.' They are interested in fiction, non-fiction, poetry, plays and music.
See also: poetry publishers p74 and prose publishers p182

SNOW LIT REV
PRINT
14 Mount Street, Lewes, East Sussex
BN7 1HL
www.abar.net/snow.pdf

Editors: Anthony Barnett, Ian Brinton
Established 2013. Mixed form.
Publication available direct from
publisher website; by direct
mail and email orders; and from

SHOOTER LITERARY MAGAZINE ☆
PRINT
98 Muswell Hill Road, London
N10 3JR
shooterlitmag@gmail.com
www.shooterlitmag.com
Editor: Melanie White

Established 2014. Mixed form:
short stories, poetry and short non-
fiction. Annual subscription £19.99
(UK); £34.99 (international) (for
two issues). Available direct from
publisher website; by post and
email order; at selected/local chain
bookshops (eg Foyles Charing
Cross); and at national and local
literary events. An e-book version
of the magazine is made available
when print editions sell out.
Shooter was nominated for
Saboteur Awards' Best Magazine
2015.
GENRES: Literary fiction; literary
journalism (essays, memoir,
reported/researched narrative
pieces); poetry; satire; biography.
Varies according to theme.
SUBMISSIONS: Open to all,
during submissions windows –
submissions must relate to the
issue theme and be of a literary
standard. Submit by email to
submissions.shooterlitmag@
gmail.com. See guidelines at
shooterlitmag.com/submissions.
Usually responds within one to
three months. Due to volume of
submissions, rejection emails are
no longer sent; successful writers
can expect a response before
or soon after the submission
deadline. Contributors are paid a
set rate and receive a print copy
of the magazine.
WE SAY: We looked at Issue 6,
entitled 'Bad Girls'. The issue
focuses on the concept of the
'nasty woman', imposing a
politically driven rejection of the
vilification of powerful women.
The cover image resonates in
the bold and assertive prose,
poetry and non-fiction pieces
that follow. A high-quality
publication, equally strong
in both physical material and
narrative voice.

257

independent bookshops.
GENRES: Literary; music; art; photography; film.
SUBMISSIONS: Open to all, although few unsolicited contributions are accepted. Guidelines at www.abar.net/snow. pdf. Usually responds within two weeks. Rejections may occasionally include unsolicited feedback.
See also: Allardyce, Barnett, Publishers (poetry publishers p16 and prose publishers p94)

SOMESUCH STORIES
DIGITAL AND PRINT
Unit 2, Royle Studios, 41 Wenlock Road, London N1 7SG
suze@somesuch.co
www.somesuchstories.co
Editor: Suze Olbrich
Established 2015. Digital publication but also publishes essays and short stories in themed collection biannually. Publication available direct from publisher website; from selected chain retailers; from independent bookshops; and from other bookshop websites.
In 2016, Somesuch Stories was shortlisted for the Stack Awards for Best Fiction and Best Non-Fiction.
GENRES: Literary fiction; biographical non-fiction; arts and culture; society and politics.
SUBMISSIONS: Pieces are commissioned following editorial prompts. Publication history is generally required. Query by email at stories@somesuch. co. Usually responds within four weeks. No feedback with rejection. Contributors are paid a flat fee.
WE SAY: These less-than-A5 eclectic magazines reflect their online origin with design choices such as a sans-serif font in Issue

3, and double-spacing between paragraphs rather than indenting in both Issues 2 and 3. But they are good quality publications; the paperback cover of Issue 2 is more inflexible than issue 3, but its black print on a silver metallic background is eye-catching. Issue 3, which curls the press' name to form its issue number, features a contents page with titles and names scattered across the page.

SOUNDINGS
PRINT AND DIGITAL
Lawrence and Wishart, Central Books Building, Freshwater Road, Chadwell Heath RM8 1RX
020 8597 0090
sally@lwbooks.co.uk
www.lwbooks.co.uk/soundings
Editor: Sally Davison
Established 1995. Mixed-form non-fiction and poetry magazine. Annual subscription costs £40 print and £25 digital, for three issues. Available direct from the publisher website; at chain and independent bookshops; and at local literary events. Some online content is available for free.
GENRES: Political analysis; cultural analysis; poetry.
SUBMISSIONS: Open to all, submit by email (submissions@lwbooks. co.uk) or post (Lawrence and Wishart, Central Books Building, Freshwater Road, Chadwell Heath RM8 1RX). Guidelines at www.lwbooks.co.uk/soundings/ submissions-information. Usually responds in one to three months. Rejections may occasionally include unsolicited feedback. Contributors receive print and digital copies of the publication.
See also: Lawrence and Wishart (prose publishers p146 and poetry publishers p50)

SOUTHLIGHT
PRINT
5 Lakeview, Powfoot, Annan,
Dumfries and Galloway DG12 5PG
01461 700396
vivien@freeola.com
www.southlight.ukwriters.net
Editors: Vivien Jones, Angus
Macmillan and John Burns
Established 2010. Mixed output.
Issues available direct from
the publisher website; from
independent bookshops; and at
local literary events.
GENRES: Poetry; prose; essays;
illustration.
SUBMISSIONS: Open to all. Submit
by post (5 Lakeview, Powfoot,
Annan DG12 5PG) or by email
(vivien@freeola.com). Guidelines
at www.southlight.ukwriters.
net. Usually responds in four to
six months. Contributors receive
copies of their issue.
WE SAY: *Southlight* prints an
eclectic mix of poetry, prose,
artwork and critical essays in
its quarterly magazine – an A4,
saddle-stitched volume of 56
pages. The cover is quite basic,
featuring an illustration and a title
on a block colour background,
while the inner pages are printed
on plain white paper. The same
font is used throughout for a
simple, homemade feel.

SOUTHWORD JOURNAL ☆
PRINT
Munster Literature Centre,
Frank O'Connor House, 84 Douglas
Street, Cork
+353 21 431 2955
munsterlit@eircom.net
www.munsterlit.ie
Editors: Patrick Cotter, Billy O'Callaghan
Established 2001. Mixed form.
Each issue £10.

GENRES: Literary fiction; poetry;
essays, interviews.
SUBMISSIONS: Submit via
Submittable at southword.
submittable.com/submit
(guidelines at the same address).
Usually responds within one to
three months. No feedback offered
with rejections. Contributors are
paid a set rate.
**See also: Southword Editions
(poetry publishers p77 and prose
publishers p184)**

SPARK YOUNG WRITERS MAGAZINE
DIGITAL AND PRINT (ONE EDITION
IN THREE)
Writing West Midlands, Studio 130
Zellig, Gibb Street B9 4AT
0121 246 2770
www.sparkwriters.org
Editors: William Gallagher
Established 2013 (previously
called '*WriteOn!*'). Mainly fiction.
Free access – all online content
available to all.
GENRES: Children's fiction; fantasy/
sci-fi; poetry; YA; teenage.
SUBMISSIONS: Open to people
aged 8-20 living or learning in the
West Midlands. Submit by email to
emma@writingwestmidlands.org.
Guidelines at www.sparkwriters.
org/get-involved.

SPONTANEITY
E-ZINE
ruth.mckee@gmail.com
spontaneity.org
Editor: Ruth McKee
Established 2013. Mixed form.
Free access – all online content
available to all.
GENRES: Literary fiction; poetry;
creative non-fiction.
SUBMISSIONS: Open to all. Submit
by email to editor@spontaneity.

org. Guidelines at spontaneity.org/ submit. Usually responds within four weeks. Rejections may include occasional unsolicited feedback. Unpaid.

WE SAY: The contents page of *Spontaneity*'s current issue is laid out like a series of newspaper articles, linking to work inspired by art (visual and written) that has previously appeared on the site. It's easy to fall down a rabbit-hole of reactions as you discover what prompted each piece. It's a unique approach to a literary magazine, and the resulting work is intense, lyrical, personal and experimental. If you're a writer who likes to work to prompts, this is one for you.

STAND ☆

PRINT AND DIGITAL

Stand, School of English, University of Leeds, Leeds LS2 9JT

stand@leeds.ac.uk

www.standmagazine.org

Editors: Jon Glover, John Whale

Established 1952. Mixed form. Subscribe online at www. standmagazine.org. Single issues may be purchased in selected bookshops or by emailing stand@ leeds.ac.uk.

SUBMISSIONS: Open to all. Submit by post to *Stand*, School of English, University of Leeds, Leeds LS2 9JT (please include an SAE if within UK). Only subscribers may submit by email. Usually responds within one to three months. Rejections may include feedback.

WE SAY: A long-established magazine producing a variety of poetry, fiction and criticism. The horizontal book and full-colour cover immediately stands out as a unique publication. Stand acts as a symbol of the need to 'Stand'

against oppression and injustice, reflected by the powerful voices it publishes. Most poets feature multiple poems each, allowing contributors an even wider platform for their writing.

STEPAWAY MAGAZINE

DIGITAL AND E-ZINE

editor@stepawaymagazine.com

www.stepawaymagazine.com

Editors: Darren Richard Carlaw, Elena Kharlamova

Established 2011. Poetry and flash fiction. Free access – all online content available to all. Winner of the Walking Visionaries Award 2015 (Walk21).

GENRES: Literary fiction; poetry; travel – literature that evokes the sensory experience of walking in specific neighbourhoods, districts or zones within a city.

SUBMISSIONS: Open to all. Submit by email to submissions@ stepawaymagazine.com. Guidelines at stepawaymagazine. com/about. Usually responds within one to three months, with feedback only if requested. Unpaid.

WE SAY: This e-zine publishes contents on a theme, particularly featuring poetry and short stories about walking and navigating urban spaces, with a contemporary lyrical aesthetic. The e-zine homepage features the magazine cover image for the current issue, with the distinctive masthead and an eye-catching image (the previous covers are archived for the curious). Clicking on the image takes you to the issue contents page, a straightforward list (Issue 24 was one essay and plenty of poetry), with a separate page displaying contributor biographies.

STINGING FLY, THE ☆
PRINT
PO Box 6016, Dublin 1, Ireland
stingingfly@gmail.com
www.stingingfly.org
Editors: Thomas Morris, Declan
Meade
Established 1997. Mainly fiction.
Subscription €30/year. Available
direct from publisher website, in
selected/local chain bookshops
and independent bookshops and
at local and national literary events.
GENRES: Literary fiction; poetry;
essays; reviews.
SUBMISSIONS: Open to all, subject
to submission windows. Submit
via Submittable at stingingfly.
submittable.com/submit.
Guidelines at stingingfly.org/
submissions. Usually responds
within one to three months.
Rejections may occasionally include
unsolicited feedback. Contributors
are paid a set rate and receive a
print copy and a discount purchase
price on the magazine.
WE SAY: We looked at Issue 33/Vol
2 of this magazine, 'In the Wake
of the Rising', which at 288 pages,
resembles a hefty anthology.
A matte laminate cover, with a
striking graphic design of old
photographs. The contents consist
of critical and artistic responses
to the Easter Rising, in the
centenary year of the event, and
so is politically and historically
rooted. The work included is
sometimes serious, sometimes
experimental – one poem is
entirely in tweets. The layout is
clean and inviting – crucial when
a magazine has as much to say as
this one does. A great read.
See also: prose publishers p186

STREETCAKE MAGAZINE
DIGITAL
streetcakemagazine@gmail.com
www.streetcakemagazine.com
Editors: Nikki Dudley, Trini Decombe
Established 2008. Mixed form.
Free access – all online content
available to all.
GENRES: Crime/thriller/mystery;
fantasy/sci-fi; literary fiction; poetry.
No non-fiction.
SUBMISSIONS: Open to all. Submit
by email to streetcakemagazine@
gmail.com. Guidelines at www.
streetcakemagazine.com/
submissions.html. Usually responds
within one to three months.
Rejection may include occasional
unsolicited feedback. Contributors
receive a digital copy. Unpaid.
WE SAY: A long-established digital
magazine, *Streetcake* keeps its
issues short and sweet. We looked
at Issue 53. The cover is a simple,
bright image: an artistic photo by
Tony Rickaby with plenty going
on; the contents, which consist of
just seven poems in this particular
issue, are cleanly laid out and
leaning towards the experimental.

STRIX
PRINT
www.strixleeds.com
strixleeds@gmail.com
Editors: SJ Bradley, Ian Harker and
Andrew Lambeth
Established 2017. Subscription
£15 for three issues over one year.
Publication available from the
publisher website.
Strix has been twice shortlisted
for the Saboteur Awards Best
Magazine category, in 2018 and
2019.
GENRE: Literary
SUBMISSIONS: Submissions open
to all, during the submissions

windows only. Submit by email to strixleeds@gmail.com. Guidelines at www.strixleeds.com/submit. Usually responds within one to three months. Contributors receive print copies of the issue.

WE SAY: A uniquely designed and eco-conscious publication, *Strix* prides itself on promoting both established and new writers in a tri-annual collection. They make use of rare Venetian typefaces to striking effect, and fully recycled paper is used to print each issue – a publication handled with care from the first word to the final product.

STRUCTO
PRINT AND DIGITAL
editor@structomagazine.co.uk
structomagazine.co.uk
Editor: Euan Monaghan
Established 2008. Mixed form. Annual subscription £14 (two issues). Available direct from publisher website; from independent bookshops and newsagents; and on other bookshop websites. All online content is available to all.

GENRES: Literary fiction; poetry; slipstream; literary interviews; essays.

SUBMISSIONS: Open to all. Submit via Submittable (guidelines and link at structomagazine.co.uk/submissions). Usually respond within six weeks. Rejections may occasionally include unsolicited feedback. Contributors receive print copy/ies and a discount purchase price on the magazine.

WE SAY: A striking cover image, overlaid by the *Structo* logo, which wraps from the front to back. The text layout uses plenty of white space, occasionally flipping sideways to accommodate the long lines of a poem. The content alternates, poetry and prose, with highlights such as an interview with Vera Chok, one of the contributors to the collection *The Good Immigrant* edited by Nikesh Shukla.

See also: Structo Press (poetry publishers p79 and prose publishers p187)

TALES FROM THE FOREST
E-ZINE
talesfromtheforest.mag@gmail.com
www.talesfromtheforest.net
Editor: Rose Fortune
Established 2016. Poetry, prose, art. Free access – all online content available to all.

GENRES: Literary.

SUBMISSIONS: Open to all, but submissions are theme-based so check the guidelines at www.talesfromtheforest.net/submissions. Submit by email to talesfromtheforest.mag@gmail.com. Usually responds within one to three months. Feedback on rejections only if requested. Unpaid.

WE SAY: *Tales from the Forest* illustrates each issue's contents with a bold illustration – very striking against the bare-tree background image and white frame. We particularly looked at Issue 5, with strong, emotional poetry and beautiful stories. The contents are listed by author name rather than piece title, which means a casual browser doesn't necessarily have a hint as to the content of what they are about to read.

TEARS IN THE FENCE
PRINT
Portman Lodge, Durweston,
Blandford Forum, Dorset DT11 0QA
tearsinthefence@gmail.com
tearsinthefence.com
Editor: David Caddy
Established 1984. Mainly poetry,
reviews and interviews. Annual
subscription £25 for three issues.
Available direct from publisher
website; by post and email
order; and at local literary events.
Nominated for Best Poetry
Magazine Pulitzer Award and
nominated for Best Poetry Editor
Pulitzer Award.
GENRES: Drama and criticism;
poetry; art, fashion and
photography; travel; literary fiction.
SUBMISSIONS: Open to all. Submit
by email to tearsinthefence@gmail.
com. Guidelines at tearsinthefence.
com/how-to-submit. Usually
responds within one to three
months, with feedback offered for
a fee. Contributors receive a print
copy of the magazine.
WE SAY: An internationalist literary
magazine producing a range of
forms, from poetry and fiction
to critical reviews and essays.
This glossy, simplistically styled
publication contains a high quantity
and quality of writing, including
some experimental and between-
genre pieces. We looked at Issue
65 in which the editorial note
fiercely asserts the importance of
independent publishing; proudly
branding their publication as an
outlet for alternative thought driven
by human issues and concerns.

TOKEN MAGAZINE
PRINT
tokenmagazine@gmail.com
tokenmagazine.co.uk
Editor: Sara Jafari
Established 2017. Mixed form.
Publications available direct from
publisher website and at select
zine fairs.
GENRES: Literary, modern,
experimental, commercial, life
writing.
SUBMISSIONS: Open to all,
focusing on those under-
represented in the arts. Submit by
email to tokenmagazine@gmail.
com. Guidelines at tokenmagazine.
co.uk/callforsubmission. Usually
responds within one to three
months. No feedback offered with
rejections. Contributors receive a
print copy.
WE SAY: We looked at a digital
version of Issue 1, which has
a colourful geometric design,
the bright borders of the cover
offset by a black and white line
drawing. This is a well-designed
magazine, with thoughtful choices
of illustration and photography,
and excellent use of colour in
the background. The contents
give voice to unheard writers,
with strong writing and imagery
exploring, for example, the
Black experience and why 'nude'
means peachy beige. Though no
theme was planned, the editorial
note points out that many of the
(beautifully written) pieces deal
with feelings of isolation.

TRAFIKA EUROPE
DIGITAL
PO Box 517, New York, NY 10029
editor@trafikaeurope.org
www.trafikaeurope.org
Editor-in-Chief: Andrew Singer
Established 2013. Quarterly online
journal. Free access – all online
content available to all.
SUBMISSIONS: Open to all. Submit

by email (editor@trafikaeurope.org) or by post (PO Box 517, New York, NY 10029). Guidelines available at www.trafikaeurope.org/wp-content/uploads/2016/03/Trafika-Europe-⊡-Submission-Guidelines-2016.03.pdf. Usually responds in one to three months.

WE SAY: We looked at Issue 15 of *Trafika Europe*, titled Lithuanian Honey Cake. With a focus on Lithuanian literature, Trafika Europe holds broad horizons and embraces different identities. The issues spans over 300 pages, providing a plethora of insightful pieces, each fronted by an author page. As a whole, the publication holds a very 'global yet local' feel.

UNDER THE RADAR ☆

PRINT

mail@ninearchespress.com
www.ninearchespress.com

Editors: Matt Merritt, Jane Commane
Established 2008. Mainly poetry, some short fiction and reviews / articles. Four-issue subscription £24.00 (UK postage included). Available direct from publisher website and by post and email order.
Winner of the 2014 Sabotage Award for Most Innovative Publisher.

SUBMISSIONS: Open to all, during submissions windows. Submit through Submittable at ninearchespress.submittable.com/submit. Guidelines at ninearchespress.com/magazine.html. Usually responds within one to three months. No feedback if rejected. Unpaid.
See also: Nine Arches Press (poetry publisher) p57

VISUAL VERSE

DIGITAL / ONLINE ANTHOLOGY OF ART AND WORDS

visualverse@thecurvedhouse.com
www.visualverse.org

Editors: Preti Taneja, Kristen Harrison
Established 2013. Mixed form. All content available to all.
GENRES: Fantasy/sci-fi; historical fiction; literary fiction; poetry; art, fashion and photography. Welcomes all genres with a literary register.
SUBMISSIONS: Submit through the submissions form at visualverse.org/submit (guidelines at same address). Cannot respond individually with acceptance/rejections – if accepted, pieces appear on the site within one week. Editors sometimes edit in collaboration with the writer. Contributors receive extensive publicity and the opportunity to be published in related projects and other journals.
WE SAY: *Visual Verse* gives their writers a gorgeous monthly picture prompt and one hour to respond to it. The work is carefully curated and cleanly presented, and each month's selection shows an extraordinary breadth of imagination. The editors also promote their writers, and maintain an easy-to-search archive. *VV* is a unique publication with an extensive readership – a great way to challenge yourself and get your work read.

WALES ARTS REVIEW ☆

E-ZINE / DIGITAL

www.walesartsreview.org
Editor: Gary Raymond
Established 2012. Mainly non-fiction. Free access – all online content available to all. Some

published fiction has been released as an anthology.

GENRES: Literary fiction; art, fashion and photography; music, stage and screen; society, education and politics.

SUBMISSIONS: Submit by email to gary@walesreview.org. Guidelines at www.walesartsreview.org/contact. Usually responds within four weeks. Rejections may include occasional unsolicited feedback. Unpaid.

WE SAY: *Wales Arts Review* is a professional e-zine, complete with eye-catching headlines, sliding images and daily updates. The focus is on reviews but creative writing and illustrations are also included – there's a handy link that take you straight to the stories, including work from some of Wales' best writers.

WASAFIRI MAGAZINE ☆
PRINT
Wasafiri, c/o School of English and Drama, Queen Mary University of London, Mile End Road, London E1 4NS
wasafiri@qmul.ac.uk
www.wasafiri.org
Editors: Susheila Nasta (founding editor), Malachi McIntosh (editor and publishing director)
Established 1984. Mixed form. Subscription approximately £50, and can only be purchased via publisher Taylor and Francis. Single issues are also available by post and email order, and at independent bookshops and local literary events. Only subscribers/ purchasers can access online content.

GENRES: Crime/thriller/mystery; drama and criticism; erotica; fantasy/sci-fi; graphic/comics; horror; historical fiction; literary fiction; poetry; romance; art, fashion and photography; biography and true stories; children and teenagers; history; society, education and politics; travel and literary criticism.

SUBMISSIONS: Open to all. Submit via our online submissions portal. Guidelines and submission: with www.wasafiri.org/submit. Usually responds in over six months. Rejections may include occasional unsolicited feedback. Contributors are paid a set rate, and receive a print copy and a discount purchase price on the magazine.

WE SAY: Perfect-bound, 100-page almost-A4 literary magazine, *Wasafiri* has a glossy, contemporary design that usually features photographic artwork on the cover. Chockful of international contemporary writing, the magazine opens with articles, interviews and art commentary (complete with full colour pictures), followed by short fiction and poetry. It ends with plenty of in-depth reviews of books from around the world. As befits an international magazine, plenty of the writing inside is translated. The issue we looked at had a particular focus on Brazilian culture.

WELL REVIEW, THE ☆
PRINT
10 Seaview Villas, Carrigaline, County Cork, Ireland
+353 871 256 136
info@thewellreview.com
www.thewellreview.com
Editor: Sarah Byrne
Established 2016. Primarily publishes poetry, plus interviews, essays and artwork in anthology-style format. Publications available

direct from the publisher website;
from chain and independent
bookshops; and at national literary
events.
A poem from Issue 1 of *The Well
Review*, by Ishion Hutchison, was
shortlisted for the Forward Prize for
Best Single Poem.
GENRES: Literary; poetry; visual
arts.
SUBMISSIONS: Submit during
submissions windows via
Submittable at thewellreview.
submittable.com/submit.
Guidelines available at the same
address. Usually responds in one
to three months. No feedback
is offered with rejections.
Contributors are paid a set rate
and receive free copies of the
issue.

WHITE REVIEW, THE
PRINT AND E-ZINE
editors@thewhitereview.org
www.thewhitereview.org
Mixed form, including poetry,
short stories, criticism, features
and essays, published as separate
online and print issues. Shortly
to launch a space for book and
exhibition reviews online. Serious-
minded but accessible work.

WILDNESS
ONLINE JOURNAL
submissions@readwildness.com
www.readwildness.com
Editors: Michelle Tudor, Peter
Barnfather
Established 2015. Mixed form.
Free access – all online content
available to all.
GENRES: Literary; poetry.
SUBMISSIONS: Open to all.
Submit by email to submissions@
readwildness.com. Guidelines at
www.readwildness.com/submit.

Usually responds within four
weeks. No feedback offered with
rejections. Unpaid.
WE SAY: The *Wildness* homepage
opens straight onto the most
recent issue, with plenty of white
space and in a large clear font,
with accents of green. The issue
is introduced with a pullquote,
and the contents divided into
two columns. Each content item
has a quote subhead, a small
picture of the author and a note
as to the type of writing you'll be
clicking through to. It's a smart
and effective layout. Once through
to the writing, more is made of
the space (no more columns). It's
easy on the eye, the writing is a
very high standard, and this is a
contemporary and pleasant read.
**See also: Platypus Press (poetry
publishers p63 and prose publishers
p170)**

WILLOWHERB REVIEW, THE
E-ZINE
07532 128558
thewillowherbreview@gmail.com
www.thewillowherbreview.com
Editor: Jessica J Lee
Established 2018. Publishes nature
writing by writers of colour. All
online content is available to all.
GENRES: Literary; nature writing.
SUBMISSIONS: Open to
writers of colour (PoC, BAME,
Indigenous) only. Submit by
email to thewillowherbreview@
gmail.com. Guidelines at www.
thewillowherbreview.com/
submissions. Usually responds in
one to three months. Rejections
include constructive feedback.
Contributors are paid a set rate.
WE SAY: *Willowherb Review*'s
website provides a simple and
delicate house for their unique

collection of content. The press is
entirely dedicated to platforming
people of colour writing about
the power, beauty and wonder
of nature. This charming press
welcomes both emerging and
established writers, but their
diversity stretches further than this.
Issue 1 includes writers from more
than seven different countries, with
writing that ranges from bold to
delicate, all centralising around a
love of nature.

WINAMOP.COM
E-ZINE
editor@winamop.com
www.winamop.com
Established 2003. Mixed form.
Free access – all online content
available to all.
GENRES: Drama and criticism;
historical fiction; literary fiction;
poetry; biography and true stories;
music, stage and screen.
SUBMISSIONS: Open to all. Submit
by email to editor@winamop.com.
Guidelines at winamop.com/
guidelines.htm. Usually responds
within four weeks. Rejections may
include occasional unsolicited
feedback.
WE SAY: *Winamop* is an
established, home-brew e-zine,
featuring work from a community
of regular contributors, which it is
actively looking to expand. The
design is wins points for being
easy to navigate and read. The
supportive vibe and encouraging
submissions blurb ('if you think it's
good enough, likely so will we')
make it a very welcoming and
inclusive publication.

Poetry magazines and e-zines

These journals and magazines are all dedicated to poetry only – any prose they publish is strictly poetry-related, in the form of interviews, news, reviews or articles.

No matter what type of poetry you write, you should be able to find a home for it. There is an astonishing range of style on display, from performance, to punk, to formal; here, poetry stalwarts jostle shoulders with scrappy zines and e-zines.

Poetry magazines and e-zines

ACUMEN LITERARY JOURNAL
PRINT
6 The Mount, Higher Furzeham Road, Brixham, South Devon TQ5 8QY
01803 851098
patriciaoxley@gmail.com
www.acumen-poetry.co.uk
Editor: Patricia Oxley
Established 1985. Annual subscription £15. Available direct from publisher website; by post and email order; at local literary events; and on Amazon. Award-winning publication.
SUBMISSIONS: Open to all. Submit by post or by email to 6 The Mount, Higher Furzeham Road, Brixham, South Devon TQ5 8QY or patriciaoxley6@gmail. com. Usually responds within four weeks. Feedback only if requested. Contributors receive a print copy.
WE SAY: *acumen* is one of our leading poetry magazines, combining poetry with reviews and articles. A5 and perfect-bound, it's well designed, with sleek, eye-catching covers and quality writing that has the knack of being serious but readable, inviting responses to previous issues and opening discussion through reviews and essays. Frequently and fairly described as one of the most wide-ranging, inclusive poetry journals around, this should be a prime target for any serious poet.

AGENDA POETRY JOURNAL
PRINT AND ONLINE BROADSHEETS
Harts Cottage, Stonehurst Lane, Five Ashes, Mayfield, East Sussex TN20 6LL
editor@agendapoetry.co.uk
www.agendapoetry.co.uk
Editor: Patricia McCarthy.
Admin: Marcus Frederick
Established 1959. Annual subscription £28. National and international printed issues, and website with supplements of poems and paintings, essays/reviews, and online broadsheets for young poets and young artists.
SUBMISSIONS: Open to all during submission windows. Submit by email to submissions@agendapoetry.co.uk. Usually responds within one to three months. Subscribers get individual, detailed feedback.
WE SAY: *Agenda* is a perfect-bound publication with an anthology aesthetic. Although the page count varies, each issue is book-length and the title and theme are chosen to reflect the submissions. We looked at Vol 49, No 1: 'Callings'. The matte cover is usually the work of a chosen artist (who is featured in the publication and online) on a block-colour background. The magazine presents lyrical, accessible poems, essays and reviews on cream paper, and offers free supplements as Broadsheets on its website. It has international reach and is highly regarded.
See also: Agenda Editions (poetry publishers) p15

ANTIPHON
DIGITAL AND E-ZINE
editors@antiphon.org.uk
www.antiphon.org.uk
Editors: Rosemary Badcoe, Noel Williams

Established 2011. Free access – all online content available to all. Includes recordings of poets reading their work on the blog. **SUBMISSIONS:** Open to all. Submit through Submittable at antiphon.submittable.com/submit. Guidelines at antiphon.org.uk/index.php/submissions. Usually responds within one to three months. Rejection may occasionally include unsolicited feedback. Unpaid.

WE SAY: This free online 61-page magazine publishes original poems, submitted through their website. The issues are designed to be downloaded in PDF format, and have a somewhat plain but nevertheless felicitous layout. We looked at Issue 21, which is set up as a theatre play with four acts, all containing seven to nine poems, plus reviews on the poets' first published book. Authors' biographies are displayed at the end of the magazine, which keep the poems clear from distracting information, displaying them in their full quality.

ARTEMIS POETRY ☆

PRINT
3 Springfield Close, E Preston, West Sussex BN16 2SZ
01903 783816
editor@poetrypf.co.uk
www.secondlightlive. co.uk
Editors: Dilys Wood and guest editors
Established 2002. Subscription £11 annual, including postage and packing. Back copies £5. Available by post and email order.
SUBMISSIONS: Open to women only. Submit by post to 3 Springfield Close, East Preston, West Sussex, BN16 2SZ. Please write *Artemis Poetry* on the envelope. Full guidelines at www.secondlightlive.co.uk/artemis.shtml#about. Usually responds within one to three months, only to successful submissions. Unpaid.

BACKLASH JOURNAL

PRINT
www.backlashpress.com
Publisher: Gretchen Heffernan
Backlash Journal is the regular publication from Backlash Press, an independent publishing house dedicated to releasing work that narrates a contemplated resistance to obedience and trend. Looks for 'experimental, yet enduring' work. Send up to three poems.
See also: Backlash Press (poetry publishers p20 and prose publishers p100)

BLACKBOX MANIFOLD

E-ZINE
www.manifold.group.shef.ac.uk
Editors: Alex Houen, Adam Piette
Established 2008. Free access – all online content available to all.
GENRES: Experimental; literary; DIY.
SUBMISSIONS: Open to all. Guidelines at www.manifold.group.shef.ac.uk/issue1/submissions.html. Usually responds within one to three months. No feedback offered with rejections. Unpaid.

WE SAY: This e-zine was easy to navigate, with archives and submissions very clearly marked. The site has a clean bold aesthetic without the use of images so the only thing for a reader to focus on is the work. Chosen submissions for each issue are organised by author, and interviews and reviews are listed separately.

BLITHE SPIRIT (THE BRITISH HAIKU SOCIETY)

PRINT
ed.blithespirit@gmail.com
www.britishhaikusociety.org.uk/journal
Editor: Shrikaanth Krishnamurthy
Established 1991. Poetry. Annual subscription costs £27 within the UK. Issues available direct from the publisher website; by direct mail and email orders; and at national literary events. Some online content available to all.

GENRES: Haiku; tanka; haibun; renku.

SUBMISSIONS: Open to members of The British Haiku Society only. Submit by email to blithespirit. editor@gmail.com. Guidelines at www.britishhaikusociety.org.uk/ journal. Usually responds within four weeks. Rejections may include occasional unsolicited feedback. Unpaid.

WE SAY: We looked at a PDF sampler of *Blithe Spirit*, which had a plain black-and-white layout with a serif font. The design makes good use of the space, scattering haiku (and senryu, tanka, haibun and sequences) down the page so the eye skips from one to the next, allowing the images to settle. The poetry included ranges from classic haiku form to more experimental approaches (we were particularly struck by Chris Luck's home intruder haiku).

BUTCHER'S DOG

PRINT
1 Jackson Street, North Shields NE30 2JA
editor@butchersdogmagazine.co.uk
www.butchersdogmagazine.co.uk
Editor: Jo Clement
Established 2012. Publishes poetry. Annual subscription £14.99 for two

issues. Available direct from the publication website; at national and local literary events; and at major and independent bookfairs. *Butcher's Dog* was a runner-up for Best Magazine in the 2017 Saboteur Awards, and nominated as Editor's choice.

GENRES: Essays; creative non-fiction; memoir; biographies; reviews.

SUBMISSIONS: Open to all writers living in the UK and the Republic of Ireland, especially writers with a connection to Northern England, during submission windows. Submit via the website at www. butchersdogmagazine.co.uk/p/ submit.html. A 'tip-jar' submission does not affect editorial decisions. Usually responds in one to three months. Feedback on submissions is provided freely, subject to the Editor's discretion and availability. Contributors receive a free copy of the issue, and a discount on further copies.

WE SAY: The Spring 2019 edition of *Butcher's Dog* (Issue 11) has a vividly illustrated jacket cover wrapped around an A5 saddle-stitched volume. Each copy of the 600-copy print run is hand-marked with a number (ours was 211), which was a lovely touch. The content is diverse and well-curated, featuring a short bio for each contributor at the end of the collection.

COMPASS MAGAZINE, THE

E-ZINE
editors@thecompassmagazine.co.uk
www.thecompassmagazine.co.uk
Editors: Lindsey Holland, Andrew Forster
Established 2015. Poetry, reviews, poetics. Free access – all online content available to all.

SUBMISSIONS: Submit by email to editor@thecompassmagazine.co.uk. Guidelines at www.thecompassmagazine.co.uk/submissions-2. Usually responds within one to three months. No feedback with rejection. Unpaid.
WE SAY: A stylish e-zine, *The Compass* is a site that's been designed from scratch to best suit its purpose (as opposed to being created from a simple template). The range of content – reviews, interviews, articles and poems – means the home page is quite crowded, but it's easy to navigate and pleasant to look at. The content is top-end: this is a poetry zine run by poets for the poetry community.

CRUNCH, THE

E-ZINE, PODCASTS AND VIDEO
www.crunchpoetry.com
Editors: Richard James Jones, Adam Sillman, Rhys Owain Williams
Established 2015. Free access – all online content available to all.
SUBMISSIONS: By invitation only. Unpaid.
WE SAY: *The Crunch* is a multimedia poetry magazine. Each issue takes up a single page of the site and focuses on a single featured poet. The content includes a 'cover' image, which includes the issue number ensconced next to a carefully considered editorial; the biography of the featured poet and a photo; a podcast interview with the poet; and videos of the poet performing. Despite the amount of content, the approach isn't too crowded or overwhelming, and it's a pleasure to focus so wholly on the work of a single writer.

CTRL+ALT+DEL

E-ZINE
Top Flat 52 High Street, Bethesda LL57 3AN
rhys.trimble@gmail.com
cad.trimbling.com
Editor: Rhys Trimble
Established 2008. Free access – all online content available to all.
GENRES: Experimental; minimalist; vispo.
SUBMISSIONS: Submission usually by invitation only, but 'if you think you fit in, have a go'. Submit by email (rhys.trimble@gmail.com). Usually responds within one to three months. Feedback offered if requested. Unpaid (except for glory).

DARK HORSE, THE

PRINT
www.thedarkhorsemagazine.com
Founded in 1995 by Scottish poet Gerry Cambridge. Publishes poetry – both free verse and in metre and rhyme – alongside essays, reviews, interviews. Welcomes submissions (in hard copy only) from new and established poets.

ENVOI POETRY JOURNAL

PRINT
Meirion House, Tanygrisiau, Blaenau Ffestiniog, Wales LL41 3SU
01766 832112
www.cinnamonpress.com
Editors: Jan Fortune, Kay Syrad
Established 1957. Poetry, reviews, translations, interviews and features. £14 for two-issue annual subscription. Publication available direct from publisher website; at local literary events; and via Inpress Books.
GENRES: All poetry forms welcome.
SUBMISSIONS: During submissions windows: please send in October

(for April). and May (for October); Submit by email only to envoi@cinnamonpress.com. Guidelines at www.cinnamonpress.com/index.php/envoi. Usually responds within one to three months. Standard email/letter rejection in most cases, but may offer feedback to those who have come close to publication.

WE SAY: We looked at Issue 182 of *Envoi*, a typically elegant publication with a moody, almost sepia photo of a graffitied and theatrical curios-shop window in late evening light. The Issue is divided into distinct sections: around 30 pages of new poetry, followed by features (covering on-the-nose topics including the poetry blogosphere, eco-poetry and prose poems), then reviews. It opens with a welcome from editor Jan Fortune, and closes with the Poets' Biographies, which show a range of writing experience from someone's first publication to recognisable names.

For a fuller description of this press, including what They Say, see also Cinnamon Press (prose publishers p109 and poetry publishers p26)

ERBACCE

PRINT
erbacce@blueyonder.co.uk
erbacce-press.com
Editor: Dr Alan Corkish
Co Editor: Dr Andrew Taylor
Established 2004. Quarterly journal, available direct from publisher website; by post and email order; at independent bookshops; at national and local literary events; and from Amazon. Note: *erbacce* is a cooperative, all profits are used exclusively to produce new books.

SUBMISSIONS: Open to all. Submit by post (Dr Andrew Taylor, 5 Farrell Close, Melling, Liverpool L31 1BU) or by email (erbacce@hotmail.com). Guidelines on the website. Usually responds within 48 hours. Contributors receive a copy of the journal and a discount on further copies.

WE SAY: *erbacce* is a 36-page journal printed on white paper. With a thin cover bearing a slight sheen, this saddle-stitched quarterly has a definite independent feel; the press is entirely owned and run by poets, and aims to present all submission and competition opportunities for free.

See also: erbacce-press (poetry publisher) p32

EYE FLASH POETRY MAGAZINE

PRINT AND DIGITAL
7 Trevor Road, Newport, Isle of Wight PO30 5DZ
07827 447532
eyeflashpoetry@outlook.com
www.eyeflashpoetry.co.uk
Editor: Charlotte Begg
Established 2017. Publications available direct from the publisher website; from independent bookshops; at national literary events; from Southbank Poetry Library; and from Amazon and other bookshop websites. Free access – all online content available to all.

GENRES: Mixed contemporary poetry.

SUBMISSIONS: Open to all. Submit by email to eyeflashpoetry@outlook.com. Guidelines at www.eyeflashpoetry.co.uk/?page_id=25. Usually responds within four weeks. Rejections may occasionally include unsolicited feedback. Contributors receive a digital copy of the magazine and a 50% discount on the purchase price of one or more print copies.

WE SAY: We looked at a PDF sample of Issue Three of the *Eye Flash Poetry Journal*. Printed in a simple black font on white background, this publication appears in a clear and professional format. The cover boasts a large, mystical image of a woodland scene, followed by an extensive collection of poems exploring relationships with nature.

See also: Eye Flash Poetry (poetry publisher) p34

FENLAND REED, THE

PRINT
thefenlandreed@gmail.com
www.thefenlandreed.co.uk
Editors: Elisabeth Sennitt Clough, Mary Livingstone, Jonathan Totman

Established 2015. Subscription £10 for two issues per year. Available direct from the publisher website; from independent bookshops; and at local literary events. Only subscribers/purchasers can view all online content, though some content is freely accessible.

SUBMISSIONS: Submissions are open to all, during submissions windows only. Submit via email to thefenlandreed@gmail.com. Full guidelines are available at www.thefenlandreed.co.uk/submissions. Usually responds in one to three months. Contributors receive a copy of the magazine.

WE SAY: We viewed a sample of poems from *The Fenland Reed*'s Issue 7. The poems explore the normality of human experiences, embedded with pensive reflections on thought and emotion. This

simplicity and value of the familiar is reflected in the publisher's website, with a background, header symbols, and of course their name, all conveying a love of nature.

FROGMORE PAPERS, THE ☆

PRINT
21 Mildmay Road, Lewes, East Sussex BN7 1PJ
frogmorepress@gmail.com
www.frogmorepress.co.uk
Editor: Jeremy Page

Established 1983. Poetry, reviews, interviews. Subscription £10 per year. Available by post and email order.

GENRES: Poetry, prose.
SUBMISSIONS: During submissions windows (April and October), submit by post to *The Frogmore Papers*, 21 Mildmay Road, Lewes BN7 1PJ. Usually responds within one to three months, no feedback offered with rejection. Contributors receive a print copy.

See also: *Morphrog* (poetry magazine) p277

HIGH WINDOW, THE

E-ZINE
3 Grovely Close, Peatmoor, Swindon, Wiltshire SN5 5DN
submissions@thehighwindow.uk
www.thehighwindowpress.com
Editor: David Cooke.

Established 2016. Free access – all online content available to all.

GENRES: Poetry; verse translations; essays; reviews.
SUBMISSIONS: Open to all. Submit by email to submissions@thehighwindow.uk. Guidelines at www.thehighwindowpress.com/submissions. Usually responds within one to three months. No feedback offered with rejection.

WE SAY: A vibrant and professional website which is clear and easy to use. The poems are divided into those selected for each journal, a featured American poet and those which have been translated from other languages. The work is on trend with other contemporary publications such as *Agenda* and *Envoi*.

See also: The High Window Press (poetry publisher) p44

IOTA POETRY
PRINT

58 Dale Road, Matlock, Derbyshire DE4 3NB
info@templarpoetry.com
www.templarpoetry.com
Founded 25 years ago. Published three times a year. Features around 25 poets per issue, plus features and reviews. £1 admin fee for submissions made by email, or submit by post.

See also: Templar Poetry (poetry publisher) p81

JOURNAL, THE
PRINT

38 Pwllcarn Terrace, Blaengarw, Bridgend, South Wales CF32 8AS
01656 857483
asamsmith@hotmail.com
samsmithbooks.weebly.com/
the-journal.html
Editor: Sam Smith
Established 1996. Subscription £11 (UK only). Available direct from publisher website; and by post and email order.

SUBMISSIONS: Publication history required. Submit by post (38 Pwllcarn Terrace, Blaengarw, Bridgend, South Wales CF32 8AS) or by email (asamsmith@hotmail.com). Usually responds within four weeks. No feedback offered with

rejection. Contributors receive a print copy.

WE SAY: The two PDF issue proofs we looked at feature a wide variety of poetry, as well as reviews and an ongoing series of Norse translations. There is a lot packed into the pages of *The Journal*, with multiple poems often appearing together on the page. Experimental and non-traditional formatting seems to be welcomed, as well as a wide variety of subjects.

See also: Original Plus (poetry publisher) p58

LITTER MAGAZINE
E-ZINE

leafepress@hotmail.com
www.leafepress.com/litter
Editor: Alan Baker
Established 2000. Poetry, reviews, interviews. Free access – all online content available to all.

SUBMISSIONS: Solicited work only. No feedback offered with rejections.

See also: Leafe Press (poetry publisher) p275

LONG POEM MAGAZINE
PRINT

20 Spencer Rise, London NW5 1AP
mail@longpoemmagazine.org.uk
www.longpoemmagazine.org.uk
Editor: Linda Black
Deputy Editor: Claire Crowther
Established 2007. Two issues per year. Single issue £10.50, annual subscription £20.50 (including P&P) within the UK; single issue £17, annual subscription £32 (including P&P) outside the UK. Available to purchase direct from website.

GENRES: Poetry plus one essay per issue on aspects of the long poem, online book reviews (long poems only).

SUBMISSIONS: Open to all; only accepts long poems or sequences of at least 75 lines of poetry (but no book length poems). Two submission months per year: June and November. Submit by email to mail@longpoemmagazine. org.uk. Guidelines at www. longpoemmagazine.org.uk/ submissions. No simultaneous submissions. Usually responds within three months. No feedback offered with rejections. Contributors receive a print copy.
WE SAY: We looked at extracts from *Long Poem Magazine* available on the publication website. The covers of the magazine are striking in their use of white space – only top and bottom of the cover contain any images, text or colour. The poems we read varied in form and style, and included translated works. Each poem includes a paragraph by the poet providing context and insight into how the poem was written or translated. The editorials – accessible for each issue – are equally in depth and thoughtful.

MAGMA ☆
PRINT AND DIGITAL
23 Pine Walk, Carshalton SM5 4ES
info@magmapoetry.com
www.magmapoetry.com
Editors: rotating editorship giving a wide range of content
Poetry and poetry-related features, in themed issues. Annual subscription (three issues per year) £22 (including P&P). Digital subscription £14.99 (free with print subscription) from exacteditions. com. Available direct from publisher website; in selected/ local chain bookshops; and in independent bookshops. Online, only subscribers/purchasers can access full content, with some content available to all.
SUBMISSIONS: Open to all. Submit through Submittable at www. magmapoetry.com/contributions (guidelines available at same address). Usually responds within one to three months. Rejection may occasionally include unsolicited feedback. Contributors receive a print copy.
WE SAY: We looked at a PDF of Issue 74. On the theme of 'work', it presents nearly 100 pages of articles, poetry, and regular features. The writing is diverse, exploring the theme to its full capacity. Each issue of *Magma* is curated by different editors, including guest editors, making *Magma* a refreshing publisher that invites new perspectives to make each issue inherently unique.

MODERN POETRY IN TRANSLATION
PRINT
c/o The Queen's College, Oxford OX1 4AW
editor@mptmagazine.com
www.modernpoetryintranslation.com
Editor: Clare Pollard
Established 1965. Subscription £23/year for three issues. Available direct from publisher website; by post and email order; in selected chain and independent bookshops; and from Amazon. Some digital content is freely available to all.
GENRES: Poetry in translation.
SUBMISSIONS: Submit during submissions windows. Visit modernpoetryintranslation. com/submit/ for current calls for submissions. May take over six months to respond. Rejections may occasionally include unsolicited

feedback. Contributors are paid a set rate.

WE SAY: The digital anthology we looked at (Issue 2, 2017) contains several mini-collections from various authors, translated from their native languages. Each poet has a short introduction, written by the translator, and some have headshots included. The colour scheme of the anthology is very crisp and clean, with red being used for page numbers, poet names, and a very powerful mantra at the beginning of the anthology.

MORPHROG ☆

E-ZINE

morphrog@gmail.co.uk
www.morphrog.com
Editors: Jeremy Page and Peter Stewart
Established 2009. 'Poetry in the extreme'. Online content is available to all.

GENRES: Poetry.

SUBMISSIONS: During submissions windows (May and November), submit by email to morphrog@gmail.com. Usually responds within one to three months, no feedback offered with rejection.

WE SAY: *Morphrog*'s simply structured website platforms its latest issue, *Morphrog 19*. Beneath a wide banner image, the site's homepage gives a link to the latest issue, followed by a simple explanation as to how to navigate the site. On the Issue page is a list of featured authors – by clicking the names readers can click through to their poems. Branding themselves as publishers of 'poetry in the extreme', *Morphrog* gives ample space to each writer, presenting their writing on individual pages, accompanied by an image that embodies that author's work.

See also: *The Frogmore Papers* **(poetry magazine) p274**

NORTH MAGAZINE, THE ☆

PRINT

0114 346 3037
office@poetrybusiness.co.uk
www.poetrybusiness.co.uk
Editors: Ann Sansom, Peter Sansom
Established 1986. Poetry, reviews, critical articles. Annual UK subscription £18 (£24 rest of the world). Available direct from publisher website; by post and email order; online at Newsstand; at Salts Mill (Shipley), Heffer's Bookshop (Cambridge), Five Leaves Bookshop (Nottingham), Magazine (Brighton), and Blackwell's Bookshop.

SUBMISSIONS: Open to all, during submissions windows. Submit by post to *The Poetry Business*, Bank Street Arts, 32-40 Bank Street, Sheffield, S1 2DS. Online submissions accepted from overseas only. Usually responds within one to three months. No feedback with rejection. Contributors receive a print copy of the magazine.

See also: Smith|Doorstop Books (poetry publisher) p75

PB MAG

PRINT

Co. Wicklow, Éire
+353 4022 3556
buspoems@gmail.com
thepoetrybusmag.wixsite.com/change
Established 2010. Available from independent bookshops and direct from the publisher website. A poem from *PB$* ('Like That Raw Engine' by George Szirtes) was shortlisted for the 2016 Forward

Prize for Best Single Poem, and included in the Forward Prize anthology.
GENRE: Urban-grit.
SUBMISSIONS: Open to all. During submissions windows, submit by email to buspoems@gmail.com. Guidelines at thepoetrybusmag. wixsite.com/change/submissions. Usually responds within one to

PENNINE PLATFORM

PRINT AND DIGITAL
PO Box 756, Wakefield WF1 9RW
07931 720056
editor@pennineplatform.com
www.pennineplatform.com
Editor: Julia Deakin

Established 1973. Annual subscription £10.50 for two issues in the UK; £14 in the EU; and £16 worldwide. Single copies available from www.pennineplatform.com and at literary events.
GENRES: Contemporary; literary; concrete.
SUBMISSIONS: Three to six unpublished poems welcome in February or September. Submit work by post (*Pennine Platform*, PO Box 754, Wakefield WF1 9RW, with SAE and contact details on each poem) or email (editor@pennineplatform.com, poems in the body of the email or attached in a single word document). Brief guidelines at www.pennineplatform.com (pending a website update). Usually responds in one to three months. Brief feedback given on all poems (up to six per issue) – please say if this is not required as it saves the editors a lot of time. Contributors receive print copies of their issue.

THEY SAY

Pennine Platform readers come from the Pennine region of northern England and far beyond. Subscribers and contributors may know the region first hand, or have yet to visit. A Pennine flavour to submissions is therefore welcome but by no means essential: more important are resonance, clarity and originality. We aim for a broad cultural mix from writers of all ages and backgrounds, especially those who see the platform more as a vantage point for looking outwards than a stage. Re-energised with new editors from 2019, we plan to enhance print output alongside new digital and spoken word opportunities.

WE SAY: We saw Issue 85 of *Pennine Platform*, a 60-page perfect-bound A5 magazine with a full-colour cover. The magazine is well designed following a revamp for this issue, and the poems inside are clearly laid out. The back cover lists the poets, who have been paired or grouped according to loose themes found within their poems.

three months. Rejections may occasionally include unsolicited feedback. Contributors receive a print copy and a digital copy of the issue.

WE SAY: *Poetry Bus* 5 (which we saw in PDF format) is a sizeable magazine, stretching to 126 pages of poetry and wonderful art: the contents cover four pages out of necessity. The poetry includes a range of styles, all presented with an eye for the space. Many of the textured images that feature every ten pages or so make use of words, and there's an extra surprise burst of colour around halfway through, with a four-page comic entry from David Timoney. Something for everyone, basically, but without feeling at all confusing for the reader. The final five pages feature short biogs of every contributor.
See also: PB Press (poetry publisher) p62

PICKLED BODY, THE
DIGITAL
thepickledbody@gmail.com
www.thepickledbody.com
Editors: Dimitra Xidous, Patrick Chapman
Established 2013. Publishes poetry and visual art. Available on Issuu and directly from the publication website: all online content is freely available to all.
GENRES: All.
SUBMISSIONS: Open to all, during submissions windows. Submit by email to thepickledbody@gmail.com. Guidelines at www.thepickledbody.com/submission-guidelines. Usually responds in one to three months. Rejections may occasionally include unsolicited feedback. Contributors receive a digital copy of the magazine.

WE SAY: *The Pickled Body*'s issues feature full-colour stylish covers utilising work by the artist featured in its pages. The layout of the magazine is clean and enticing, with plenty of white space and careful consideration given to the layout of the poetry it features including prose poetry, fragmented poetry and visual poetry – we were taken with Richard Biddle's collage art poetry in Issue 3.3. Full contributor biographies are featured on the final page.

PN REVIEW
PRINT AND DIGITAL
4th Floor Alliance House, 30 Cross Street, Manchester M2 7AQ
0161 834 8730
info@carcanet.co.uk
www.pnreview.co.uk
Editors: Michael Schmidt and Andrew Latimer
Established 1973. Publishes poetry and non-fiction articles. Print and digital annual subscriptions at £39.50 (UK), (£45) Europe, or £49 (ROW) for six issues. Available direct from the publisher website, from independent bookshops, at national and local literary events, and from Amazon. Some online content is freely available to all.
SUBMISSIONS: Guidelines at www.pnreview.co.uk/contact.shtml. Usually responds in one to three months. Rejections may occasionally include unsolicited feedback.
WE SAY: An A4, perfect-bound bi-monthly publication printed on creamy matte paper. We looked at three issues of the magazine. On each one, the cover is minimalistic and full-colour, in the vein of an academic journal, while the inner pages are monochrome, featuring a mix of poetry and essays. We

thought it felt high-brow and serious, both in content and in design.

See also: Carcanet (poetry publishers p25 and prose publishers p106)

POETRY IRELAND REVIEW ☆

PRINT
11 Parnell Square, Dublin 1, Ireland
+353 1 6789815
publications@poetryireland.ie
www.poetryireland.ie
Editor: Eavan Boland

Established 1981. Annual subscription €38/€42. Available direct from publisher website; by post and email order; at chain and independent bookshops nationwide; at literary events; and from Amazon and other bookshop websites.

GENRE: Literary.

SUBMISSIONS: Open to all. Submit by post to *Poetry Ireland*, 11 Parnell Square, Dublin 1, Ireland. Guidelines at www.poetryireland. ie/writers/submission-to-pir. Usually responds within four to six months. Rejection may occasionally include unsolicited feedback. Contributors are paid a set rate.

WE SAY: We looked at the online catalogue for this journal. We were struck by the artwork on the cover – all professional and eye-catching, using muted, expressive imagery whether paintings, photography or ink drawings. We hope this sort of craftsmanship appears in the published work, of which there are 121 pages, packed with poetry and essays (the website also lets us view the contents page). We recognised more than a few names in the list (Nessa O'Mahony, Eleanor Hooker and Chris Preddle, for example).

See also: Poetry Ireland (poetry publisher) p64

POETRY LONDON ☆

PRINT
Goldsmiths, University of London,
New Cross, London SE14 6NW
020 8228 5707
admin@poetrylondon.co.uk
www.poetrylondon.co.uk
Editors: Martha Sprackland (Poetry);
Dai George (Reviews)

Established 1988. Print magazine, with some content available online to all. Subscribe for £28 (or £25 by Direct Debit) for three issues over one year. Available direct from the publisher website; by direct mail and email order; from independent bookshops; and at local literary events, including the magazine's issue launches, which take place three times a year at Kings Place, London.

GENRES: Contemporary poetry.

SUBMISSIONS: Open to all. Submit via Submittable or by post: guidelines at www.poetrylondon. co.uk/submissions. Usually responds in four to six months. No feedback offered with rejections. Contributors are paid a set rate and receive a print copy of the issue.

POETRY REVIEW, THE

PRINT AND DIGITAL
The Poetry Society, 22 Betterton Street, London WC2H 9BX
info@poetrysociety.org.uk
www.poetrysociety.org.uk/
 publications-section/the-poetry-review
Editor: Emily Berry

The quarterly journal of The Poetry Society, this barely needs an introduction. Includes work by new and established poets, as well as interviews, articles on poetry, critiques and art. Wide readership, as it is distributed to every full member of The Poetry Society. Hard copy submissions only.

POETRY SPACE SHOWCASE ☆
PRINT AND DIGITAL
www.poetryspace.co.uk
Editor: Susan Sims
Subscription ('Friend of Poetry Space') £15 per year. Available direct from publisher website and on Amazon. Free access – all online content available to all.
SUBMISSIONS: Open to all. Submit by email to susan@poetryspace. co.uk. Usually responds within one to three months. Rejections may include occasional unsolicited feedback. Unpaid.
WE SAY: The *Poetry Space Showcase* is slightly hidden in the Poetry Space website (the link is part-way down the menu to the left) and is less showy than the name suggests: a single, easy-on-the-eye web page, followed by the featured poems. But showiness isn't everything, and this is still a professional, understated site. A different photograph heralds the start of each new poem, which all share the virtues of striking imagery and memorable metaphors.
See also: Poetry Space (poetry publisher) p65

POETRY WALES ☆
PRINT AND DIGITAL
57 Nolton Street, Bridgend CF31 3AE
01656 663018
info@poetrywales.co.uk
www.poetrywales.co.uk
Established 1965. Poetry, reviews, articles. Annual subscription £27. Available direct from publisher website; by post and email order; and at local literary events. Only subscribers/purchasers can access online content.
SUBMISSIONS: Open to all. Submit through Submittable at poetrywales.submittable.com/

submit. Usually responds within four to six months. No feedback offered with rejections. Contributors are paid a set rate and receive a print copy of the magazine.
WE SAY: Perfect-bound 96-page magazine on thick quality paper. The copy we looked at (Vol. 51, No. 1) featured a landscape photo on the matte cover, and explored how Patagonia and Wales might imagine each other. The content included some translated poetry, as well as in-depth articles alongside the many poems, which ranged from strict structure to free-verse.
See also: Seren Books (prose publishers p181 and poetry publishers p72)

PULSAR POETRY MAGAZINE
E-ZINE
34 Lineacre, Grange Park, Swindon, Wiltshire SN5 6DA
pulsar.ed@btopenworld.com
www.pulsarpoetry.com
Editor: David Pike
Established 1994. Poetry and reviews. All online content freely available to all.
GENRES: Hard-hitting work with message and meaning. Not keen on religious or epic poems.
SUBMISSIONS: Open to all – up to three unpublished poems, but no simultaneous submissions. Submit by post or by email to *Pulsar* Editor, 34 Lineacre, Grange Park, Swindon, Wiltshire SN5 6DA or pulsar.ed@btinternet.com. Usually responds within four weeks. No feedback offered with rejection. Contributors receive exposure.
WE SAY: *Pulsar Poetry* has a simple, but unconventional, old-fashioned layout, on a yellow background with rather a small font. With dropdown menus and menu-bars

now the norm, it's not easy to find the poems, but once found the content is clearly signposted. The poetry and discourse are modern and the zine works hard to promote its poets and other publications.

QUID
PRINT
www.barquepress.com/quid.php
'Name = cost = image.' An occasional journal of 'poetics, criticism, invective and investigation'. Copies available online to download and print out.
See also: Barque Press (poetry publisher) p21

RAUM POETRY
PRINT
raumpoetry@gmail.com
www.raumpoetry.com
Keen to experiment with unconventional poetry as well as traditional forms, any form of good poetry or poetry in translation is welcomed. Submissions are accepted on a rolling basis.

REACH POETRY
PRINT
24 Forest Houses, Halwill, Beaworthy, Devon EX21 5UU
publishing@indigodreams.co.uk
www.indigodreams.co.uk
Editor: Ronnie Goodyer
Established 1997. A monthly publication. Subscription £51/ year for 12 monthly issues or £4.50 single UK. Available direct from publisher website; and by post and email order.
Indigo Dreams' Editors won the Ted Slade Award for Services to Poetry 2015.
GENRES: All styles considered and wide range in each monthly issue.

SUBMISSIONS: Open to all. Submit by post (IDP, 24 Forest Houses, Halwill, Beaworthy, Devon EX21 5UU) or by email (publishing@ indigodreams.co.uk). Guidelines at www.indigodreams.co.uk. Poetry, lively letters section, readers' votes. Usually responds within four weeks. Occasional feedback offered with rejection. Contributors receive a monthly monetary prize, shared by the top three as voted for by readers.
WE SAY: A5 monthly publication by Indigo Dreams which showcases both new and experienced poets. The perfect-bound, full-colour design is attractive and the issue engages readers through interactive elements in which readers can vote for their favourite poems. Publishing around 500 poems each year, this magazine is a fruitful source of diverse forms, projecting a range of voices through high quality writing.
For what They Say, see Indigo Dreams Publishing Ltd (poetry publisher) p46. See also *The Dawntreader* p223 and *Sarasvati* p253 (mixed-form magazines)

RIALTO, THE ☆
PRINT
c/o 74 Britannia Road, Norwich NR1 4HS
info@therialto.co.uk
www.therialto.co.uk
Editor: Michael Mackmin
Established 1984. Poetry, poetry news and views. Annual subscription £24 (overseas £24+£12 shipping; concessions £19). Available direct from publisher website and at a few selected/local chain bookshops and independent bookshops.
SUBMISSIONS: Open to all. Submit by post (*The Rialto*, 74 Britannia

Road, Norwich NR1 4HS) or Submittable (therialto.submittable.com/submit). Guidelines on the website. Usually responds within one to six months. Returns may include occasional unsolicited feedback. Contributors are paid a set rate.

WE SAY: Perfect-bound, 64-page A4 magazine with an artistic edge. The screamingly bright cover of Issue 83 featured a full-page illustration of reds, oranges and yellows, on a bold blue ground. Inside on thick white paper, poems are laid out with clear thought as

SHEARSMAN MAGAZINE
PRINT
50 Westons Hill Drive, Emersons Green, Bristol BS16 7DF
editor@shearsman.com
www.shearsman.com/shearsman-magazine

Editor: Tony Frazer

Established 1981 (2003 in its current form). Poetry and literary criticism. Available direct from publisher website, by post and email order, at selected/local chain and independent bookshops and on Amazon and other bookshop websites.
SUBMISSIONS: Open to all, only during submissions windows. Submit by post (Shearsman Books Ltd., 50 Westons Hill Drive, Emersons Green, Bristol BS16 7DF) or by email (editor@shearsman.com), avoiding attachments other than PDFs. Full guidelines at www.shearsman.com/shearsman-magazine-submissions. Usually responds in up to three months. No feedback offered if rejected. Contributors receive two free copies of the magazine.
See also: Shearsman Books (poetry publisher) p73

WE SAY: We looked at *Shearsman* Issue 119 and 120, a double issue containing over 100 pages of diverse writing, unbound by strict themes or patterns. Editor Tony Frazer emphasises the magazine's love for writing on the experimental end, whilst also appreciating more conservative and traditional work. The layout emphasises the poets' names at the head of each poem, with names, poem titles and the title page of the issue balancing a pleasing sans serif font against the serif font used for the poetry. The layout is clean and bright with wide margins.

to their shape and size, so there's no feeling of overcrowding, and even the title page has a couple of poems on it (Wordsworth and Hopkins).
See also: The Rialto/Bridge Pamphlets (poetry publisher) p68

SALON OF THE REFUSED
E-ZINE
refusedpoems@gmail.com
www.salonoftherefused.com
Editors: Jacqueline Saphra and Norbert Hirschhorn
Established 2017. Free access – all online content available to all.
SUBMISSIONS: Open to all. If the poet believes in their work and it has been rejected a minimum of four times, *Salon of the Refused* will publish it. Submit by email to refusedpoems@gmail.com. Guidelines at www.salonoftherefused.com/send-us-a-poem. Usually responds within four weeks. Unpaid.

SKYLIGHT 47
PRINT AND DIGITAL
Skylight 47, Treanlaur, Maree, Oranmore, County Galway, Ireland
skylightpoets47@gmail.com
www.skylight47poetry.wordpress.com
Editors: Ruth Quinlan, Nicki Griffin, Bernie Crawford,
Established 2013. Mixed form. Subscription €13.10/year within Ireland or €14.90/year outside Ireland for two issues. Publications available direct from publisher website; by direct mail and email orders; from independent bookshops; and at local literary events. Some online content available to all.
Skylight 47 was nominated for the Galway Cathaoirleach Community Awards in 2016.

GENRES: Literary.
SUBMISSIONS: Open to all, during submission windows. Submit by email to skylightpoets47@gmail.com. Guidelines at www.skylight47poetry.wordpress.com/submissions. Usually responds within one to three months. No feedback offered with rejections. Contributors receive a print copy.
WE SAY: With a digital newspaper style, this 24-page magazine showcases a great deal of work in a short space, fitting multiple poems or prose pieces on each page. Illustrations complement the poems, as does a beautifully designed cover, with one artist featured per issue.

SMITHEREENS LITERARY MAGAZINE
DIGITAL
smithereens.press@gmail.com
www.smithereenspress.com
Editor: Kenneth Keating
Established 2018. Publishes poetry. Free access – all online content available to all.
SUBMISSIONS: Open to all, during submissions windows. Submit by email to smithereens.press@gmail.com. Guidelines at www.smithereenspress.com/submissions/submissions.html. Usually responds in one to three months. Rejections may occasionally include unsolicited feedback. Currently unpaid.
WE SAY: We looked at Smithereens Press' website, which contains their full catalogue of chapbooks and magazine issues. It takes a few clicks to get to the most recent issue, but once there the magazine is viewable via Issuu. We looked at Issue 3, which had a bright blue cover, with a more monochrome

285

sea image set as though viewed through a porthole. The cover also displays the names of the

contributing writers. Inside, there is a tremendous range of poetry styles, formatted in sans serif font.

SOUTH BANK POETRY ☆
PRINT
Kemp House 152-160 City Road,
London EC1V 2NX
020 7117 6193
editor@southbankpoetry.co.uk
www.southbankpoetry.co.uk
Editors: Katherine Lockton and Peter Ebsworth

Established 2008. Publishes poetry. Annual subscription £16.50 for three issues. Publications available direct from the publisher website; by direct mail and email order; from chain bookshops nationwide; and from independent bookshops.
GENRES: Poetry.
SUBMISSIONS: Open to all. Submit via the website at www.southbankpoetry.co.uk/ submit-a-poem (guidelines at the same address) or by post to *South Bank Poetry*, The Editors, Kemp House 152-160 City Road, London EC1V 2NX. Usually responds in four to six months. No feedback offered on submissions. Contributors receive a free copy of the issue.
WE SAY: We looked at two issues of *South Bank Poetry* (30 and 31). The magazine is a perfect-bound A5 paperback publication which is well laid out and has a polished feel. The poems published within are fresh and diverse in terms of style and subject. *South Bank Poetry*'s website continues the

South Bank POETRY

professional feel with an easy submissions process and a sleek design.

THEY SAY

South Bank Poetry is always on the lookout for the best new poems being written now, especially poems about life and current affairs. We publish clear and accessible poetry that is enjoyable to read. Work that has featured in our magazine has gone onto be highly commended in the Forward Prize for Poetry and featured in the *Forward Anthology*.
South Bank Poetry aims to be an all-inclusive poetry hub where everyone can feel like they belong. We open up access to the poetry world through our magazine, workshops, classes and readings in venues such as residential homes and church halls.

The poets' names head the pages, in serif font and in the same bright blue as the cover.

See also: Smithereens Press (poetry publisher) p76

SOUTH POETRY MAGAZINE
PRINT
PO Box 9338, Wimborne BH21 9JA
south@southpoetry.org
www.southpoetry.org
Editors: Penny Dale, Peter Keeble, Anne Peterson, Chrissie Williams
Established 1990, published twice annually. Poetry, reviews, profiles. Annual subscription £12 (or £22 for two years). Available by post and email order.
SUBMISSIONS: Open to all. Submit by post to *South Poetry Magazine*, PO Box 9338, Wimborne BH21 9JA. Hard copies only, please, using the submissions form. Full guidelines at www.southpoetry. org/submissions. Individual responses not possible. Successful submitters' names are posted on the website eight to ten weeks after the deadline for that issue's submissions. Contributors receive a print copy.
WE SAY: We looked at a copy of *South Poetry's* 59th issue, a slightly-larger-than-A5 perfect-bound magazine with a glossy cover and bright white pages. The poems are laid out in a clear way, and there's a reviews section at the back of the magazine, as well as a news section and comments from the poetry selectors, which is a nice touch.

Prose magazines and e-zines

We define prose quite widely for this section: short stories, long short stories, flash fiction, creative non-fiction and more – even comics. Any magazine that publishes work that's literary, but not poetry, is included. However, the majority of these magazines focus on what we would normally think of as straight short stories. There are also some stunning publications for writers (and readers) of genre fiction.

Prose magazines and e-zines

AD HOC FICTION ☆

E-ZINE
helpdesk@adhocfiction.com
www.adhocfiction.com
Editor: John O'Shea
Established 2015. Fiction. Free access – all online content available to all. *Ad Hoc Fiction* was longlisted for the Saboteur Awards, Wild Card Category in 2016 and 2017.
GENRES: Micro-fiction.
SUBMISSIONS: Open to all. Submit online at www.adhocfiction.com/write. Usually responds within one week. Feedback is not available. The winning contributor of *Ad Hoc Fiction*'s weekly contest is rewarded with free entry to the Bath Flash Fiction Award, worth £9.
WE SAY: *Ad Hoc Fiction* presents all entries to its weekly competition as a website-based, read-and-vote e-book. It's a simple design: one piece of flash fiction to a page (there were 88 pages in the week we looked at). The e-book is set to perfectly fit a phone screen, and it saves reading location. It's a nifty set up, allowing for access to a range of writing styles – but if you only want to read the winning stories, simply click the obvious tab for the crowd-agreed best of the best.
See also: prose publishers p92

BLACK STATIC

PRINT, DIGITAL AND E-ZINE
5 Martins Lane, Witcham, Ely, Cambridgeshire CB6 2LB
andy@ttapress.com
www.ttapress.com
Editor: Andy Cox
Established 1994 (under the title The Third Alternative – renamed in 2005). Mainly fiction. See www.ttapress.com/shop/ for subscription rates. Publication available direct from the publisher website; by post and email order; in chain bookshops nationwide; in independent bookshops; and at literary events. Free access – all online content available to all. Winner of several British Fantasy Awards and The International Horror Guild Award.
GENRES: Horror and dark fantasy; book reviews; film reviews; interviews; comment.
SUBMISSIONS: Submissions open to all. Stories of up to 10,000 words. Submit via Submittable at tta.submittable.com/submit (guidelines at same address). Usually responds within four days. Contributors receive money and a copy of the magazine. Rejections may occasionally include unsolicited feedback.
WE SAY: We saw the digital version of this slick-looking horror magazine, which features both fiction and articles about the genre, as well as reviews of both books and film. The issue also includes a novella by Carole Johnstone. The cover shows a black and yellow figure resembling a blindfolded Statue of Liberty, and the issue is punctuated by black-and-white artwork, mostly photo manipulated. The fiction in this issue is very subtle, literary horror, and the magazine seems to favour slightly longer works. A very distinguished horror magazine – well worth a look!
See also: TTA Press (prose publisher) p194

BOOKANISTA
E-ZINE
editors@bookanista.com
newvoices@bookanista.com
www.bookanista.com
Editors: Farhana Gani, Mark Reynolds
Welcomes general submissions from publishers and established writers for articles, interviews and short fiction. For open submissions, try their New Voices for short fiction.

BOUDICCA PRESS
E-ZINE
boudiccapress.wordpress.com
boudiccapress@gmail.com
Publishes weird, literary and relationship fiction by women in the UK for publication online. Stories should be no longer than 1,000 words. Boudicca Press also published short story anthology *Disturbing the Beast.*

CRIMEWAVE
PRINT
5 Martins Lane, Witcham, Ely, Cambridgeshire CB6 2LB
andy@ttapress.com
www.ttapress.com
Editor: Andy Cox
Established 1999. Short stories. Published irregularly – see www.ttapress.com/shop/ for subscription rates. Publication available direct from the publisher website; by post and email order; in chain bookshops nationwide; in independent bookshops and at literary events. Free access – all online content available to all. Award-winning stories.
GENRES: New modern crime and mystery.
SUBMISSIONS: Submissions open to all. Stories of up to 10,000 words. Submit via Submittable

at tta.submittable.com/submit (guidelines at same address). Usually responds within four days. Rejections may occasionally include unsolicited feedback. Contributors receive money and a copy of the magazine.
See also: TTA Press (prose publisher) p194

DUBLIN REVIEW, THE
PRINT
PO Box 7948, Dublin 1, Ireland.
order@thedublinreview.com
www.thedublinreview.com
Editor: Brendan Barrington
Established 2000. Mixed form: fiction and non-fiction. See www.thedublinreview.com/subscribe for subscription information. Available direct from publisher website; by post and email order; and from Amazon.
GENRES: Literary fiction; essays; memoir; travel writing; criticism; reportage.
SUBMISSIONS: Open to all. Submit by email to submissions@thedublinreview.com. Guidelines at thedublinreview.com/submissions. Usually responds within one to three months. No feedback offered with rejection. Contributors are paid a set rate and receive a discount purchase price on the magazine.

EAST OF THE WEB
E-ZINE
submissions@eastoftheweb.com
www.eastoftheweb.com/short-stories
Fiction – short stories across multiple genres, rates by age and length for easy browsing. Receives about half a million unique visitors per month, and the site offers the chance to receive reader feedback.

ELLIPSIS ZINE

DIGITAL AND PRINT
www.ellipsiszine.com
Editor: Steve Campbell
Established 2017. Fiction.
Publication available direct from
publisher website. Free access – all
online content available to all.
SUBMISSIONS: Submit by email
to ellipsiszinesubs@gmail.com.
Guidelines at www.ellipsiszine.
com/submissions. Contributors
receive print copies and a share of
the royalty fee.
WE SAY: Though we didn't see a
print version of the zine, we did
look at the online content. The
website uses a simple but stylish
template to present a range of
short fiction, with a new piece
added every few days. Each story
is illustrated with a photographic
image appropriate to the tale. The
writing featured is striking, packing
a punch in few words – as the best
short fiction should.

ELSEWHERE: A JOURNAL OF PLACE

PRINT AND DIGITAL
paul@elsewhere-journal.com
www.elsewhere-journal.com
Editor: Paul Scraton
Accepts submissions for both the
print journal (when submissions
window is open) and for the
blog. 'Dedicated to involved and
intelligent writing about place',
which should also be combined
with the current Issue theme.

FAIRLIGHT BOOKS

DIGITAL
Summertown Pavilion, 18-24 Middle
Way, Oxford OX2 7LG
01865 957790
submissions@fairlightbooks.com
www.fairlightbooks.com

Established 2017. Publishes
short stories on their website on
a weekly basis. Free access – all
online content available to all.
GENRES: Literary short stories.
SUBMISSIONS: Open to all.
Submit by email to submissions@
fairlightbooks.com. Guidelines
at www.fairlightbooks.co.uk/
submissions. Usually responds in
one to three months. Rejections
may occasionally include
unsolicited feedback.
WE SAY: Fairlight Books' online
short story selection is easily
accessed via the website's menu
bar, where a drop-down list also
gives you the option to display
stories according to time-taken-to-
read. The list of stories is displayed
with a large bright image alongside
each title, plus the author name
and the opening sentences of the
work. The stories themselves are
displayed in a reasonably sized
sans serif font. They are, as you'd
expect from an award-winning
publisher, great reads.
See also: prose publishers p124

FICTION POOL, THE

E-ZINE
thefictionpool@gmail.com
www.thefictionpool.com
Editor: Jo Simmonds
Established 2016. Fiction. Free
access – all online content available
to all.
GENRES: Experimental; literary;
realist; surrealist; quirky.
SUBMISSIONS: Open to all. Submit
by email to thefictionpool@
gmail.com. Guidelines at www.
thefictionpool.com/submit. Usually
responds within four weeks.
Rejection may occasionally include
unsolicited feedback. Unpaid.
WE SAY: The homepage of this zine

292

is stacked with colour-rich, moody photographic images drawing the eye to the corresponding story title overlaid on the pictures. It's a little like scrolling through the spines of books on a shelf. The Fiction Pool seems to have a propensity for interesting titles. The stories are laid out clearly, in a large font, and the content of them is often visceral, cleverly told, and unflinching. Take, for example, 'Twenty-First Century Mr Chips' by Michael Bloor, which lays out the tale of a paedophile investigation in the form of answerphone messages.

FLASH: THE INTERNATIONAL SHORT-SHORT STORY MAGAZINE ☆

PRINT
Department of English, University of Chester, Parkgate Road, Chester CH1 4BJ
01244 513152
flash.magazine@chester.ac.uk
www.chester.ac.uk/flash.magazine
Editors: Peter Blair, Ashley Chantler
Established 2008. Mainly fiction. Subscription £11/year. Available direct from publisher website.
GENRES: Literary fiction of up to 360 words, with reviews and literary criticism.

FICTIVE DREAM

E-ZINE
fictivedream@gmail.com
www.fictivedream.com
Editor: Laura Black

Established 2016. Fiction. Online content available to all.
GENRES: Literary fiction; general fiction.
SUBMISSIONS: Open to all. Submit by email to fictivedream@gmail.com. Guidelines at www.fictivedream.com/submissions-guidelines. Responds within four weeks. Unpaid.
WE SAY: This e-zine is easy on the eye, with a dusky blue header, sans-serif fonts and a clear menu to follow. We looked at a number of the stories available, considering 'Drive' by Amy L Bethke, 'A Trick of the Light' by Susan McLeod, 'Works in Progress' by Mike Fox and 'Migration' by Michelle

They say

We're interested in stories that focus on those moments that change people's lives. Stories with a distinctive voice, clarity of thought and precision of language. They may be on any subject. They may be challenging, dramatic, playful, exhilarating or cryptic. Above all, they must be well-crafted and compelling.

Ross. These texts all appeal deeply to the human experience and consciousness, inviting the reader into their own world. All of them are formatted with the title, followed by an appropriate image, the date of publication and the name of the writer. The biogs appear at the end, next to the handy tagging options.

SUBMISSIONS: Open to all. Submit by email to flash.magazine@chester.ac.uk. Guidelines at www. chester.ac.uk/flash.magazine/submissions. Usually responds within six weeks, no feedback with

GHASTLING, THE
PRINT AND DIGITAL
editor@theghastling.com
www.theghastling.com
Editor: Rebecca Parfitt

Established 2014. Fiction.
Print available on Amazon and via the publication website; e-book available on Kobo; all online content available to all.
GENRES: Horror; ghost stories, literary fiction; the macabre and peculiar. No non-fiction.
SUBMISSIONS: During submissions windows, submit by email to editor@theghastling.com. Usually responds within one to three months. No response by indicated time means a rejection unless you are a subscriber. Subscribers receive a line of feedback with their submission. Unpaid at the moment.
WE SAY: The Ghastling calls itself a 'modern-day penny dreadful', but its production values are far higher than that implies. Slightly smaller than A4, with a page count that varies depending on the contents (it started out at 54 pages and has climbed from there), this magazine is perfect bound, using quality materials with a design that harks back to woodcut prints, but with touches of colour and contemporary art mixed in. The cover images so far have been unnerving – and that sense of slowly unveiled horror perfectly invokes the stories within.
See also: The Ghastling Press (prose publisher) p130

THEY SAY

A magazine of short contemporary fiction and illustration devoted to horror, the macabre, ghost stories and the oh-so-strange that pays homage to the penny dreadful of yesteryear. By the nature of its design it is a highly coveted and collectable magazine that never ceases to surprise and delight those that encounter it. We publish twice a year during specific windows and are particularly interested in the following horror subgenres: quiet horror, psychological horror and folk horror. We also welcome relevant reviews for publication on our website, please contact: editor@theghastling.com to pitch an idea or enquire.

rejection. Contributors receive a print copy of the magazine.

WE SAY: Perfect-bound 111-page magazine that includes flash fiction, essays and reviews. The cover is matte, with a photographic image on the front and appropriately flashy silver spine and back. Reasonable quality white paper inside, and no illustrations, but plenty of very short fiction. After the original fiction, there's a section called 'Flash presents', which presents classic work (Virginia Woolf, in the issue we looked at – Vol. 7 No. 2), followed by an essay on her work. Then several reviews and advertisements thoughtfully kept to the last few pages.

GREEN BOOK, THE
PRINT
brian@swanriverpress.ie
swanriverpress.ie
Editor: Brian J Showers
Established 2013. Non-fiction commentaries, articles, reviews. Available direct from publisher website; by post and email order; from independent bookshops and online book dealers; and at national and local literary events.
GENRES: Literary criticism and history based around Irish Gothic, supernatural and fantastic. No fiction.
SUBMISSIONS: Open year-round. Usually responds within four weeks. Rejection may occasionally include unsolicited feedback. Contributors receive a print copy.
See also: Swan River Press (prose publisher) p187

HAPHAZARD REVIEW
DIGITAL / E-ZINE
editor@haphazardreview.com
www.haphazardreview.com
Editor: Sam Murphy
Established 2018. Publishes non-fiction. Available directly from the publication website: all online content is freely available to all.
GENRES: Essays; creative non-fiction; memoir; biographies; reviews.
SUBMISSIONS: Open to all. Submit by email to editor@ haphazardreview.com. Guidelines at www.haphazardreview.com/ haphazard-review/2018/10/28/call-out-for-writing. Usually responds within four weeks. Submission feedback is provided only if requested, for a fee. Currently unpaid.
WE SAY: The *HapHazard Review* website features an easy to follow, picture-tile homepage, with links to each piece, and a large front drop-down menu to the left of the screen – a very clear, easy to read and navigate template site. The content is unique, bringing together both podcasts and writing about podcasts. In particular we looked at 'A Show for Readers and Writers' where Rachel Gilman writes about the experience of recording each episode of her radio talk show 'The Write Stuff', in a series of funny and engaging vignettes. We did have to scroll right to the end of the lengthy piece to discover who the writer was, but the layout is otherwise clear and easy on the eyes for screen-reading.

INTERZONE
PRINT, DIGITAL AND E-ZINE
5 Martins Lane, Witcham, Ely, Cambridgeshire CB6 2LB
andy@ttapress.com
www.ttapress.com
Editor: Andy Cox

Founded 1982, and taken over by TTA Press in 1994. Fiction, interviews, reviews. See ttapress.com/shop/ for subscription rates. Publication available direct from publisher website; by post and email order; in chain bookshops nationwide; in independent bookshops; at literary events; and from Amazon, Apple, and Weightless Books. Free access – all online content available to all. Winner of British Science Fiction Association award and British Fantasy Award; nominated many times for the Hugo Award.

GENRES: Sci-fi and fantasy; book reviews; film reviews; interviews; comment.

SUBMISSIONS: Submissions open to all. Stories of up to 10,000 words. Submit via Submittable at tta.submittable.com/submit (guidelines at same address). Usually responds within four days. Rejections may occasionally include unsolicited feedback. Contributors receive money and a copy of the magazine.

WE SAY: The cover of the digital copy we saw of this sci-fi/fantasy magazine is a photo manipulation of a woman, with red and blue light obscuring some of her face. The look is 90's futurism – but stylishly done. The art inside also includes hand-drawn illustrations. The issue itself features articles, fiction and reviews of sci-fi and fantasy media, as well as interviews with authors. The work itself is innovative, almost literary sci-fi – an interesting read.

See also: TTA Press (prose publisher) p194

NECESSARY FICTION
E-ZINE
editor@necessaryfiction.com
www.necessaryfiction.com
Editors: Steve Himmer, Michelle Bailat-Jones (translations), Helen McClory (fiction), Susan Rukeyser (reviews)

Book reviews, short stories, 'Research Notes' and occasional interviews and essays, updated throughout the week. Particularly supportive of independent publishers in their reviews, and all areas of writing are open to submissions.

OPEN PEN
PRINT
sean@openpen.co.uk
www.openpen.co.uk
Editor: Sean Preston
Established 2011. Fiction only. Publication is free to read, and available direct from publisher website and from independent bookshops.
In the 2016 Saboteur Awards, *Open Pen* was shortlisted for Best Magazine and Best Anthology.

GENRES: Literary; hipster; urban-grit; humour.

SUBMISSIONS: Open to all. Submit by email to submissions@openpen.co.uk. Guidelines at www.openpen.co.uk/submit/. Usually responds within one to three months, with feedback only if requested. Contributors receive free print copies.

See also: prose publishers p163

PARAGRAPH PLANET
E-ZINE
www.paragraphplanet.com
A creative writing website that publishes one 75-word paragraph every day. Going since 2008, it accepts a range of writing, including 'a mixture of twist-in-the-tale flash fiction, evocative short,

short fiction, openings of published novels or brief moments captured'.

REFLEX FICTION ☆
E-ZINE
16 Glyme Close, Abingdon OX14 3SY
dave@reflexfiction.com
www.reflexfiction.com
Editor: David Borrowdale
Established 2016. Fiction. Free access – all online content available to all.
GENRES: Literary.
SUBMISSIONS: Open to all. Submit online at www.reflexfiction.com/flash-fiction-submissions-entry-form. Guidelines at www.reflexfiction.com/flash-fiction-competition-rules. Usually responds within one to three months. The top three contributions from each quarter win a cash prize.
WE SAY: We looked at the online publication of the most recent *Reflex Fiction* flash winners. 'Barely Casting a Shadow' by Alicia Bakewell is displayed in a framed space on the page, with an image above the title – frankly a very spooky image, that looks like someone struggling to breathe through cloth stretched over their face. The fiction is (as flash fiction should be) a whole vivid world, complete with broken relationships, in just a few words. High quality and evocative writing.

SCOOP
PRINT
Studio 3, The Print House,
18-22 Ashwin Street, London E8 3DL
hello@scoopthemag.co.uk
www.scoopthemag.co.uk
A monthly magazine for ages 8+ that includes original fiction and non-fiction and promises 'never to talk down to [its] readers'.

SHADOW BOOTH, THE
PRINT AND DIGITAL
dan@theshadowbooth.com
www.theshadowbooth.com
Editor: Dan Coxon
Established 2017. Publishes short fiction in book-length volumes (see also p181). Available direct from the publisher website; by post and email order; at national and local literary events; and from Amazon.
GENRES: Horror; ghost stories; weird fiction; literary.
SUBMISSIONS: During submissions windows only, submit by email to submissions@theshadowbooth.com. Guidelines at www.theshadowbooth.com/submit. Usually responds in one to three months. No feedback offered with rejections. Contributors are paid a flat fee and receive free copies of the issue.
For further information, including what We Say, see also: prose publishers p181

SHORELINE OF INFINITY ☆
PRINT, DIGITAL AND E-ZINE
0131 208 1900
editor@shorelineofinfinity.com
www.shorelineofinfinity.com
Editor: Noel Chidwick
Established 2015. Mainly fiction. Available direct from publisher website, post and email order. Only subscribers/purchasers can access online content.
GENRES: Fantasy/sci-fi; reviews; commentary on science fiction related topics.
SUBMISSIONS: Open to all, during submissions windows. Submit via the online manager at www.shorelineofinfinity.com/submissions (guidelines at same address). Usually responds within one to three months. Standard

rejection may occasionally include unsolicited feedback. Contributors are paid a set rate and receive a digital copy of the magazine.

WE SAY: This magazine continues to go from strength to strength. The digital copy of Issue 8 that we looked at comes in at a whopping 134 pages, complete with multiple high-quality illustrations on different styles, a graphic novel section, title pages for stories, drop caps galore and an eye-catchingly illustrated cover. As well as stories, *Shoreline* includes interesting reviews of sci-fi novels (so many that the mag publishes the rest on the website). Noel Chidwick's editor's letter, gently humorous and also illustrated, points out that the theme that has emerged is people whose humanity is being tested.

SHORT FICTION ☆
ONLINE
shortfictionjournal@gmail.com
www.shortfictionjournal.co.uk
Editor: Ruby Cowling
Established 2007. Short fiction. Free access – all online content available to all.

GENRES: Literary. No non-fiction or poetry.

SUBMISSIONS: Open to all, during submissions window only. Submit by email to shortfictionjournal@gmail.com. Guidelines at www.shortfictionjournal.co.uk. Usually responds within two months. Contributors are paid up to £50 for work up to 5,000 words and their stories matched with bespoke illustrations.

WE SAY: *Short Fiction Journal's* modern and artistic website proudly displays links to their authors' work on the homepage using large square, slightly dimmed out, illustrations to highlight the names and titles, and, more discreetly, to list when a piece was published and roughly how long it will take to read. On clicking through, the illustrations spring to life in full colour, with a link to the author's website beneath, followed by the story. If you love a story, you can 'like' it (think social media-style). The writing they publish is often hard-hitting and thoughtful, exploring a wide range of themes.

SPELK
E-ZINE
spelkfiction@gmx.com
www.spelkfiction.com
Editor: Gary Duncan
Established 2014. Flash fiction. Free access – all online content available to all.

GENRES: Crime/thriller/mystery; literary. No non-fiction.

SUBMISSIONS: Open to all. Submit by email to spelkfiction@gmx.com. Guidelines at spelkfiction.com/submit-2. Usually responds within four weeks. Rejection may occasionally include unsolicited feedback.

WE SAY: *Spelk's* layout is a simple template. The homepage features the most recent published story, a basic menu and an alphabetical list of contributors linking to their featured stories, so you can hunt for your favourite writers. The browse function is a bit awkward – if you click on the archives, only the last story posted in the month appears, giving the false impression that *Spelk* only updates once a month. In fact, it's more like once a week, so readers keep coming back for a regular hit of sharp flash fiction – and the fiction is edgy, packing a punch in 500 words or fewer.

SPLICE

E-ZINE
48 Milner Road, Birmingham B29 7RQ
07783 909469
thisissplice@gmail.com
www.thisissplice.co.uk
Editor: Daniel Davis Wood

Established 2017. Publishes non-fiction in the form of author interviews and literary criticism, posted online twice weekly. Free access – all online content available to all. *Splice* was nominated for the 2019 Republic of Consciousness Prize for Small Presses.

SUBMISSIONS: Open to all. Submit by email to thisissplice@gmail.com. Guidelines at www.thisissplice.co.uk/submissions. Usually responds within four weeks. Rejections may occasionally include unsolicited feedback. Contributors are paid a flat fee.

WE SAY: *Splice*, whilst publishing fiction and anthologies (see p184), also operates as an e-zine publishing regular reviews and interviews. Their reviews are published around twice per week and present a long, in-depth and honest exploration into the texts they cover. At around 2,000 words each, their reviews make a significant contribution to the press' overall output, and sit proudly within their site.
See also: Splice (prose publisher) p184

STORGY MAGAZINE ☆

DIGITAL AND E-ZINE
www.storgy.com
Editors: Tomek Dzido, Anthony Self, Ross Jeffery

Established 2013. Fiction. Free access – all online content available to all.

GENRE: Literary; non-fiction; flash fiction.

SUBMISSIONS: Open to all. Submit by email to submit@storgy.com. Guidelines at storgy.com/touch-us. Usually responds within one to three months. No feedback offered with rejection.

WE SAY: *Storgy* is a prime example of what an e-zine can be. The fonts are clear, the site is slick and the home page is loaded with images, but not overwhelming. We get the impression that a lot of thought has gone into making the reading experience a pleasant one: *Storgy* has more than 13,000 likes on Facebook, so this e-zine clearly has readers. One thing we do miss is a comprehensive archive list, but you could argue that this just gives the new work a sense of immediacy.
See also: Storgy (prose publisher) p186

WORMWOOD

PRINT
Coverley House, Carlton, Leyburn, North Yorkshire DL8 4AY
01969 640399
markl.valentine@btinternet.com
www.tartaruspress.com
Editor: Mark Valentine

Established 1990. Mainly publishes non-fiction. Available direct from publisher website; by post and email order; and in independent bookshops.
Wormwood was nominated for a World Fantasy Award in 2012.

GENRES: Supernatural; decadent; fantastic.

SUBMISSIONS: Open to all. Submit by email to markl.valentine@btinternet.com. Guidelines at

tartaruspress.com/wormwood.html.
Usually responds within four weeks.
No feedback offered with rejection.
Contributors receive a print copy of
the magazine.
**See also: Tartarus Press (prose
publisher) p189**

Part 3:
Competitions

Entering writing competitions can feel like casting your precious words into an abyss, only to watch them drop out of sight without so much as a faint splash. Nevertheless, it can be a worthwhile endeavour.

For winners, there is the prize money, of course, plus the glow of achievement and validation, and the notch on your CV. But even if you don't win, there's the camaraderie on social media amongst people who have entered, and the flurry of anticipation when the longlists are announced. More importantly, there is the insight that can be gained from reading the winners' work and critically applying that same eye to your own work.

Bear in mind, too, that when the competition is run by a small press or magazine, the entrance fees play a vital part in helping the press to survive. If those entrance fees are out of your price range, don't despair. Check the competition website carefully, and trawl social media. In the past two years great strides have been made in increasing competition accessibility. Many competition organisers, including Mslexia, run bursary schemes for low-income writers, or have generous previous winners who want to donate entries for others. Don't be shy – apply!

Once you believe you're ready to send in your work, we recommend you check down our handy list of tips to improve your chances of winning:

- We've said it before, but please (please) read the rules carefully, and stick to them. If they call for anonymous entries, make sure your name is confined to a cover sheet only. If they call for entries by post rather than email, then post your work. If the competition is for unpublished work only, make sure your story hasn't appeared anywhere – if you win, you will be found out and disqualified. Managing a competition is hard work; don't give the organisers and judges any reason to exclude you.
- If you've read the rules and the FAQs and are still uncertain about any aspect of your entry, then get in touch with the organiser and ask them directly – preferably with plenty of time before the deadline!
- Don't go for the obvious idea. Try stepping out of your comfort zone of gender, sexuality, setting. Judges will be reading hundreds of entries so it helps if there is something (other than your brilliant writing) that makes your entry stand out.
- Avoid rushing to finish an original poem or story just minutes before the deadline. Give yourself time to step away from it for a few days

– the longer the better – and edit it at least once more before you submit.

- Check that your story is actually telling a story and that your poem has something to say. Judges often comment that story entries read like an extract from a longer manuscript; or that a poem doesn't seem to have a point.
- Cut the padding. Start your story as late as possible in the narrative. With poems, ask yourself whether you really need that opening stanza. Judges, far more than normal readers, need to be ensnared by your very first line.
- Obviously you will check carefully for typos and punctuation mistakes, but look out for clichés and obvious word pairings too. Clichés leap off the page for sifters and judges, so spend time identifying and rewriting each one.

If the results come through and your entry isn't on the longlist:

- Don't take it personally. Remember that when there's a panel of judges, the winners are often the result of argument and compromise. With a single judge, individual taste plays a part, too.
- Don't abandon the work. Reread it critically. Could you make it stronger? If so, redraft it and try again. If it's already as good as it can be, try again with a different competition – or submit it to one of the many magazines we've helpfully listed in this book for that purpose.

Good luck!

A3 REVIEW, THE
thea3review.submittable.com/submit
Cross-category monthly
competitions.
CATEGORIES: Single poem; poetry
collection; short story; flash fiction.
ENTRY FEE: $5.
PRIZES: £475 total prize money
every six months, plus publication.

A NEW ULSTER
anuanewulster.wixsite.com/anewulster
Occasional competition offering
free editing and formatting services
for novels and first-time collections.
CATEGORIES: Single poem; novel.
PRIZES: Professional feedback and
mentoring.

AD HOC FICTION
www.adhocfiction.com
CATEGORIES: Flash fiction.
PRIZES: Free entry to the Bath
Flash Fiction Award, worth £9.

AESTHETICA CREATIVE WRITING AWARD
www.aestheticamagazine.com/cwa
CATEGORIES: Poetry (up to 40
lines per poem); short fiction (up to
2,000 words).
ENTRY FEE: Short fiction £18; poetry
£12. Multiple entries allowed.
PRIZES: £1,000 (poetry winner);
£1,000 (short fiction winner);
publication in the *Aesthetica
Creative Writing Anthology*; a
selection of books from Vintage
and Bloodaxe Books; one-year
print subscription to *Granta*; full
membership to The Poetry Society
(poetry winner); consultation with
Redhammer Management (short

fiction winner); a complimentary
copy of the *Anthology*.

ALMOND PRESS
www.dystopianstories.com/terms-and-
conditions
CATEGORIES: Short stories (under
5,000 words).
PRIZES: £100 first prize; shortlisted
works published in electronic and
print format; visibility.

AMBIT MAGAZINE
www.ambitmagazine.co.uk
CATEGORIES: Poetry; short fiction
(no more than 1,000 words).
ENTRY FEE: £6 per poem; £8 per
story.
PRIZES: Each category £500 first
prize, £250 second prize, £100
third prize; publication; invitation
to read at launch party.

ARTEMIS POETRY / SECOND LIGHT PUBLICATIONS
www.secondlightlive.co.uk
CATEGORIES: Long poems (over 50
lines, no upper limit); short poems
(up to 50 lines).
ENTRY FEE: £6 per long poem;
£4 per short poem (or £9 for
three/£14 for eight).
PRIZES: Each category £300 first
prize, £150 second prize, £75 third
prize, book prize for commended;
publication.

AURORA METRO
The Virgina Prize for Fiction
www.aurorametro.com/newsite/
virginia-prize/
Open to women fiction writers,
writing in English.

CATEGORIES: Novel, any genre.
PRIZES: £1,000 and conditional offer of publication.

BANGOR LITERARY JOURNAL, THE

www.thebangorliteraryjournal.com/
forty-words-competition
www.thebangorliteraryjournal.com/
the-bangor-poetry-competition
CATEGORIES: Bangor Poetry Competition (themed poetry) and Forty Words Competition (flash fiction and poetry).
ENTRY FEE: Bangor Poetry Competition: free until shortlisted (£8). Forty Words Competition: £3.50 per piece, or 2@£6, or 4@£10.
PRIZES: Bangor Poetry Competition: £100 first prize, £50 second prize, £30 third prize, fourth and fifth place £10 each. Forty Words Competition: reading and publishing in journal.

BLUE NIB, THE

www.thebluenib.com/chapbook-
contest-intro
The Blue Nib has run four chapbook contests to date, each judged by a well-known poet.
CATEGORIES: Poetry chapbook; short story.
PRIZES: Money and publication go to the top three poets selected by the guest judge. Other prizes include feedback/mentoring.

BRITTLE STAR

www.brittlestar.org.uk/competition
Runs bi-annually.
CATEGORIES: Poetry (no longer than 60 lines); short fiction (no longer than 2,000 words).
ENTRY FEE: £5 for first entry, £3.50 subsequent entries.
PRIZES: Each category £250 first prize, £50 second prize, £25 third

prize; publication; invitation to launch and prize-giving.

CATERPILLAR, THE

www.thecaterpillarmagazine.com
CATEGORIES: The *Caterpillar* Poetry Prize (no line limit); The *Caterpillar* Story for Children Prize (stories up to 1,500 words).
ENTRY FEE: The *Caterpillar* Poetry Prize €12 per poem; The *Caterpillar* Story for Children Prize €12 per story.
PRIZES: Poetry €1,000, publication. Short story €500 first prize plus two-week stay at The Moth Retreat, €300 second prize, €200 third prize, publication.

CHICKEN HOUSE
The Times/Chicken House Children's Fiction Competition

www.chickenhousebooks.com/
submissions
CATEGORIES: Children's/YA Novel.
ENTRY FEE: £18
PRIZES: A worldwide publishing contract (including a £10,000 advance), professional feedback and mentoring. Previous winners include Nicki Thornton, Laurel Remington and Jasbinder Bilan.

CINNAMON PRESS

www.cinnamonpress.com/index.php/
competitions/our-awards
CATEGORIES: Poetry pamphlet (15-25 poems up to 50 lines each); Cinnamon Literature Award (first 10,000 words of a novel; or two short stories 2,000-4,000 words; or 10 poems); Cinnamon Pencil (for free mentoring or bursary) and mini competitions (see website).
ENTRY FEE: £10 for pamphlet prize; £16 per entry for Literature Award; £12 Cinnamon Pencil; £4 mini competitions.

PRIZES: Poetry pamphlet: publishing contract plus 30 copies of pamphlet x 2. Literature Award: publishing contract. Cinnamon Pencil: one year of mentoring and bursaries for two runners up.

COMMA PRESS
www.commapress.co.uk
New writer showcase.
CATEGORIES: Short story (between 2,000 and 6,000 words).
PRIZES: Paid publication.

COMMA PRESS
The Dinesh Allirajah Prize for Short Fiction
www.commapress.co.uk/resources/
prizes
CATEGORIES: Short story (between 2,000 and 6,000 words).
PRIZES: £500 to the winner and publication in *Northern Soul*, shortlist published in Comma e-book.

CRYSTAL MAGAZINE
Surprise competitions open to all.
CATEGORIES: Single poem; short story; article.
ENTRY FEE: £1.23.
PRIZES: Publication, plus surprise small gift.

DAHLIA PUBLISHING
www.leicesterwrites.co.uk/2017/01/18/
rules/
CATEGORIES: Short story.
PRIZES: Monetary prize; publication.

DEMPSEY & WINDLE
The Brian Dempsey Memorial Prize and National Poetry Day Competition
www.dempseyandwindle.com/
competition.html
CATEGORIES: BDMP - pamphlet

and single poem; NPD - single poem.
PRIZES: BDMP Pamphlet - £100 and publication. BDMP Single Poem - First prize: £75; second prize £50; third prize £25. Longlisted poems published in an anthology, with a free copy for each contributor. NPD - Book prizes to the value of £30, and publication.

DOG HORN PUBLISHING
www.doghornpublishing.com
CATEGORIES: Poetry (single poem); poetry (collection/pamphlet); novel; short story; flash fiction.
PRIZES: Publication; professional feedback/mentoring; introduction to agent/publisher.

EARLYWORKS PRESS
www.earlyworkspress.co.uk/
competitions.htm
CATEGORIES: Short story, flash fiction and poetry held annually. Occasional novel and poetry collection competitions.
PRIZES: Minimum of £100 for first place in short story competitions, others vary. Complimentary copy of the anthology for shortlisted authors, plus opportunity to join the Earlyworks Press writers' club and/or join in further publication projects.

EYRIE PRESS
www.eyriepress.co.uk/short-story-
competition
CATEGORY: Short story (up to 1,000 words)
ENTRY FEE: £5 per entry
PRIZES: Winner receives £75 plus publication in *The Fens* lifestyle magazine.

FISH PUBLISHING

www.fishpublishing.com/writing-contests

CATEGORIES: Single poem; short story; flash fiction; memoir.
PRIZES: Money; writing retreats; publication (see p35 and p127); and professional feedback/mentoring.

FITZCARRALDO EDITIONS
The Fitzcarraldo Editions Essay Prize

www.fitzcarraldoeditions.com/prizes
CATEGORIES: Book-length essays (submit a proposal of up to 5,000 words for an essay that will be minimum 25,000 words).
PRIZES: £3,000; writing retreat; publication; introduction to agent/publisher.

The Fitzcarraldo Editions Novel Prize

CATEGORIES: Complete novel manuscript (minimum length 30,000 words).
PRIZES: £3,000; publication.

FLASH: NATIONAL FLASH FICTION YOUTH COMPETITION

www.chester.ac.uk/flash.fiction/youthcompetition
CATEGORIES: Flash fiction.
PRIZES: Up to £100.

FLASHBACK FICTION

www.flashbackfiction.com/index.php/competition
CATEGORIES: Single prose poem; flash fiction (themed).
ENTRY FEE: First entry free; £3 per subsequent entry.
PRIZES: Publication and money – the amount varies depending on the competition.

FLY ON THE WALL PRESS

www.flyonthewallpoetry.co.uk
Competitions run yearly, under different themes connected in some way to world issues and politics.
CATEGORIES: Single poem; short story.
PRIZES: Roughly £50 per winning piece.

FROGMORE PRESS, THE

www.frogmorepress.co.uk
The Frogmore Poetry Prize
CATEGORIES: Poetry (no longer than 40 lines).
ENTRY FEE: £4 per poem.
PRIZES: First prize 250 guineas (£262.50) and two-year subscription to *The Frogmore Papers*; first runner up 75 guineas (£78.75) and one-year subscription; second runner up 50 guineas (£52.50) and one-year subscription. Shortlisters receive a selection of books.

GALLEY BEGGAR PRESS

www.galleybeggar.co.uk
CATEGORIES: Short story (up to 6,000 words).
ENTRY FEE: £10 per submission.
PRIZES: Winner chooses between £2000 or year-long editorial support for a writing project.

GRIMBOLD BOOKS

www.grimboldbooks.com
CATEGORIES: Short story and flash fiction.
PRIZES: Usually giveaways of books, small monetary prizes, and the occasional prize involving an e-reader.

HALF MOON BOOKS

www.halfmoonbooks.co.uk
A 'competitions' page is available

on the site only when the competitions is open.
CATEGORIES: Single poem.
PRIZES: First prize £250; second prize £50; Only Otley Prize £25.

HAPPENSTANCE PRESS
www.happenstancepress.com/index.
php/poetry-submission/monthly-competition
CATEGORIES: Poetry (single poem); short quizzes/fun competitions.
PRIZES: Books.

HASHTAG PRESS
www.hashtagpress.co.uk/hashtag-press-2020
CATEGORIES: Novel.
ENTRY FEE: Free.
PRIZES: Publication and professional feedback/mentoring.

HOLLAND PARK PRESS
www.hollandparkpress.co.uk
CATEGORIES: Poetry (single poem); short story.
ENTRY FEE: Free.
PRIZES: £200 and publication.

INDIGO DREAMS PUBLISHING
www.indigodreams.co.uk
CATEGORIES: Poetry (collection/pamphlet) and single poem.
PRIZES: Publication.

INK SWEAT & TEARS
Pamphlet Commission
www.inksweatandtears.co.uk
Competition held every two or three years in association with Café Writers.
CATEGORIES: Poetry pamphlet (12 pages of sample poems plus a proposal).
ENTRY FEE: £10.
PRIZES: £2,000 and publication, plus 100 copies of the pamphlet.

JOTTERS UNITED LIT-ZINE
jottersutd.wix.com/jotters-united
CATEGORIES: Poetry; short story (max 2,000 words).
PRIZES: Publication; selection of books.

LINEN PRESS
www.linen-press.com
CATEGORIES: Short story; first novel chapter.
PRIZES: Professional feedback and mentoring; choice of Linen Press books.

LONDON MAGAZINE, THE
www.thelondonmagazine.org/category/tlm-competition/
CATEGORIES: Poetry (up to 40 lines); short story (up to 4,000 words, no flash fiction).
ENTRY FEE: £7 first poem; £5 per subsequent poem. £10 per story.
PRIZES: Poetry £300 first prize; £200 second prize; £150 third prize. Short story £500 first prize; £300 second prize; £200 third prize. Publication.

LUNA PRESS PUBLISHING
Beyond Realities
www.lunapresspublishing.com
Luna Publishing ran Beyond Realities writing contests for three years. The competition is currently closed, but looking to reopen. Please check their website for up-to-date information.
CATEGORIES: Single poem; short story.
PRIZES: Beyond Realities had £100 for the winner and runners-up, and publication. In the future the press may revisit this.

MAGIC OXYGEN
www.magicoxygen.co.uk/molp/
Plants a tree in Boré, Kenya, for

every entry received.
CATEGORIES: Single poem (up to 50 lines); short story (up to 4,000 words).
PRIZES: across each category: first prize £1,000; second prize £300; third prize £100; highly commended x2 £50.

MAGMA
Magma Poetry Competition
www.magmapoetry.com/competition
CATEGORIES: Editors' prize for poems up to ten lines; Judge's Prize for poems 11-50 lines.
ENTRY FEE: £5 single poem, or £15 for four poems.
PRIZES: Judge's Prize: £1,000 first prize, £300 second prize, £150 third prize. Editors' Prize: £1,000 first prize, £300 second prize; £15 special mentions x10. Publication. Contributors receive a print copy and are often invited to read at the launch.

MOTH, THE
www.themothmagazine.com
CATEGORIES: The *Moth* Poetry Prize (no line limit; entry fee €12 per poem); The *Moth* Short Story Prize (stories up to 6,000 words; entry fee €12 per story); The *Moth* Art Prize (portfolio of 5-10 2D artworks; entry fee €20 per portfolio).
PRIZES: Poetry: €10,000 first prize, €1,000 runner-up x3, publication. Short story: first prize €3,000; second prize writing retreat (w/€250 stipend), third prize €1,000, publication. Art: two-week retreat with €1,000 stipend.

MOTHER'S MILK BOOKS
www.mothersmilkbooks.com/index.
php/writing-prize
www.mothersmilkbooks.com/index.
php/pamphlet-prize

CATEGORIES: Poetry (pamphlet); poetry (single poem); prose.
PRIZES: Money; publication.

MSLEXIA
www.mslexia.co.uk/competitions
Women writers only.
CATEGORIES: Children's novel (first 3,000 words for a book of at least 15,000 words); adult novel (first 5,000 words for a book of at least 50,000 words) short story (up to 3,000 words); flash fiction (up to 300 words).
ENTRY FEE: £25 per novel entry; £10 per short story; £5 per flash fiction.
PRIZES: Novel: £5,000 for the winner. Short story: first prize £3,000; three finalists £100; publication for all. Flash fiction: first prize £500; three finalists £50; publication for all.

NEW WELSH REVIEW
The New Welsh Writing Awards
www.newwelshwritingawards.com
CATEGORIES: Include novel and short story, but categories change every year.
ENTRY FEE: £10 (but entry fee waivers available).
PRIZES: £1,000 per category, a two-night stay at Gladstone's Library, and £300 towards a Tŷ Newydd course, as well as publication and professional feedback/mentoring.

NINE ARCHES PRESS
Primers: publication and mentoring scheme
ninearchespress.com/primers.html
CATEGORIES: Poetry pamphlet (initial six poems; further 14 if shortlisted).
ENTRY FEE: £15 per submission.
PRIZES: Publication; professional

feedback and one-to-one mentoring with acclaimed poets and editors, programme of live showcase events.

NORTH MAGAZINE, THE
The Poetry Business Book & Pamphlet Competition; and **The Wordsworth Trust Single Poem Prize**
www.poetrybusiness.co.uk/
competition-menu/competition
CATEGORIES: Collection/pamphlet (20-24 pages of poems; full-length manuscript if shortlisted).
ENTRY FEE: £28.
PRIZES: Main competition: equal share of £2,000; pamphlet publication x3; book publication x1; launch readings; magazine publication. Single Poem Prize: £1,000, £300, and £200 prizes; launch readings.

ORBIS QUARTERLY INTERNATIONAL JOURNAL
Readers' Award
www.orbisjournal.com/about-orbis
CATEGORIES: Open to all contents of the magazine - poetry, prose and reviews.
ENTRY FEE: Free.
PRIZES: £50 to the winner as chosen by Orbis readers. £50 divided between the runners up.

OUEN PRESS
www.ouenpress.com
CATEGORY: Short story (run every second year – new theme each time).
PRIZES: First prize £300; 2x runners up receive £100.

PAPER SWANS PRESS
www.paperswans.co.uk
CATEGORIES: Poetry (collection/

pamphlet), single poem and flash fiction.
PRIZES: Publication.

PEIRENE PRESS
www.peirenepress.com
CATEGORIES: Flash fiction.
PRIZES: Books.

PENNY DREADFUL, THE
www.thepennydreadful.org/index.
php/novellaprize/
CATEGORIES: Novella (between 15,000 and 35,000 words).
ENTRY FEE: €10 per manuscript, maximum two manuscripts per entry.
PRIZES: €2,000 and publication.

PENNYSHORTS
www.chiplitfest.com/short-story-
competition-rules
Sponsors ChipLitFest Short Story competition.
CATEGORIES: Short stories (not exceeding 3,000 words).
ENTRY FEE: £5 per submission.
PRIZES: £500 first prize, £100 second prize, £50 third prize.

POETRY IRELAND
Trócaire Poetry Ireland Poetry Competition
www.poetryireland.ie/education/
trocaire-poetry-ireland-poetry-
competition/
CATEGORIES: Single poem.
PRIZES: Money; tickets to a writing retreat; and professional feedback/mentoring.

POETRY LONDON
www.poetrylondon.co.uk/competition
CATEGORIES: Single poem.
PRIZES: First prize £5,000; second prize £2,000; third prize £1,000, plus four commendations at £500 each. Prize winners are published

in the print magazine, commended entries are published online.

POETRY SPACE
www.poetryspace.co.uk/poetry-space-competition
CATEGORIES: Poetry (up to 40 lines).
ENTRY FEE: £5 per poem.
PRIZES: £250 first prize; £100 second prize; £50 third prize. Publication for top 20 poems, plus complimentary copy of the magzine for poets.

POETRY WALES
www.poetrywales.co.uk
CATEGORIES: Single poem (the Wales Poetry Award); poetry pamphlet (20-24 pages long).
ENTRY FEE: Wales Poetry Award - £5 per poem, up to five poems allowed. Free entry for writers of low-income backgrounds residing in the UK (less than £16k per year).
PRIZES: Wales Poetry Award - first prize £100, second prize £50, third prize £25, plus book bundle and publication. Poetry Pamphlet - win up to £250 and publication.

PROLEBOOKS
www.prolebooks.co.uk/poetry%20 competition.html
CATEGORIES: Poetry (collection/ pamphlet), single poem and short story.
PRIZES: Monetary prize; publication.

REFLEX FICTION
www.reflexfiction.com/flash-fiction-competition-rules
CATEGORIES: Flash fiction.
PRIZES: First prize £1,000; second prize £500; and third prize £250.

RETREAT WEST BOOKS
www.retreatwest.co.uk/competitions
CATEGORIES: First chapter; novel; short story; flash fiction (annual and themed quarterly); micro fiction (monthly).
ENTRY FEE: Flash fiction (annual and quarterly) £8; short story £10; micro-fiction; £4; first chapter £10; novel £15.
PRIZES: Varies per category, but includes money (up to £400 for first place); mentoring and feedback; and publication (including a publishing contract with Retreat West Books for the novel competition).

RIALTO, THE
The RSPB and The Rialto Nature Poetry Competition
www.therialto.co.uk
CATEGORIES: Poetry (single poem; Poetry (collection/pamphlet).
ENTRY FEE (SINGLE POEM): £6 for first poem, £3.50 for subsequent poems.
PRIZES (SINGLE POEM): £1,000 first prize, £500 second prize; writing retreat worth £550 third prize; day out with Mark Cocker.

SHARPE BOOKS
www.sharpebooks.com
CATEGORIES: Novel.
PRIZES: Vary, but are usually £500, plus publication.

SHOOTER LITERARY MAGAZINE
www.shooterlitmag.com
Annual short story and poetry competitions.
CATEGORIES: Short story (any theme, up to 5,000 words long) and poetry (any theme, up to 100 lines long).
DATES: Poetry 2019: November

24th deadline. Short story 2020: opens January with April deadline.
ENTRY FEE: Poetry: £3 per poem, or £8 for three poems. Short story: £7 per story, or £10 for two. All entrants of both competitions receive an e-copy of the magazine issue featuring the winning writing.
PRIZES: 2019 poetry prizes: first prize £150, runner-up £50. Short story 2020: first prize £500, runner-up £150. Winners are published in print and online; runners-up are published online.

SHORT FICTION

www.shortfictionjournal.co.uk
CATEGORIES: Short fiction (up to 6,000 words).
ENTRY FEE: £8 per story.
PRIZES: £500 plus publication for first prize; £200 plus publication second prize.

SMITH|DOORSTOP BOOKS

The Poetry Business Book & Pamphlet Competition; and **The Wordsworth Trust Single Poem Prize**

www.poetrybusiness.co.uk/
competition-menu/competition
CATEGORIES: Collection/pamphlet (20-24 pages of poems; full-length manuscript if shortlisted).
ENTRY FEE: £28.
PRIZES: Main competition: equal share of £2,000; pamphlet publication x3; book publication x1; launch readings; magazine publication. Single Poem Prize: £1,000, £300, and £200 prizes; launch readings.

SOUTH BANK POETRY

www.southbankpoetry.co.uk/
competition/
CATEGORY: Single poem.
ENTRY FEE: £4 first poem, £3

second poem, £2 per subsequent poem.
PRIZES: First prize £300, second prize £150, third prize £50.

SOUTHWORD JOURNAL/ EDITIONS

www.munsterlit.ie
CATEGORIES: Gregory O'Donoghue Poetry Prize; The Seán Ó Faoláin Short Story Competition; The Fool for Poetry Chapbook Competition; Fiction Chapbook Competition.
PRIZES: Poetry: first prize €1,000, a week's residency, publication and a trip to Cork, Ireland; second prize €500 and publication; third prize €250 and publication. Ten runners-up paid €30 publication fee. Poetry pamphlet: first prize €1,000; second prize €500. Both receive 50 complimentary copies of their chapbook. Short story: first prize €2,000, publication and week-long residency; second prize €500 and publication; four shortlisted writers receive publication fee of €120. Fiction chapbook: Best International Entry and Best Irish Entry each win publication, 20 complimentary copies and advance fee payment of €250.

STAND

www.standmagazine.org
CATEGORIES: Runs occasional competitions; see website for details.

STINGING FLY, THE

www.stingingfly.org
The Davy Byrnes Short Story Award, run every five years.
CATEGORIES: Short story.
PRIZES (AS OF 2014): €15,000 first

prize; €1,000 for five runners-up; publication.

STORGY – YEARLY SHORT STORY COMPETITION

www.storgy.com
CATEGORIES: Short story (max 5,000 words).
ENTRY FEE: £5.
PRIZES: Cash prizes offered to winners (first, second and third place).

WALES ARTS REVIEW

www.walesartsreview.org
CATEGORIES: Short story; flash fiction; non-fiction.
PRIZES: Various prizes.

WASAFIRI MAGAZINE

www.wasafiri.org/new-writing-prize/
Open to anyone without a complete book in the category entered.
CATEGORIES: Poetry; fiction; life writing. 3,000 word limit or five poems max.
ENTRY FEE: £6 (one category); £10 (two categories); £15 (three categories).
PRIZES: £1,000 for the winner of each category; publication.

WAYWISER PRESS, THE

waywiser-press.com/category/hecht-poetry-prize/
CATEGORIES: Book-length poetry collection.
ENTRY FEE: $27.
PRIZES: £2,000; publication; invitation to read to read with judge.

WELL REVIEW, THE

www.thewellreview.com
CATEGORIES: Single poem (annual).
PRIZES: First prize €1,000; second prize €500; third prize €250. All winners published in print and online.

WRECKING BALL PRESS

www.wreckingballpress.com
CATEGORIES: Poetry collection/ pamphlet).
PRIZES: Publication.

We hope this Guide will be useful for you during your publishing journey. If you know of a publisher that should have been included (or one that has closed down since the publication of this book), please contact us so that we can include them in (or omit them from) the fourth edition. indiepressguide@mslexia.co.uk

With special thanks to...

...all those writers and editors who alerted us about additional presses to include – or defunct ones to omit. Your help is so appreciated.

...all the indie press editors, assistants and publicity directors who helped us compile this Guide by patiently filling out surveys, answering questions, sending sample copies and spreading the word.

...all those writers who helped us discover presses by sharing their work on social media.

...the Mslexia team and Charlea Harrison for their unflagging enthusiasm in the face of piles of publication samples, and for their hard work in reviewing them.

Index

#

3:AM Magazine **213**
404 Ink **91, 213**

A

A3 Press, The **15, 91**
A3 Review, The **213, 305**
A New Ulster **214, 305**
A Void **214**
Abaddon Books **92**
Accent Press **92**
acumen literary journal **269**
Ad Hoc Fiction **92, 289, 305**
Aesthetica Creative Writing
    Award **305**
Aesthetica Magazine **93**
African Writing **214**
Against The Grain Poetry Press
    16
Agenda Editions **15**
Agenda Poetry Journal **269**
Alanna Max **93**
Alba Publishing **15, 93**
Alchemy Press **94**
Allardyce, Barnett, Publishers
    16, 94
All-New Swimmers Club, The
    214
All The Sins **215**
Almond Press **94, 305**
Ambit Magazine **215, 305**

Amorist, The **216**
And Other Stories **17, 94**
Angry Robot **95**
Anima Poetry Press **17**
Antiphon **269**
Aquifer Books **17**
Arachne Press **17, 96**
Archipelago **216**
Arc Publications **18**
Areté Books **18**
Areté Magazine **216**
Arlen House **19, 97**
Artemis Poetry **270**
Artemis Poetry / Second Light
    Publications **305**
ASLS **19, 97**
Aston Bay Press **98**
As Yet Untitled **19, 97**
Atlantic Press **98**
Augur Press **20, 98**
Aurora Metro **98, 305**
Avery Hill Publishing **99**
Awen Publications **20, 99**

B

b small publishing **100**
Backlash Journal **270**
Backlash Press **20, 100**
Bad Betty Press **20**
Bangor Literary Journal, The
    217, 306

Banipal (Magazine of Modern
   Arab Literature) 217
Banipal Publishing 21, 100
Banshee 217
Banshee Press 21, 100
Barbican Press 101
Barque Press 21
BHP Comics 101
Bi'an: The UK Chinese Writers'
   Network 218
Birlinn Press 21, 101
Bitter Lemon Press 102
Black & White Publishing 102
Black Dog 102
Black Light Engine Room, The
   22
Black Pear Press 22, 102
Black Shuck Books 103
Black Static 289
Blackbox Manifold 270
Blackheath Books 22, 103
Blithe Spirit (The British Haiku
   Society) 271
Bloodaxe Books 22
Blue Diode 23
Blue Nib, The 23, 103, 218, 306
Bluemoose Books 104
Boatwhistle Books 24
Boiler House Press 24, 104
Bookanista 290
Book Guild, The 24, 104
Boudicca Press 290
Bridge House Publishing 105
British Journalism Review 218
Brittle Star 218, 306
Broken Sleep Books 24

Brown Watson 105
Burning Eye Books 24
Burning House Press 219
Burnt Roti 219
Butcher's Dog 271

C
Cabinet Of Heed, The 219
Cambridge Literary Review 220
Canbury Press 105
Candlestick Press 25, 105
Canongate 105
Carcanet Press 25, 106
Cardiff Review, The 220
Carysfort Press 106
Cassava Republic 106
Caterpillar, The 221, 306
Catnip Publishing 106
CB Editions 26, 107
Chapman 221
Charco Press 107
Chicken House 108, 306
Choc Lit 108
Cillian Press 110
Cinnamon Press 26, 109, 306
Circaidy Gregory Press 27, 110
Claret Press 110
Clearing, The 221
Clinic 27
Clover and White Magazine 222
Clutag Press 27
Columba Press 27, 110
Comma Press 111, 307
Compass Magazine, The 271
Cōnfingō 222

Copy Press **28, 111**
Corona Books UK **112**
Crannóg **222**
Crater Press, The **28**
Cressrelles Publishing Company
     Limited **112**
Crimewave **290**
Crinkle Crankle Press **112**
Crown House Publishing **113**
Crunch, The **272**
Crystal Magazine **222, 307**
ctrl+alt+del **272**
Curly Mind, The **223**
Currach Press **28, 113**

D

Dahlia Publishing **28, 114, 307**
Dancing Bear Books **114**
Darf Publishers **114**
Dark Horse, The **272**
Daunt Books Publishing **115**
Dawntreader Magazine, The **223**
Dead Ink **115**
Dedalus Ltd **115**
Dedalus Press **29**
Dempsey & Windle **29, 307**
Dirt Pie Press **30, 116**
Dissections **224**
DNA Magazine **224**
Dodging The Rain **224**
Dodo Ink **116**
Dog Horn Publishing **30, 117,
     307**
Doire Press **30, 117**
Dome Press, The **117**

Dostoyevsky Wannabe **31, 118**
Dream Catcher **225**
Dublin Review, The **290**
Duckworth Books **118**

E

Earlyworks Press **31, 118, 307**
East of the Web **290**
Egaeus Press **119**
Egg Box Publishing **32**
Elementum **225**
Elliott & Thompson **119**
Ellipsis Zine **291**
Elsewhen Press **119**
Elsewhere: A Journal Of Place **291**
Emma Press, The **33, 120**
Enitharmon Press **32**
Envoi Poetry Journal **272**
époque press **120**
époque press ezine **225**
Equinox Publishing **121**
erbacce **273**
erbacce-press **32**
Erotic Review **226**
Etruscan Books **34**
Everything With Words **121**
Eye & Lightning Books **123**
Eye Flash Poetry **34**
Eye Flash Poetry Magazine **273**
Eyrie Press **122, 307**

F

Fahrenheit Press **123**
Fair Acre Press **34, 123**

What's the next step on your writing journey? Whatever it is, whoever and wherever you are, we can help you achieve your writing dreams.

Global Words press

"She really is the very best editor I've worked with, and I worked with the number one guy at Simon & Schuster."
Nicole Conn, Writer and Director

"The course boosted my confidence with writing. You're both brilliant at what you do."
Francesca, National Justice Museum

Our Services

• Development editing, copy editing, proof reading
• Self-publishing packets/submission letters
• Professional cover design and legal requirement fulfilment
• Typesetting for eBooks and printed books
• Author marketing and social networking
• Workshops and International writing retreats
Our long time editors and multi-published authors
specialise in delivering a personalised service.

Nicci and Victoria are both experienced, professional, & very attentive...providing an immense learning experience."
Gill, Writing Retreat Participant, Spain 2019

If you're looking for a personal touch to getting your book published, look no further. This is a team that will do their very best to give you the best result."
John Parsons, author of children's books

Get in touch today to see how we can
help you with your writing goals.
www.globalwords.co.uk
info@globalwords.co.uk
07545 623 218

Fairlight Books **124**, **291**
Farrago Books **125**
Fenland Reed, The **274**
Fentum Press **125**
Fiction Desk, The **125**
Fiction Pool, The **291**
Fictive Dream **292**
Fincham Press **35**, **125**
Fine Feather Press Ltd **126**
Fine Press Poetry **35**
Firefly Press **126**
Firewords **226**
Fish Publishing **35**, **127**, **308**
Fitzcarraldo Editions **126**, **308**
Five Dials **226**
Flapjack Press **36**
Flarestack Poets **36**
Flash: National Flash Fiction Youth Competition **308**
Flash: The International Short-Short Story Magazine **292**
Flashback Fiction **227**, **308**
Fledgling Press **128**
Flipped Eye Publishing **37**, **128**
Fly On The Wall Press **37**, **128**, **308**
Fly On The Wall Webzine **227**
For Books' Sake **38**, **129**, **227**
Fox Spirit Books **38**, **129**
Foxtrot Uniform **39**, **228**
Frogmore Papers, The **274**
Frogmore Press, The **308**
From Glasgow To Saturn **228**
Fur-lined Ghettos **229**

G

Gallery Press, The **39**
Galley Beggar Press **129**, **308**
Gatehouse Press **39**, **130**
Ghastling Press, The **130**
Ghastling, The **293**
Girasol Press **39**
Gold Dust Magazine **229**
Gorse **229**
Graffeg **130**
Graft Poetry **40**
Granta Books **131**
Granta Magazine **230**
Green Bean Books **131**
Green Book, The **294**
Green Bottle Press **40**
Grey Hen Press **40**
Grimbold Books **131**, **308**
Grist **41**, **132**
Guildhall Press **132**
Guillemot Press **41**, **132**
Guppy Books **41**, **132**
Gutter Magazine **230**
Gylphi Limited **133**

H

Hafan Books (Refugees Writing in Wales) **41**, **133**
Half Moon Books **42**, **308**
HapHazard Review **294**
Happenstance Press **42**, **309**
Hashtag Press **133**, **309**
Haverthorn **231**
Head of Zeus **134**

Headpress 134
Hearing Eye 42
Hedgehog Press 43
Henningham Family Press 43, 135
Hera 135
Hercules Editions 43
Here Comes Everyone 231
Hi Vis Press 44, 135
High Window Press, The 44
High Window, The 274
History Press, The 136
Hogs Back Books 136
Holland House Books 138
Holland Park Press 44, 137, 309
Honest Publishing 44, 138
Honno Welsh Women's Press
        138
Hoperoad Publishing /
        Small Axes 139
Horrific Tales Publishing 139
Hotel 231
Hurst Street Press 45, 140
Hypnopomp 232

I

I Am Not A Silent Poet 232
Idle Ink 232
If A Leaf Falls Press 45
if p then q 45
Ignite Books 140
Indigo Dreams Publishing Ltd
        46, 309
Indigo Press, The 140
Infinity Plus 141
Influx Press 141

Ink Sweat & Tears 233, 309
Ink Sweat & Tears Press 47
Inspired Quill 141
Interpreter's House, The 233
Interzone 294
Iota Poetry 275
IRIS 233
Irish Literary Review 234
Iron Press 47, 142
Island Review, The 234
Istros Books 142
Ivy Press 143

J

Jacaranda Books 143
John Catt Educational 143
Jotters United Lit-zine 234, 309
Journal, The 275
Junction Box 234

K

Katabasis 47, 144
Kenilworth Press 144
Khidr Collective 48, 144
Khidr Collective Zine 235
Knight Errant Press 48, 144
Knights Of 145
Knives Forks And Spoons 48
Kristell Ink 145

L

LabLit.com 235
Lagan Press 49, 145

Lampeter Review, The **235**
Lantana Publishing **145**
Lapwing Publications **49**
Laudanum **49**
Laurence King Publishing **146**
Lawrence and Wishart **50, 146**
Leafe Press **50**
Learned Pig, The **235**
Legend Press **147**
Les Fugitives **147**
Letters Page, The **236**
Liars' League **236**
Liberties Press **51, 148**
Lighthouse **237**
Lilliput Press, The **148**
Linen Press **149, 309**
Literary Pocket Book, The **51**
Litro Magazine **237**
Litro Magazine Ltd **149**
Litter Magazine **275**
Little Island Books **51, 150**
Little Toller Books **150**
London Magazine, The **238, 309**
Lonely Crowd, The **238**
Lonely Press, The **52, 151**
Long Poem Magazine **275**
Loose Chippings **151**
Losslit Magazine **239**
Low Light Magazine **239**
Luath Press **52, 151**
Luna Press Publishing **151, 309**
Lune **240**

M

Magic Oxygen **52, 152, 309**
Magma **276, 310**
Manchester Review, The **240**
Mandrake Of Oxford **152**
Mantle Lane Press **152**
Margō Collective **153**
Mariscat Press **53**
Matthew James Publishing **153**
Maybe Later Press **240**
Mayfly Press **153**
Meanwhile... **240**
Mechanics' Institute Review, The **241**
Melos Press **53**
Mercier Press **153**
Mica Press **53**
Minor Literature[s] **241**
Mira Publishing **155**
Modern Poetry in Translation **276**
Monstrous Regiment **242**
Monstrous Regiment Publishing **54, 155**
Moormaid Press **54**
Morbid Books **54, 155**
Morphrog **277**
Moth, The **242, 310**
Mother's Milk Books **54, 154, 310**
Moving Worlds: A Journal Of Transcultural Writings **243**
Mslexia **244, 310**
Mudfog Press **55, 155**
Mudpress **55**

Mulfran Press 56
Murder Slim Press 156
Muswell Press 156
Myriad Editions 157
Myrmidon Books Ltd 157

N

Necessary Fiction 295
Neem Tree Press 158
Neon Books 56, 158
Neon Literary Magazine 243
New Island 56, 158
New Walk Editions 56
New Welsh Review 159, 243, 310
New Writing Scotland 245
NewCon Press 57, 159
Nightjar Press 159
Nine Arches Press 57, 310
No Exit Press 160
North Magazine, The 277, 311
Northwords Now 245
Nosy Crow 160
Notting Hill Editions 160
Nottingham Review, The 161, 246

O

O'Brien Press, The 161
Offa's Press 57
Offord Road Books 57, 161
Ogham Stone, The 246
Old Street Publishing 162
Oldcastle Books 162
Oneworld 162

Onslaught Press, The 58, 162
Onstream Book Publications 163
Open Pen 163, 295
Orbis Quarterly International
    Journal 247, 311
Orenda Books 163
Original Plus 58
Otter-Barry Books 58, 163
Ouen Press 164, 311
Out-Spoken Press 59, 164
Oversteps Books Ltd 59
Own It! 164
Oystercatcher Press 59

P

Paekakariki Press 60
Palewell Press Ltd 60, 164
Paper and Ink 247
Paper Swans Press 60, 311
Papillote Press 61, 165
Paragraph Planet 295
Parallel Universe Publications
    61, 166
Parthian Books 166
Patrician Press 62, 167
PB Mag 277
PB Press 62
Peepal Tree Press 62, 167
Peirene Press 168, 311
Peninsula Press 168
Penkhull Press 168
Penned In The Margins 63, 169
Pennine Platform 278
Penny Dreadful, The 247, 311
Pennyshorts 169, 311
People's Friend, The 248

Peridot Press 169
Peter Owen Publishers 169
Phaeton Publishing Ltd 170
Pickled Body, The 279
Pilot Press 170
Pilrig Press 170
Pindrop Press 64
Pinter & Martin Ltd 170
Pixel Heart Literary Magazine 248
Planet and Planet Extra 248
Platform For Prose 248
Platypus Press 63, 170
Pluto Press 171
PN Review 279
Poetry Ireland 64, 311
Poetry Ireland Review 280
Poetry London 280, 311
Poetry Review, The 280
Poetry Space 65, 312
Poetry Space Showcase 281
Poetry Wales 281, 312
Poolbeg Press 171
Popshot Magazine 249
Porridge Magazine 250
Profile Books 171
Prole 249
Prolebooks 65, 171, 312
Prototype 65, 172, 249
PS Publishing 66, 172
Publishing Project, The 66, 172
Pulsar Poetry Magazine 281
Push – The Writing Squad 251
Pushing Out The Boat 66, 173, 251
Pushkin Press 173

Q

Quartet Books 173
QUID 282
Quiller Publishing 173

R

Rack Press 67, 173
Raum Poetry 282
Reach Poetry 282
Reader, The 252
Red Ceilings Press, The 67
Red Hare Publishing 174
Red Press 68, 174
Red Squirrel Press 68, 174
Reflex Fiction 296, 312
Retreat West Books 175, 312
Rialto, The 282, 312
Rialto, The/Bridge Pamphlets 68
Riggwelter 252
Riptide Journal 252
Rockingham Press 69
Route Publishing Ltd 69, 176
Rowman & Littlefield Publishing Ltd 176
Ruby Fiction 177
Rufus Stone Limited Editions 177

S

Sable 253
Sacristy Press 69, 177
Sad Press 70
Salmon Poetry 70
Salò Press 71, 178

Salomé 253
Salon of the Refused 284
Salt Publishing Ltd 71, 178
Sandstone Press 178
Sapere Books 179
Saqi Books 72, 179
Saraband 180
Sarasvati 253
Scoop 296
Scores, The 254
Scotland Street Press 72, 180
Scribe 180
Scrittura Magazine 254
Sea Lion Press 180
Selkie, The 255
Sentinel Literary Quarterly 255
Seren Books 72, 181
Shadow Booth, The 181, 296
Sharpe Books 182, 312
Shearsman Books Ltd 73
Shearsman Magazine 283
Shoestring Press 74, 182
Shooter Literary Magazine 256, 312
Shoreline of Infinity 296
Short Fiction 297, 313
Sidekick Books 74
Silkworms Ink 74, 182, 255
Sine Wave Peak 74
Singing Apple Press 75
Skylight 47 284
Smith|Doorstop Books 75, 313
Smithereens Literary Magazine 284
Smithereens Press 76
Smokestack Books 76

Snowbooks Ltd 182
Snow Lit Rev 256
Soaring Penguin Press 183
Solaris 183
Somesuch Stories 257
Soundings 257
Soundswrite Press 77
South Bank Poetry 285, 313
Southlight 258
South Poetry Magazine 286
Southword Editions 77, 184, 313
Southword Journal 258, 313
Spark Young Writers Magazine 258
Speculative Books 77, 184
Spelk 297
Splice 184, 298
Spontaneity 258
Stairwell Books 77, 185
Stand 259, 313
Stepaway Magazine 259
Stewed Rhubarb Press 78
Stinging Fly Press, The 186
Stinging Fly, The 260, 313
Stonewood Press 78, 186
Stony Thursday Poetry Book, The 79
Storgy 186
Storgy Magazine 298
Storgy – Yearly Short Story Competition 314
Strange Attractor Press 187
Stranger Press 79
Strangers Press 187
Streetcake Magazine 260
Strix 260

Structo **261**
Structo Press **79, 187**
Swan River Press **187**
Sweet Cherry Publishing **188**
Sylph Editions **188**

T

Tales From The Forest **261**
tall-lighthouse **80**
Tangent Books **188**
Tangerine Press **80, 189**
Tapsalteerie **80**
Tartarus Press **189**
Team Angelica Publishing **189**
Tears in the Fence **262**
Telos Publishing Ltd **190**
Templar Poetry **81**
Tenebris Books **190**
Thistle Publishing **191**
Three Hares Publishing **191**
Thunderpoint Publishing **191**
Tiny Owl Press **192**
Tiny Tree Children's Books **192**
Tirgearr Publishing **193**
Token Magazine **262**
Trafika Europe **262**
Tramp Press **192**
Trigger Publishing **194**
TTA Press **194**
Tuba Press **81**
Turas Press **81, 195**
Two Rivers Press **195**

U

UKAuthors/UKApress **195**
Unbound **81, 195**
Under The Radar **263**
Uniformbooks **82, 196**
Unsung Stories **196**
Unthank Books **197**

V

V. Press **82, 197**
Vagabond Voices **83, 198**
Valley Press **83, 198**
Vane Women Press **83, 198**
Vanguard Editions **84, 199**
Vertebrate Publishing **199**
Verve Books **199**
Victorina Press **84, 200**
Visual Verse **263**
Voidery Aperture, The **84, 200**

W

Wales Arts Review **263, 314**
Walker Books **200**
Ward River Press **200**
Ward Wood Publishing **84, 201**
Wasafiri Magazine **264, 314**
Waywiser Press **85, 201, 314**
Well Review, The **264, 314**
White Review, The **265**
Whittrick Press **202**
Wild Things Publishing **202**
Wild Wolf Publishing **202**
Wildness **265**
Willowherb Review, The **265**

winamop.com 266
Wordwell Books 202
Wormwood 298
Worple Press 85
Wrecking Ball Press 85, 202, 314
Wundor Editions 86, 203

Y

Y Lolfa 203
Yew Tree Press 86
Ylva Publishing 203
Yolk Publishing 204

Z

Zed Books 204
Zenopress 86, 204
ZimZalla 87
Zuntold 204

Submission notes